# THE WAY THAT I FOLLOWED

# The Way that I followed

A NATURALIST'S JOURNEY AROUND IRELAND

Frank Mitchell

COUNTRY HOUSE

Published in 1990 by
Country House
41 Marlborough Road
Donnybrook
Dublin 4


British Library Cataloguing in Publication Data
Mitchell, Frank 1912-
The way that I followed: a naturalist's journey around Ireland
1. Ireland. Description & travel
I. Title
914.1504824
ISBN 0-946172-20-X (pbk)
0-946172-21-8 (hbk)

Managing editor: Treasa Coady
Text editor: Elaine Campion
Text designed by Q Design
Typeset by Printset & Design Ltd, Dublin
Colour separation by Kulor Centre, Dublin
Printed in Ireland by Criterion Press, Dublin

ACKNOWLEDGEMENTS

The author and publishers wish to thank the following for permission to reproduce photographic material:
Aerofilms (p 79), Derek Hill and the Ulster Museum (Pl. 2), Seamas Caulfield, (p 111), J. K. St Joseph: Cambridge University Collection (p 156), Ordnance Survey Office, Permit nos. 5311 and 5313 (pp vi, 168, Pl. 6), Liam de Paor and the RSAI (p 169), Ashe Studios (p 184), The National Library of Ireland (p 189), The Environmental Sciences Unit, TCD and Co. Offaly VEC (p 212), The Irish Times (pp 221 and 248), The Royal Irish Academy (p 232), Department of Foreign Affairs (Pl. 1).
Photographs by J. C. Coleman (p 4), T. H. Mason (pp 17, 115), A. J. Sutcliffe (p 26 top), R. Shepherd (p 55), L. Dunne (p 26 bottom).

The route maps at the opening of chapters, and maps on pages 199, 212 and 214 are by Tom McConville; the illustration on p 24 and maps on pages 200, 201, 206, 210, 217, 220, 225 and 244 are by Mary Davies.

*To Elizabeth*

*scholar, physician, artist and companion*

# CONTENTS

*List of illustrations* IX
*Introduction* XI

1 THE EARLY DAYS *1*
FAMILY INFLUENCES / ARTHUR STELFOX / J. P. BRUNKER

2 THE COLLEGE YEARS *7*
DECISION TIME / OPTING FOR NATURAL SCIENCES / THE QUATERNARY RESEARCH COMMITTEE

3 THE REAL BEGINNING *13*
KNUD JESSEN / BALLYBETAGH BOG

4 BEES IN MY BONNET *21*
ORTHODOX GEOLOGY / THE TERTIARY PERIOD · EROSION OF LIMESTONE · CHEMICAL WEATHERING · TECTONIC MOVEMENT / THE QUATERNARY PERIOD

5 CAVING *32*
SHANDON / CASTLEPOOK / KILGRAENY / KESH, SLIGO / CASTLETOWNROCHE

6 SOUTH-EAST CORNER *38*
**1. WATERFORD AND WEXFORD, QUATERNARY**
KILBEG / LATER GLACIAL HISTORY / PINGOS / GLACIO-MARINE PROCESSES
**2. SOUTH-EAST COAST, ARCHAEOLOGY**
WICKLOW AND WEXFORD / DUBLIN · DALKEY ISLAND · SUTTON · WOOD QUAY

7 NORTH LEINSTER *52*
DRUMGOOSAT (KNOCKNACRAN) RADIOCARBON DATING: HARRY GODWIN / NORTH LOUTH / COOLEY PENINSULA / ROCKMARSHALL

8 NORTH-EAST CORNER *65*
**1. COUNTY DOWN AND BELFAST**
MOURNE MOUNTAINS / STRANGFORD LOUGH / WOODGRANGE / THE PALAEOECOLOGY CENTRE / THE BRITISH ASSOCIATION FOR THE ADVANCEMENT OF SCIENCE
**2. LOUGH NEAGH**
LIGNITE DEPOSITS / GLENAVY / LIFE IN THE LAKE
**3. LARNE**
RAISED-BEACH GRAVELS / THE BROIGHTER HOARD / HALLAM MOVIUS'S EXCAVATIONS
**4. GOODLAND**
CHALK DOWNLAND / ESTYN EVANS / EVIDENCE OF EARLY AGRICULTURE
**5. NORTH COAST**
BALLYCASTLE / RATHLIN ISLAND / COLERAINE

9 NORTH DONEGAL *85*
INISHOWEN / MULROY BAY / SHEEP HAVEN / TORY ISLAND / BLOODY FORELAND

10 SOUTH-WEST DONEGAL *96*
DAWROS PENINSULA / PORTNOO / ROSSAN PENINSULA

11 SLIGO *101*
LIMESTONE COUNTRY / CARROWKEEL / KNOCKNAREA / CARROWMORE / SKREEN

12 MAYO *109*
EARLY AGRICULTURAL PRACTICES / BEHY / BELDERG / GLENAMOY / BELMULLET / INISHKEA / BLANKET-BOG / ACHILL ISLAND / LETTERKEEN / BURREN (MAYO) / KILLADANGAN / CLARE ISLAND

13 GALWAY *129*
INISHBOFIN / ROUNDSTONE / POLLNAHALLIA

14 CLARE *137*
THE BURREN / SOUTH-WEST CLARE / SCATTERY ISLAND / LOOP HEAD

15 NORTH KERRY *144*
KERRY HEAD / BALLYLONGFORD / BALLYBUNNION / FENIT TO SPA

16 DINGLE PENINSULA *153*
CAHERCONREE / MAHAREE ISLANDS / LOUGH ADOON / COUMANARE / BALLINLOGHIG

17 SOUTH-WEST KERRY *161*
BEHY VALLEY / EN ROUTE TO VALENCIA ISLAND / VALENCIA ISLAND / GREAT SKELLIG / ISLAND MONASTERIES / PORTMAGEE TO BALLINSKELLIGS / PUFFIN ISLAND / BALLINSKELLIGS / CARRIGACAPPEEN

18 CORK *178*
GLENGARRIFF / SKULL / LOUGH HYNE / SOUTH CORK UPLANDS

19 WATERFORD *187*
SURFACES IN WEST WATERFORD / LISMORE CASTLE

20 LIMERICK *192*
LOUGH GUR / PARTEEN

21 THE SHANNON *198*
SHANNON SOURCE AND LOUGH ALLEN / LOUGH ALLEN TO LOUGH REE · LOUGH GARA · GLACIAL DIVERSION · TERMONBARRY / LOUGH REE / LOUGH REE TO LOUGH DERG · ATHLONE · CLONMACNOISE · BOORA · MEELICK / LOUGH DERG · GLACIAL DIVERSION / KILLALOE TO LIMERICK · CASTLECONNELL

22 ERNELAND *223*
POT-HOLING / ERNE BASIN / LOWER LOUGH ERNE / UPPER LOUGH ERNE

23 THE MIDLANDS *228*
DRUMURCHER / CROGHAN / CLONSAST BOG / LITTLETON BOG / DERRYNAFLAN BOG

24 THE BOYNE *242*
UPPER COURSE / LOWER COURSE · BRÚ NA BÓINNE · NEWGRANGE · KNOWTH / TOWNLEY HALL / DROGHEDA / THE ESTUARY

*Bibliography* 259
*Index of Topics* 260
*Index of Personal Names* 263
*Index of Irish Localities (with National Grid references)* 265

# ILLUSTRATIONS

## Colour Plates


1 Geological map of Ireland
2 Tory Island, Donegal
3 Ballylongford Estuary, Kerry
4 Ballinloghig, Kerry
5 Valencia Island, Kerry
6 Lough Gur, Limerick
7 Knowth, Meath
8 Baltray standing-stones, Baltray, Louth


## Black and White Photographs


A.W. Stelfox 3
J.P. Brunker 4
Jessen and Jonassen 17
Tropical limestone, Tanga, Tanzania 26
Fenit limestone pinnacle 26
W.A. Watts and pollen diagram 39
Sir Harry Godwin 55
Jessen, Mitchell and Iversen 62
Knud Jessen 63
Goodland, Antrim 79
Skreen tombstone, Sligo 108
Phalaropes, near Belmullet, Mayo 115
Burren droving-road, Formoyle, Clare 140
Illauntannig monastery, Kerry 156
Great Skellig, Kerry 168
Great Skellig, Kerry 170
Carrigacappeen, near Kenmare, Kerry 177
John Jackson and boulder-dolmen: near Dunmanus, Cork 182
Lough Hyne, Cork 184
Brosna floods: near Rahan, Offaly 221
George Eogan and others at Knowth 248
Kilsharvan statue, Meath 255


## Location Maps


Cave sites 32
South-east Ireland 38
North-east Ireland 52, 65
North Donegal 85
South-west Donegal 96
Sligo and Mayo 101, 109
Galway, Clare and north Kerry 129, 137, 144
South-west Ireland 153, 161, 178
The midlands 228
The Lower Boyne 242


## Illustrative Maps


Great Skellig 169
Shannon Basin 199
Former midland lakes 200
Lough Allen 201
Derrycarne diversion 206
Clonmacnoise to Meelick 210
Mongan Bog 212
Killaloe diversion 217
Castleconnell 220
Erne Basin 225
Brú na Bóinne 244


## Line Drawings


Limestone features 24
Behy field-systems, Mayo 111
Old Lismore Castle 189
Shannonbridge, Galway 214
Map of lateglacial beetles 232

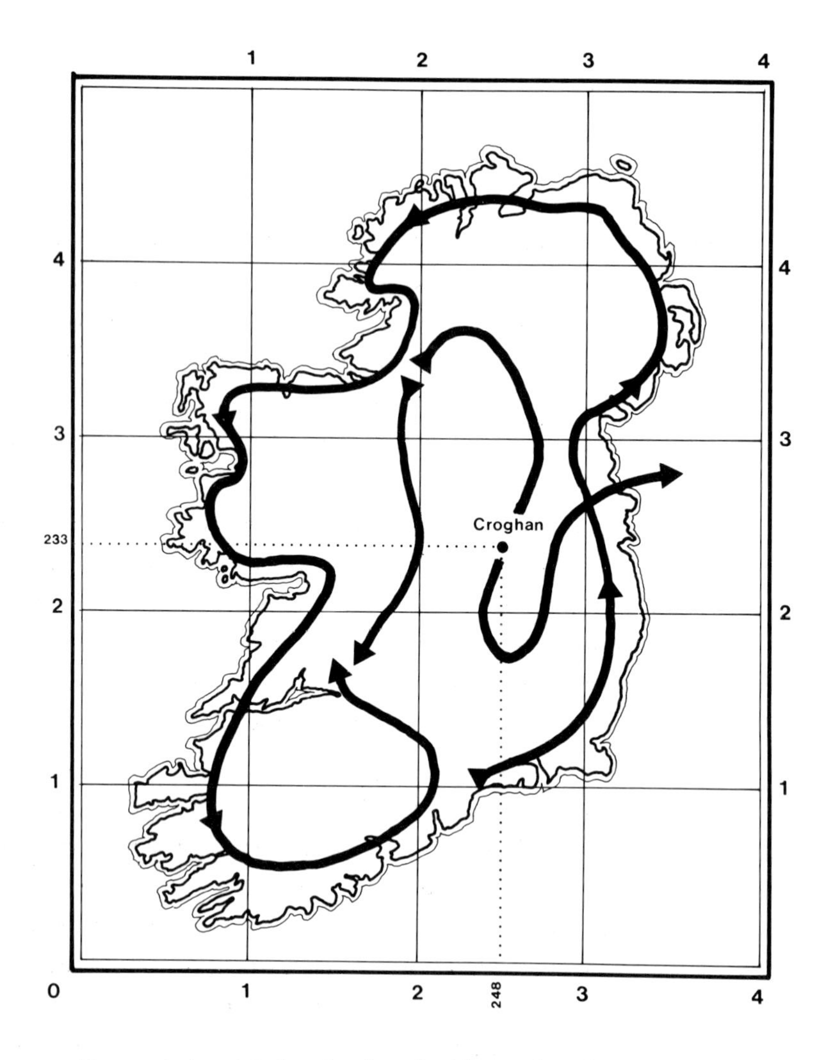


*The approximate route is shown by a heavy line. The map shows the National Grid, and named localities can be found by reading the co-ordinate numbers in the Locality Index, and measuring from the left and bottom margins, in that order. The location of Croghan (248 233) is shown. Any gridded map may be used.*

# INTRODUCTION

I trust that I shall not seem presumptuous or underhand if I publish a book entitled *The Way that I Followed*. Presumptuous, because I attempt, not to follow in the footsteps of, but to provide a companion volume for a most successful book published more than fifty years ago. I refer of course to Lloyd Praeger's *The Way that I Went*, first published in 1937, and re-issued many times since. Underhand, because some might think that by choosing a similar title, I seek to draw some of the success of Praeger's book down upon my own.

Praeger presented his book as a thank-offering for seven decades of happy and beneficial wandering throughout the length and breadth of Ireland. I have enjoyed the same privilege, though my wanderings were through an Ireland very different to that which Praeger explored, and my curiosity and that of my colleagues were armed with many techniques that were unknown to Praeger and his times. And it is that contrast between the world of science in Praeger's day and mine that has prompted me to write this book.

A book of this type can be presented in three ways, chronological, thematical, or geographical—as Praeger chose. If I were to take the chronological route, the book would inevitably have a strongly autobiographical tinge, and this I was determined to avoid, except inasfar as some personal explanation is occasionally unavoidable. The thematic course would turn it into a textbook, and of these there are already too many. I try to give running comment, rather than detailed argument. I am aware that there may be errors and omissions, and these I regret. The geographical course may be confusing for those who do not know Ireland, and has the further complication that sometimes several years may separate my visits to sites described successively on my route; also some sites had great claims on my personal interests, and were re-visited many times, often over long periods of years. At such places I try to provide a chronological pointer.

But the geographical course was really mandatory if my book was to be moulded the way Praeger moulded his. Praeger zig-zagged down Ireland, but I have tried to follow a continuous if winding route. After some unavoidable marking time in Dublin, I set off from the south-east corner of the country, and proceed anti-clockwise right round the island till I reach Cork. I then move in a northerly direction to Limerick, where I meet the Shannon. There is then a hiatus, as I follow the Shannon, not northwards from Limerick, but southwards from its source at the Shannon Pot. With another hiccup I jump back to the Erne and its lakes, and then wander through the east midlands till I arrive at the source of the Boyne. I then follow the Boyne till it reaches the sea below Drogheda, where our peregrination ends.

As will be seen from my story, many colleagues and friends joined me at various places along the way, or contributed illustrations to the book. From all of them I drew both information and friendship, but as they are too numerous to arrange their names in a readable alphabetical list, I make here one simple, but sincere, expression of my thanks. But special thanks must go to Elizabeth FitzPatrick, for helpful comments as the text made its way through successive drafts, and to Treasa Coady, for her skilful production of the book.

CHAPTER 1

# The Early Days

FAMILY INFLUENCES

ARTHUR STELFOX · J. P. BRUNKER

## Family Influences

I do not know what brought out a *naturalist* streak in me so strongly. My father was educated in Dr Benson's famous school in Rathmines, but although Benson made strenuous efforts to inculcate a love of birds in his pupils, his enthusiasm did not stir my father. However, he did love the outdoors, and before his marriage he went camping with Tommy Mason, writer and photographer, and after his family was reared went caravanning with Isaac Swain, then Professor of Geology in Cork. The open air attracted him, but he did not look at nature in detail.

It was Tommy Mason—or more correctly Thomas Holmes Mason, MRIA—who showed me my first scientific specimen. The Mason and the Mitchell families holidayed in Rush during and after the First World War. In those days road surfaces were made of small lumps of broken limestone crushed down by a steam-roller, and if a road was to be repaired, piles of broken limestone would be dumped along it. The quarry at Milverton outside Skerries was the source of the limestone, which at that locality was very fossiliferous, and if one looked through the lumps at the roadside, quite a good specimen could quickly be found. I can still see—I suppose I was about seven at the time—Mr Mason poring over the lumps of stone and distributing fossils to the little group standing round. At the time he was also interested in moths, and he added to his attractiveness for children by taking them out after dusk to help him paint patches of a scented sugary concoction on telegraph poles. He would return in the early morning to collect the moths that had got stuck in his mixture. I was very touched when I learned after his death of his wish that I should have any books I cared to choose from his archaeological library.

My mother would pick blackberries or collect mushrooms, and there was an annual pilgrimage on Ascension Thursday to Ballycorus to hear the cuckoo, but she was more interested in people than in nature. In his younger days my brother was a successful angler, and when he retired went to live in the country near Poulaphuca, where his garden was his chief interest. My sister frequently visited the countryside of western Ireland, as this was the area where the rural crafts of spinning, dyeing and weaving still survived, but like my brother, gardening is her chief outdoor interest. In the book-cases of an aunt I found—and carried off—the four volumes of Thompson's *Natural History of Ireland,* published in the 1850s—how they got there, I do not know.

When I was about eleven I started to look at birds and to keep a notebook about what I saw. This led me to the Natural History Museum in Merrion Square to examine the displays of native Irish birds. I suppose I must have gone several times, and so attracted the attention of one of the staff, Arthur Stelfox, who came and spoke to me. The ensuing conversation was one of the turning-points in my life, as it was the beginning of an influence, and friendship, that lasted till his death at the age of eighty-nine in 1972.

## Arthur Stelfox

Arthur Stelfox was a genius, but at the same time bordered on the eccentric. He was most renowned as an entomologist, specialising in ichneumon-flies, and as a conchologist, specialising in freshwater pond-snails, but he also carried on the museum tradition of identification of animal-bones; here he was of great assistance to archaeologists, though he always complained that they were over-rough with the bones they found. He bred generations of snails in his garage, and produced results that gave geneticists much food for thought.

*Arthur Wilson Stelfox*

Stelfox was a man of habit. His dress never varied: tweed jacket and knickerbockers, open-necked shirt. He left the museum at 5 pm and cycled home to Harold's Cross where his evening-meal—usually roast pork—was waiting. As soon as the meal was over, he crossed the room, and resumed the task of mounting his specimens by the light of an oil-lamp at his side. Mrs Stelfox—a botanist in her own right—sat at the opposite side of the fire with a basket of mending on her knee. If I called in the evening, as I often did, he would comment on Irish natural history—and historians—without pausing in his work. He bought one motor-car, a Talbot tourer, and when, after many years, it was damaged in a collision, he never bought another. Every June he went for one week to Ben Lawyers in Scotland to feast on its Alpine flowers, which were then in full bloom.

Such was the man who spoke to me. He tried to interest me in insects, suggesting bees as a group little studied in Ireland; but I stayed with birds. At the time the Dublin Naturalists'

Field Club had a small Active Service Unit, the ASU, which went out into the field every Sunday. Stelfox, Tony Farrington, later to be another friend and colleague, and Louis Smyth, later, as Professor of Geology, to be my chief in Trinity College, were regulars, and there was a floating population of younger men. Stelfox suggested I should join them, but, as my father had Sabbatarian leanings, that was not possible. He then introduced me to J.P. Brunker, who was employed in Guinness's brewery, but who lived for natural history in all its forms, particularly plants in Co. Wicklow.

## J. P. BRUNKER

*James Ponsonby Brunker*

Brunker had a bull-nosed Morris two-seater, and we would drive down on Saturday afternoons to Kilcoole or Newcastle on the coast where he would look for rare clovers and at the same time show me birds. We would then go to Hunters' Hotel in Newrathbridge for tea, and I saw for the first time the famous notice 'Ladies and gentlemen will not, others must not, pick the flowers'. Brunker, too, was a man of habit. Like Stelfox, his dress never varied: trench-coat, cap and pipe. Every third week of March he would haunt the river Dodder, just above Orwell Bridge, listening for the first chiff-chaff. Watching Brunker watching for the chiff-chaff was quite a sound piece of ornithology, and although he is gone for many years, I still try to visit the spot at the right time each year.

On one occasion he presented me with a dead brambling, which I had stuffed by Teddy Williams, the last survivor of a family of distinguished taxidermists. The firm was in an attic at the top of Dame Street, and I went there many years later to see a black redstart, which was frequenting the local roof-tops. Teddy and I became friends, and we went shooting together. Brunker told me that if you ever see a flock of winter chaffinches, you must watch closely as they fly away to see if you can spot a white rump which lies fore-and-aft, not side-to-side as in the bullfinch. If you see such a rump, you are looking at a brambling. It was sixty years before such a sight burst upon me, and most appropriately it was on one of Brunker's favourite stamping-grounds, the Murrough, just north of Wicklow town, that I saw several brambling among a flock of chaffinches.

As well as tips like this, he also gave me a small book on bird identification, but it had no photographs, only some sketchy line-drawings. As various school prizes I acquired *Our Resident Birds* and *Our Migrant Birds*, each with about thirty black-and-white photographs. One has only to pick up Roger Petersen's *Field Guide* with its hundreds of colour illustrations to realise how much bird-books—and all natural history books—have advanced during the past fifty years.

In 1926, when I was thirteen, Stelfox had another suggestion. A group of cave-diggers was coming from Bristol to Ireland to look for bones in a cave in Co. Waterford, some Irish people were going to join them, and I should go along too. The next thing that happened was that the Stelfox family came to Sunday afternoon tea in our home; I thought it was a simple social occasion, but looking back I suppose it was an opportunity for my parents to 'vet' the man about whom they had heard so much from me, to see if it would be safe to let their son go to Waterford.

Stelfox must have passed the test, and so in the wet summer of 1926 I found myself outside a cave in a bell-tent in a field at Kilgraeny, near Dungarvan, with three companions, all students in Trinity College, two of them protégés of Stelfox. Arthur Gwynn (later to be my brother-in-law), a member of the ASU, had entered Trinity as a medical student, but had been persuaded by Stelfox to switch to entomology; in middle life he reverted to medicine. Arthur Lisney, another medical student, was also a keen entomologist, and maintained this interest throughout his professional life. Lisney suffered acutely from asthma (which shortened his life); no one told me of this, and I awoke in the middle of one night, thinking I was suffocating, but it was merely Arthur smoking some type of herb cigarette, in an effort to relieve a spasm.

Bill Riley, who took his degree in physics and chemistry, had an interest in caves and bones. We will return to Kilgraeny later.

Stelfox had another protégée, Nora McMillan from Belfast. Nora became an expert conchologist, and made her career in the Liverpool Museum. After Stelfox retired, I sent any freshwater or marine shells I came upon in my fieldwork off to Nora for identification and comment. This happy collaboration still continues.

CHAPTER 2

DECISION TIME

OPTING FOR NATURAL SCIENCES

THE QUATERNARY RESEARCH COMMITTEE

## Decision Time

A number of years have elapsed, and now I am approaching the end of my schooldays. Following on the death of his father, my father left school prematurely, and entered a stockbroker's office. His elder brother, George, was anxious to enter business, and he suggested to my father that they should pool their resources and buy Hodges, an ironmongery and furniture establishment on Aston's Quay. The premises are today occupied by a student travel bureau. I am sure that when my father took this step he had hopes that his sons might follow him in the trade.

My brother and I attended the High School, then in Harcourt Street. In school he was a whiz-kid, carrying all before him, while I was a slow learner. At the exam for entrance exhibitions into Trinity College he took second place, and then entered the Medical School, to take the first steps on a road that led to a distinguished career in medicine.

When I sat for the same examination some years later, I was eighteenth on the list. Everybody was very kind, thought I had gone up too young and that I should try again the following year. I did, and was placed sixteenth, not a profitable return for a further year at school. This should have ended my prospects of a university course, and I did spend some time working in Hodges. But my mother insisted that as my brother had had some years in the university, I should have the same. My sister, when her turn came, decided to follow the arts—music, painting, weaving—outside the walls of a university.

But then the goddess Chance intervened on my behalf. The High School was an Erasmus Smith foundation, and there was a special entrance exhibition, open only to boys who had been educated at an Erasmus Smith school. I had a school colleague, Jimmy Bridle, and we usually sat together towards the top of the class. He was placed far ahead of me in the results list, and secured the Erasmus Smith exhibition. But he opted for a career in the Bank of Ireland and did not take up the award, which then, somewhat unworthily, arrived on my shoulders, despite my lowly position on the examination list.

What was I to read?—the idea being still afloat that after graduating I would return to Hodges, Honours French and English were decided on, on the basis that proficiency in French would be helpful in a commercial career. Nowadays courses in adjustment are available to help teenagers at school to proceed, without dislocation, to the university scene. Nothing of the sort existed in 1930, although I would have benefited greatly from such a course. English consisted of watching Professor W.F. Trench, an authority on Shakespeare, walk backwards and forwards on the rostrum, eyes closed, hands clasped behind his back, descanting on Hamlet's problems. Sam Beckett had no use for lightweights in his classes, and was rude to those who showed no promise. I took the hint and fled.

I had not yet learned to work, and spent some time in the billiard-room and at the Four Courts. I sometimes think I would have done well at the Bar, because I can speak glibly and can make up a subject in some detail and then dismiss it. I attended several *causes célèbres*: the Emilio Scala case, in which the ownership of a winning sweepstake ticket was disputed; the Burroughs Wellcome case, where it was claimed that a number of children had become infected following an injection of one of the company's products; the Gogarty libel case. Oliver St John Gogarty, a swash-buckling medical figure, noted in *Ulysses* as Buck Mulligan, had published his autobiography, and two Dublin dealers claimed they had been libelled. Sam

Beckett was called for the plaintiffs, and was cross-examined by John Mary Fitzgerald, a very keen advocate, who had taken a first-class honours degree in modern languages before turning to the Bar. He asked, 'You have written a book, *The Whoroscope*, Mr Beckett?'—'Yes'—'Begins with W, Mr Beckett?'—'Yes'—'And there's another, ''*More Pricks than Kicks*'' '—'Yes'—'You are an authority on Proust' (the vowels pronounced as in 'Faust'). The unsuspecting Beckett rose to the fly, 'Are you referring to the French author Proust (the vowels pronounced as in 'roost')?' Fitzgerald did not speak, but as he sat down he gave the jury a sharing glance which said more clearly than words 'Plain people like you and me can't be expected to know how to pronounce the names of dirty French writers'. But at the Bar I would inevitably have become personally involved in the affairs of my clients, and I would have torn my nerves to shreds.

## Opting for Natural Sciences

I turned to Natural Sciences, thinking that here the field naturalist would find a congenial home. I won't say 'Foiled again', but it was not quite what I expected, as study was entirely confined to the lecture-room and the laboratory.

In geology there was Professor John Joly, a most distinguished geophysicist with a very inventive mind, and indeed a man before his time. It was just beginning to be realised that the decay of radioactive substances in the earth's crust created heat there, and that if this heat continued to accumulate, melting and volcanic activity must follow. It is unfortunate that he is not alive today, when it is fully realised that much volcanic activity does take place on ocean floors, and that this activity causes the continents to move. Continental movement was one of the chief themes in his famous book *The Surface History of the Earth*, published in 1926. But he was over eighty by the time I reached his lectures, unable to control noisy students, and my chief reaction was one of embarrassment.

Botany was under the charge of Henry Dixon, a famous plant physiologist, who made his reputation through his studies of the way in which water and other substances are conducted from the ground up through the trunk of a tree to the leaf canopy at the top. He had no interest in the flowers of the field.

Nor had zoology any interest in animals in the wild. James Brontë Gatenby, a New Zealander who had taken his doctorate in Oxford, was a man of strong views, with a taste for polemics. A cytologist, he had an interest in detailed cell-structures. Among these were *mitochondria*, tiny rod-like structures in the nucleus of the cell. But before the tiny slivers of tissue appeared on Brontë's microscope slide, they had undergone considerable chemical treatment and staining. Other workers claimed that the mitochondria had only appeared as a consequence of the treatment, and had formed no part of the original cell. For a time his work went under a cloud, but then the electron-microscope appeared, and showed the mitochondria as plain as a pikestaff in the living cell. It was a very happy thing that in the last years of his working-life his reputation soared again.

My first years in college were just like my last years in school. I did not know how to work; I can see myself lying on the floor at home, listlessly turning over the pages of a textbook, with the radio playing beside me. But the college dangled a bait in front of its brighter students, Scholarship. There was only a restricted number of such awards, and they brought with them a small salary, free rooms and a free dinner. Quite suddenly I decided to work for one, and moved into rooms in college to make study easier. I got a scholarship when I was twenty years of age. Thus I only learned to *work* at this relatively late age, and it is a question I often ask of my colleagues—When did you start to *work*?

We had to specialise in one subject in our final year, and I chose zoology simply because birds were animals, and animals were zoology. Tissue-culture, trying to grow implanted living tissue in other animals, was becoming all the rage, and Brontë told me that I was to do tissue-culture in snails. This involved taking a piece out of one living snail and implanting it in another, and then after a certain interval killing the second snail, and trying to discover what had happened to the implant. I was finding the whole process most distasteful, when chance again intervened on my behalf.

Professor Joly had died, and his assistant, Louis Bouvier Smyth, was promoted to the Chair of Geology. I had been interested in Smyth's lectures in invertebrate palaeontology, the subject of his personal research. He spoke about a limestone quarry in north Co. Dublin, at St Doulagh's on the Malahide road, where the rock was especially rich in well-preserved fossils. I organised some of my classmates and we went out to the quarry. Incidentally, this was the only excursion into the field that I had throughout the whole four years of my course. I worked on some of the fossils I had collected in order to lessen the rock-matrix which surrounded them, then I showed them to Smyth. This may have created a good impression, because shortly afterwards he asked me to go to see him. At our interview he said that if I would switch from zoology to geology as my special subject, and if I were to get a good honours degree, he would ask the board of the college to appoint me as his assistant.

## THE QUATERNARY RESEARCH COMMITTEE

A further intervention followed almost immediately. A group of field scientists in the Royal Irish Academy decided that the time had come when a serious effort must be made to unravel the history of the development of bogs in Ireland, and of the formation of the glacial deposits on which they rested. A leading Danish expert in this field, Knud Jessen, Professor of Botany in the University of Copenhagen, had indicated that he would be interested in the task, and Mr de Valera, then Taoiseach, was willing to make funds available. A Quaternary Research Committee was set up, and Praeger, Farrington and Adolf Mahr, Director of the National Museum, formed an executive committee.

Praeger had had such a project in mind for many years, as he knew that study of the plant fossils preserved in the bogs would yield a rich record of the history of Irish vegetation. Because of problems he met in his geological mapping of the glacial deposits in Co. Wicklow, Farrington was most anxious to have the techniques of studying late-glacial deposits that had been developed in Scandinavia applied in Ireland. Mahr, who had recently come to Dublin, was greatly impressed by the quantity of antiquities that peat-cutting produced every year. He knew that the statistical counting of pollen grains—wrongly called pollen-analysis—embedded in bogs could lead to a dating of the layers building up the bog, and so to the dating of archaeological objects found in the layers. Statistical counting is now only one element of a wider field of pollen studies, known as *palynology*.

The triumvirate's first tasks were to organise Jessen's visit, and to recruit Irish students who would both guide Jessen round the country and be trained in the new techniques by him. Smyth became aware of the project, and suggested to me that I should send my name forward as a candidate even though, should I be successful, it would mean missing two months of summer study for my final examination in October. Smyth was confident that it was an opportunity not to be missed by someone with my tastes, and needless to say I was entranced by the prospect of two months in the Irish countryside. Better still, the project would replace tissue-culture as my fourth-year specialisation.

Praeger already had some knowledge of me, because I was then fairly active in the Dublin Field Club, whose meetings Praeger rarely missed. Tony Farrington and I soon formed an easy acquaintanceship, which quickly grew into friendship. I approached my meeting with Mahr with some reserve, because I had earlier been interviewed by an archaeologist, and been found wanting.

In the early thirties Harvard University, largely through the influence of Professor Kingsley Porter who had installed himself in Glenveagh Castle in Donegal (now a national park), conducted several large-scale investigations in Ireland, including archaeology. The latter was under the direction of Hugh Hencken, Director of the Peabody Museum in Boston. Like the Quaternary Research Committee, Hugh was anxious to enlist young assistants. Somebody, probably Stelfox, must have mentioned me to him, and I was summoned, much overawed, to lunch in the Buttery, the basement bar of the old Royal Hibernian Hotel, where Hugh always stayed. Something must have gone wrong during our meeting, and an invitation to join him never emerged. His last dig in Ireland was at the big crannog at Lagore, outside Dunshaughlin in Co. Meath, in 1933 and 1934, where Joe Raftery from the National Museum and Eleanor Hardy from Cambridge were student assistants. But there were no ill-feelings. Jessen visited the Lagore dig in 1934 with me in attendance, and later, at Hugh's request, I went back to the site of one of his earlier digs at Ballinderry in Co. Westmeath, and did some pollen work which was incorporated in his publication. In later life he was crippled by a stroke, but he refused to abandon his work. I called on him many years afterwards in Harvard, and found him, though struggling with disability, at his desk.

Mahr was very enthusiastic about the whole project, and was convinced that it would be a success. He contributed to that success by preparing for Jessen a long list of sites to be visited, sites from which some archaeological object dug up in a bog had recently reached the National Museum. For each site there was a short report and a 6-inch map. The sites were then arranged in geographical order, and Jessen would visit each in turn. At one point Mahr's enthusiasm reached such a level that he leaned forward in his chair and jabbed his forefinger repeatedly into my thigh—an attention I could well have done without—and said, 'Mr Mitchell, if you work hard, in ten years you will have a European reputation'.

It was a tragedy for Irish archaeology—and for the man himself—that Mahr allowed himself to be carried away by his enthusiasm for Hitler and his cause. He was number two in the hierarchy of Dublin supporters of the Nazis; he happened to be in Europe when war was declared, and he never returned to Dublin. After Germany's defeat, he was disgraced, and died some years later in unhappy obscurity. But during his short period of office in Dublin, he did great things, not only for the museum, but for Irish archaeology in general.

I emerged as the successful candidate.

CHAPTER 3

# The Real Beginning

KNUD JESSEN · BALLYBETAGH BOG

## KNUD JESSEN

Jessen and his assistant, Hagbard Jonassen, arrived in Dublin, and were lodged in the Hibernian Hotel, across the road from the Royal Irish Academy. It had been arranged for them to meet the committee in the evening, and as I turned up the Academy steps, where Tony Farrington was standing waiting to receive them, Jessen and Jonassen were walking up the other side of the steps, and I was introduced to them. I will not at this point attempt to sum up either Jessen's capabilities or my reaction to him; I will allow these to transpire as the story of my relationship with him develops.

Jonassen, or Jonas, as he was always referred to, was also very able. At first sight he was earnest, but he was quite capable of fun. He obviously had pored over Dublin street-maps before his arrival, and as he walked up the Academy steps he already knew that Dawson Street ran from St Stephen's Green to Nassau Street, and that Molesworth Street, leading to the National Museum, was just a few yards away. He cared passionately about people, and was a keen pacifist; he was chairman of the Danish branch of War Resisters International. He found it very difficult not to explode when having to listen to Mahr's fascist tirades, and after the war he worked in reconstruction camps in Greece. He visited Ireland several times after the first quaternary campaign was over, and we remained close friends until his death in 1975.

Ballybetagh Bog, 15km south of Dublin, near Kilternan, was the first target. Meltwater, spilling over across a rock-ridge from one ice-impounded lake into another, had cut a narrow channel through the ridge. There is a second similar channel near by, the Scalp, through which the road to Enniskerry runs. The channel at Ballybetagh had held narrow lakes, and at the close of the Ice Age many Irish giant deer—and a smaller number of reindeer—had been drowned there, and their bones had been preserved in the lake-muds. Giant deer bones were first found there in the late nineteenth century, and there had been a steady trickle of finds through the ensuing years. In addition, in 1926 Stelfox had brought one of the early practitioners of pollen studies, the Swede Gunnar Erdtman, to Ballybetagh, and they found a fossil leaf of the dwarf willow (*Salix herbacea*). This willow is very common in arctic regions, and still survives in a few isolated localities on Irish mountain-tops. The possibility of finding a fossil arctic flora in Ireland was a further bait to Jessen.

Gunnar Erdtman's achievements in the development of pollen work did not receive adequate recognition in his lifetime, because another Swede, Lennart von Post, considered that Erdtman was treading on his coat-tails. Von Post was a powerful figure in the Swedish scientific establishment, and was able to block Erdtman's promotion. This was very unfair, because already in the twenties Erdtman had visited the British Isles, and had published diagrams—admittedly crude by modern standards—from England, Ireland and the Isle of Man. He produced a book of drawings of pollen grains, which went for years without a rival, and he crossed the Atlantic with a vacuum-cleaner running constantly so that he could get some idea of how far pollen could travel. But he was stiff in his manner, and always dressed like a Swedish cavalry officer; his wife was also aristocratic in appearance.

Pollen grains, which are microscopic in size, have a very durable outer case, within which the living tissue is protected. Most cases are provided with exits or pores through which the inner tissue can emerge, and the shape of the case, and the number and arrangement of the pores, varies from plant to plant. Most cases are readily identified under suitable magnification. Many plants cast their pollen into the air, where, carried by the wind, some grains will reach female flowers, but the vast majority fall to the surface of the earth. If kept wet and protected from oxygen, the pollen cases have great resistance to decay. Those which fall into lakes or onto the surfaces of bogs may survive in an identifiable state for thousands of years.

The idea of the value of studying fossil pollen had been around for a long time, but von Post, in the early twenties, was the first to take a series of samples down through a depth of peat, count the tree-pollen grains in each sample systematically, and then deduce from changing proportions of different tree-pollens corresponding changes in the composition of the local forests. In a sample of peat, however, pollen grains provided only a tiny proportion of the bulk, and to identify them among the other debris was a lengthy task. Von Post was content to place a small piece of peat on a microscope slide, moisten it with an alkaline solution (usually potassium hydroxide), warm the slide over a Bunsen burner to encourage the alkali to macerate the peat, put a cover slip on the sample, and begin the laborious task of counting 150 pollen cases.

Erdtman began to look for short-cuts. He reckoned that the bulk of the vegetable debris in the sample was not as resistant to decay as the pollen-cases, and that suitable chemical treatment would get rid of the debris without harming the pollen. His brother was a chemist, and together they worked out a treatment using first oxygen and then acid to lessen the quantity of debris. These chemical treatments involved dispersing the pollen through a volume of fluid; how were they to be collected again? Erdtman put the fluid into tubes which he whirled around in a centrifuge, and centrifugal force pushed the pollen down to the bottom of the tubes. The concentrated pollen was mounted on a slide, and counting was much more rapid. Most pollen-workers took up the new method, but von Post was furious and would not admit either chemical treatment or a centrifuge into his laboratory. Jessen adopted the Erdtman technique, and such was the state of the art when I was instructed in it in Copenhagen some months later.

That I was to go to Copenhagen for further study carried a double significance, first that I had been accepted by Jessen as suitable material, and second that Hodges would never see me. Despite a summer careering round Ireland with Jessen—we visited every county—I had secured a good degree. The trip solved one of my tasks. As part of the final examination in botany, candidates had to produce a dried collection of not less than thirty plants; as we moved around Ireland Jessen was collecting plants for the Copenhagen herbarium, and he nearly always had a few spare specimens. These he passed on to me, I stuck them on sheets of paper, and in no time I had my collection.

Louis Smyth was as good as his word, and I was appointed to be his assistant at a salary of £50 in the first year and £100 in the second—payable quarterly in arrears, in addition to my modest emoluments as a Scholar. It was characteristic of Louis's kindly nature that he wrote a very thoughtful letter to my father, saying that while he knew my father would regret my not joining him in Hodges, he felt confident that my new career would be one in which he could take pride. In a letter to my father from Copenhagen, I tried to say something on similar lines, and I admired him because he never once, either by word or implication, gave utterance to any disappointment at my opting for science rather than commerce.

## Ballybetagh Bog

It was decided to open up a series of trenches at Ballybetagh so that interpretation of the stratigraphy would not have to depend on the borings that Jessen could make with a hand-drill of narrow diameter. Bill Riley, whom we met in Chapter 1, had just returned after a spell of meteorological work in East Africa, and was at a loose end; he was recruited to oversee the excavations. This had a comic sequel. The early thirties were a time of high unemployment in Ireland, and de Valera's government had started a relief scheme for unskilled workers, chiefly on public works. But de Valera extended public works to include archaeological excavations, an intelligent arrangement which continues to this day. This extension was of the greatest value to Hugh Hencken, and it also covered the Ballybetagh dig.

One Saturday afternoon de Valera decided, without notice, to visit the site himself. The paying-out of state money required a certain amount of paper-work, and Bill decided to stay on and catch up with this chore on the holiday afternoon. He looked out of his tent and saw a tall figure in black peering into the trenches. There were other men present, but they kept a short distance from the figure in black. He shouted a warning not to fall in, and said he would be out in a moment.

Bill joined the stranger, explained what was going on in the dig, and listened to the visitor speculating on the placename *Ballybetagh*, and wondering what position those who were referred to as *betaghs* had held in early Irish society. The tour came to an end and the visitor concluded his expression of thanks by enquiring what the name of his guide was. Bill said 'Riley', and not to be outdone in politeness, added 'and what's yours?' The man, looking a little surprised, said 'Oh, de Valera'. The surprise was probably occasioned by the fact that de Valera would have expected that a ganger on a government relief scheme would have been a supporter of his party, Fianna Fáil. Because of his absence in Africa, Bill must have been one of the very few men in Ireland at the time who did not know what de Valera looked like. I didn't have many meetings with de Valera, but when we did have a conversation, the topic of Ballybetagh inevitably recurred.

*In action. With a forceps, Jessen places a peat sample in a tube. The chamber of the bog-drill lies on the peat-bank before him. Jonassen, with pencil in hand and notebook by his knee, will make the necessary record. The levelling apparatus stands behind them.*

The Ballybetagh excavations gave a fine send-off to Jessen's Irish programme. The open-water lake-muds at the bottom of the sections were divided by a layer of grey sandy clay, rich in leaves of the dwarf willow, and this was exactly the stratigraphy with which Jessen was familiar in Denmark. The end of the Ice Age in north-west Europe was marked by a sudden warming in climate, and temperate plants started to come back. Then climatic conditions reversed, and frost returned. Repeated freezing and thawing of the surface layers of the ground enabled sand and clay to slide down the sloping sides of the Ballybetagh valley and out over the mud, carrying the remains of cold-loving plants with them. Warmth returned, soil movement ceased, and first temperate herbs and shrubs, and then trees, returned to Ireland.

Jessen's work was especially important because he identified not only the microscopic pollen, but also leaves and seeds which were visible to the naked eye and so often grouped together as *macrofossils*. For macrofossils large samples were necessary, and these were subsequently washed and sieved in the laboratory. Not at Ballybetagh, because there he had specially cut sections available to him, but at other sites he considered worthy of examination, he would start by making with his hand-drill a line of borings across the deposit to be examined. The relative heights of these were then determined with a level, and Jonassen would spend the evening—after he had finished making a fair copy of the day's field-notes—drawing up a cross-section of the deposit. Jessen would inspect this and decide on the most profitable point at which to make his detailed boring to collect pollen samples. During this time he would also have prepared herbarium specimens. Sometimes he would make two detailed borings, or possibly a second cross-section. Many of today's workers have at their disposal more sophisticated techniques for examining and identifying their material, but they tend to be specialists. The pollen workers go to a site and make one boring to get their detailed samples. The macroscopic people go to a 'good' site where previous workers have shown that suitable material exists, and collect a large sample to examine in detail. Neither take an overview of the site as a whole. The breadth and carefulness of Jessen's work has not been surpassed.

A minor but interesting point may perhaps be made. All Jessen's work in Ireland was done before plastic bags came on the scene. It was important that his large samples should be kept wet, and of course some considerable time was going to elapse before they could be examined in the laboratory. Jessen had waterproofed paper bags, but they were quite unsatisfactory. Plastic bags, which we now all use as a matter of course, would have made his fieldwork much simpler.

Before Jessen's visit, the name Ballybetagh connoted the extinct Irish giant deer, because of the many bones and antlers of this animal that had been found there. This splendid deer stood about 2m high at the shoulders, and the male had huge antlers with a spread of 3m. But the antlers were only thin plates of bone, and were probably used for display rather than combat. The chief aim of the Ballybetagh campaign was to try to put the giant deer into context, and one of the trenches revealed part of a head embedded in the mud immediately below the arctic clay layer. Since then I have investigated many other finds of giant deer in different parts of Ireland, and all have lain in the same stratigraphical position. So it is reasonable to suppose that this animal flourished in Ireland for the last time in that early temperate stage, and that it was killed off through lack of sufficient nutritious food when the cold period came on.

The technique of radiocarbon dating was unknown when Jessen was here, but a further investigation at Ballybetagh has put the date of disappearance at 10,600 years ago. This Ballybetagh date arose from work that was done there lately by Tony Barnosky of the Carnegie Museum in Pittsburgh. Like other workers before him, Tony was puzzled as to why remains of male deer at Ballybetagh greatly outnumbered female remains. Most of the early digging was done by collectors who wanted to assemble skeletons for sale to museums, as well as discarded broken bones. Tony kept every scrap he found, and was amazed by the number of scraps. His explanation, which I find quite satisfactory, is that the sheltered valley at Ballybetagh provided a winter refuge for the males, while the females and young kept to open country. At the beginning of winter, mortality among males exhausted by the autumn rut was high; the survivors trampled on the carcasses, damaging the bones and smashing the fragile antlers to pieces, hence the abundance of debris.

Ballybetagh has one further connotation for me—corncrakes. Tommy Mason had four sons, and the second, Alec, was a contemporary and a friend of mine in school and college. As schoolboys we experimented with egg-collecting, but Alec took to photography, and I can remember photographing rooks' nests in pine trees in Rathfarnham. In the early forties corncrakes were still abundant in south county Dublin, and Alec, with the aid of serrated horse-ribs, a stuffed decoy bird, and a net, combined ringing and photography; I was a general technical assistant. A very few of the birds we ringed were recovered; one we recovered ourselves. A bird approached in response to Alec's calls, and we saw that it had a ring on its leg. Needless to say we were going to stay put for ever if necessary, but catch it we had to. We did, and it was a bird we had ringed in the adjoining field the year before. We learned about bird-nature. One male was puzzled by the lack of response from the decoy; he thought he was at fault and went off to get a present. He came back with a fat caterpillar in his beak, and held it close to the beak of the decoy. Again no response. I cannot recall if we ever caught him.

We had a major success just up the road from Ballybetagh, at Glencullen crossroads. We ringed a bird, and as it was a warm May evening we went into Johnny Fox's pub for a drink. The pints had barely been put before us when another bird started up on the opposite side of the road. We asked the barman to mind our drinks, went out, ringed the bird, and were back to the pub in twenty minutes. Today, a Dubliner has to cross the Shannon if he wants to hear the corncrake.

Alec, after he had graduated, spent a year with a scientific company in Germany before returning to the family firm in Dublin, which dealt in optical goods, cameras and scientific supplies. Some irony here was not, I am sure, lost on my father. His friend, Tommy Mason, had four boys, and three of them entered the firm. My father had two boys, but neither followed in his footsteps. Later in life, after his brother's retirement from the firm, my father switched to a smaller business, Lennox Chemicals, where he felt he could draw at least technical advice from my brother and myself.

Irony again, because Masons and Lennox were operating in the same field; at one time the possibility of a merger was discussed, but nothing came of it.

I may be over-labouring the nagging feeling that I had in some way let my father down, but I am unfortunately full of what Thomas Mann describes as 'the true Protestant's passionate, relentless sense of personal responsibility'.

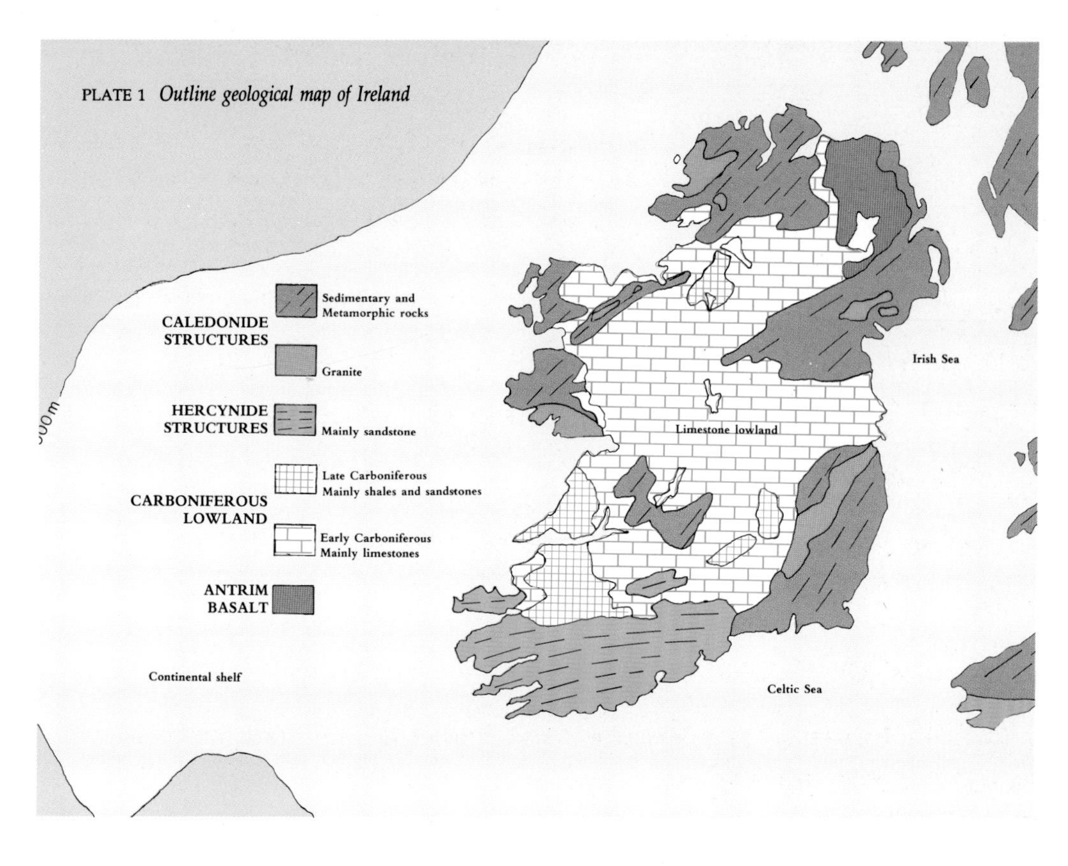


PLATE 1 *Outline geological map of Ireland*

PLATE 2 *Tory Island, Donegal. Derek Hill placed himself high on the east corner of the island, and from there looked south-westwards. The cliffed north coast, and the gentle tilt from there to the south, are clearly depicted.*

PLATE 3 *Ballylongford Estuary, Kerry. From the wharf at Saleen we look north down the estuary at high tide. Carrickafoyle Castle rises from the salt-marsh.*

PLATE 4 *Ballinloghig, Kerry. Low cloud, grey rock and pale bog-vegetation create a doomful landscape.*

PLATE 5 *Valencia Island, Kerry. On this north slope of the island, one is alone with wind, sky and sea.*

PLATE 6 (BELOW) *Lough Gur, Limerick. The limestone knolls of the Lough Gur area rise from the Limerick plains. The peninsula of Knockadoon, guarded by a small 15th-century castle, projects into the lake. Knockadoon was farmed intensively in Neolithic and Bronze Age times.*

PLATE 7 *Knowth, Meath. The great tumulus at Knowth lies on a low hilltop. A ring of large kerb-stones, many lavishly decorated, surrounds the main mound. The gash in its left-hand side is exposing a large passage-grave, similar to Newgrange. Four small mounds in the foreground cover minor reconstructed tombs.*

PLATE 8 *Baltray, Louth. These stones stand on the edge of a cliff, which overlooks low ground, which was formerly a tidal lagoon at the mouth of the Boyne Estuary. Were they erected to welcome—or to deter—prehistoric immigrants?*

CHAPTER 4

# Bees in my Bonnet

ORTHODOX GEOLOGY · THE TERTIARY PERIOD

EROSION OF LIMESTONE · CHEMICAL WEATHERING

TECTONIC MOVEMENT · THE QUATERNARY PERIOD

Here I must make an abrupt digression, and return to that boy of fourteen in the field at Kilgraeny. I had never seen a cave before I dug at Kilgraeny as a teenager, when I was happily free of any pre-conceived notions. Now, more than sixty years on, I have seen many other caves and many other geological phenomena, and have had all too much time to fill my head with notions, some of which are known to my colleagues as bees in poor old Mitchell's bonnet.

But many geological phenomena are difficult to explain rationally, and I cannot help forming concepts as to how they might have taken place. Further work often shows some of the concepts to be wrong, and they are then discarded, or the topic is abandoned. Others tend to persist, and as several bees will take to the wing at various stages of my narrative, I will try to make my readers aware of them now.

## Orthodox Geology

My unorthodox geological comments will be largely confined to events of the last two stages of the earth's history, the Quaternary, roughly speaking the period in which human-like forms have been present on earth, which probably stretches back some two million years from the present, and the Tertiary, the age of mammals, which preceded it. By the opening of the Tertiary, which probably took place about 70 million years ago, the great reptiles of the preceding stage had disappeared, and the Tertiary showed great development among the mammals. A vast period of geological history lies before the opening of the Tertiary, and I now give an orthodox outline of that period, as far as it affects my story (Pl. 1).

We begin about 600 million years ago, when the land area of Ireland as we know it today was below the sea. Primitive life-forms were confined to the sea, and geologists call the time-period the *Lower Palaeozoic*. Rivers on surrounding land discharged clay and sand into the sea, and a thick blanket of these materials was deposited on its floor. Moderate consolidation changed these sediments into shales and sandstones.

About 400 million years ago tremendous earth-pressures uplifted these sedimentary rocks, crushing them into ridges running north-east/south-west. Molten rock, much of which solidified into granite, was injected into these earlier rocks, which were altered by the heat and pressure, and metamorphosed into slate and quartzite. Later erosion has dissected the rocks into ridges and valleys with the same trend. These structures extend from Scandinavia, through Scotland (from which they take their name, *Caledonides*), into Donegal and Connemara. They also appear in south-east Ireland, and in a wedge of country running in from the coasts of Down and Louth.

Following uplift, erosion under conditions of heavy seasonal rainfall attacked these rocks, releasing large quantities of sand which were swept along by torrential floods. Great sheets of sand and gravel built up over most of Ireland, and these were consolidated into what geologists call Old Red Sandstone. Primitive vertebrate animals began to venture onto land, and plants also began their invasion of the continents. These evolutionary developments characterise the *Upper Palaeozoic*.

A warm sea with corals flooded in over Ireland, and this time little sediment was carried in by neighbouring rivers. As a result, calcareous debris derived from the dead shells of numerous animals accumulated on the sea floor; the debris later consolidated into limestone, usually grey in colour because of a small content of clay. The shells were built up by the animals, extracting calcium and carbon dioxide from the sea water and combining them into calcium carbonate (calcite, $CaCO_3$). After very great thicknesses of such sediment had built up in some areas, in what is known as the *Lower Carboniferous* period, clay and sand again began to reach the sea floor, and shales and sandstones were formed, in what we call the *Upper Carboniferous* period. Vertebrate amphibians and large trees developed as the Upper Palaeozoic continued. In places, tree debris accumulated in sufficient quantity to be transformed into coal, hence the term Carboniferous.

Tremendous earth upheavals followed about 300 million years ago. Rocks were folded along a west-east axis from Kerry far into Germany, and the structures produced are known as the *Hercynides,* taking their name from a European locality. The Old Red Sandstone was much more resistant to erosion than the limestone, with the result that in south-west Ireland high ridges of sandstone are separated by valleys, some of which have a surviving limestone floor. In other parts of Ireland where erosion of the limestone and the sandstone has been heavy, the older sedimentary and metamorphic rocks are exposed over wide areas.

By now the reptiles, who culminated in the great dinosaurs, had appeared, and we enter the *Mesozoic* phase of development. At first there was little formation of rock in Ireland, but then warm tropical water again flooded in, and calcareous ooze was deposited on the sea floor. Very little debris of land origin reached the sea, and the pure ooze was later consolidated and uplifted as *chalk,* a white limestone. At first almost the whole land area of Ireland was blanketed by chalk, which, being a weak limestone, was quickly stripped away by erosion. Today, on land, it only survives in the north-east corner, but we now know, thanks to exploration for oil and gas, that it covers great areas of sea-floor south of Waterford and east Cork.

Temperatures then fell, the great reptiles disappeared, mammals and flowering plants flourished, and we enter the *Tertiary* period, about 70 million years ago.

## THE TERTIARY PERIOD

As I reach the Tertiary, my bees start to hum as my interest quickens, although the field evidence remains elusive and there is little room for dogmatism. I shall discuss three topics only—the dissolving of limestone by rainwater, the rotting to a great depth of other types of rock following prolonged chemical attack, and the raising or lowering of blocks of the earth's crust due to tectonic movement.

### Erosion of limestone

Much of Ireland's rock surface is covered by Carboniferous limestone, a rock essentially composed of *calcite*, with a small content of clay, which gives it a grey colour. The limestone was formed in layers beneath the sea, and the irregular movements of uplifting tectonic forces produced many cracks and fissures, known as *joints*, through it. Rain which falls on limestone proceeds down the joints as *ground-water* till it reaches the level at which all cavities are flooded by water, the *water-table*. It then tends to move laterally, seeking a passage through the joints, more or less following the slopes of the land-surface above.

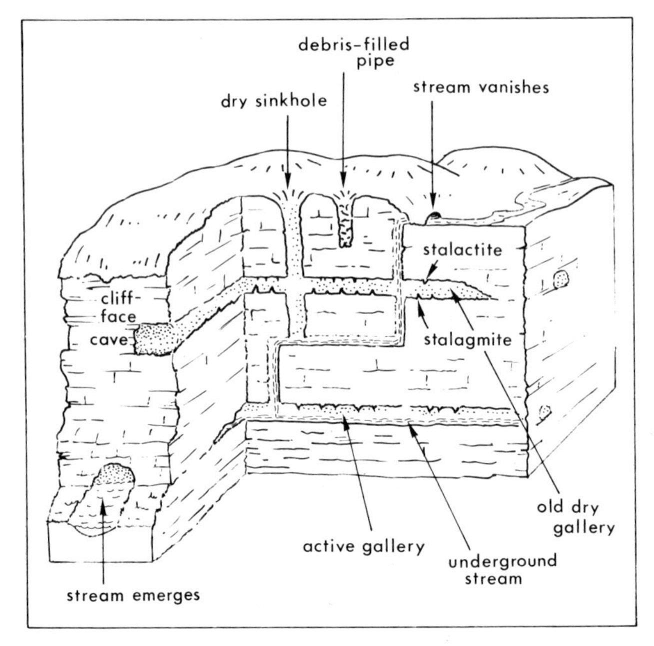


*Where limestone occurs extensively at the surface, drainage goes underground following the joint pattern. Galleries are opened up and then abandoned as streams seek out new routes.*

The atmosphere through which the water ($H_2O$) falls contains some carbon dioxide ($CO_2$), and when the rains reach the limestone, complex chemical reactions occur, which result in some calcite passing into solution and being carried away in the ground-water. At first the attack is concentrated on the cracks where the water drops down, which widen into fissures, or grikes, and the walls of the underground lateral channels which waste away, producing caves. Ultimately the whole of the original rock surface may be destroyed, and there remains a streamless, fretted area of bare rock. Such landscapes are common in Yugoslavia, and are known internationally by the Slovene name *karst*. Upstanding residual blocks of rock are known as *hums*, and the intervening hollows, if small, are *dolines*: if large, they are *poljes*.

In parts of Africa and Asia the process still continues uninterruptedly, and we get a 'mountains of the moon' landscape with towering pinnacles of limestone, a scene well loved by Chinese artists. But ice-sheets swept across Ireland's pinnacles, and stream-lined the surface of the rock from which they rose. This is well demonstrated in the Burren in Clare, where Ireland's most important karst is seen. Karst also occurs in the tablelands east of Sligo, and around Colgagh Lough, about 5km east of Sligo town, fretted karst can be seen. Near Fenit in Kerry some pinnacles still survive.

Big underground channels also developed, and as the whole land-surface fell, consequent on continued solution, the water-table also fell, and the channels became dry caves, some of considerable size. Praeger mapped the caves near Mitchelstown in Tipperary, and followed the passages, which in places opened up into spectacular chambers, for a distance of 500m. In Clare some cave passages can be followed for a distance of 12km. A very slight change in water conditions will precipitate the calcium carbonate out of solution, even from dripping water, and calcite icicles, known as *stalactites*, will hang down from the cave roof. A second erect 'icicle', known as a *stalagmite*, may arise from the cave floor immediately below the stalactite. If the two unite, a decorative column is formed: such columns are often on a spectacular scale, and are well developed at Mitchelstown.

This cave system has long been open to tourists, and it has now been joined by four others, scattered down Ireland from Fermanagh to Kerry. The existence of these five big cave complexes of passages and chambers gives the clearest indication of the extent to which the limestone of Ireland has been turned into a sponge-like mass, dissected by prolonged solutional activity in pre-Ice Age times. This is a concept that has been slow to dawn on me and other geologists.

**Chemical weathering**

The Tertiary lasted for about 65 million years, and for most of that time the climate in Ireland varied between warm temperate and sub-tropical. Water is one of the most powerful of

*Tanga, Tanzania. In tropical Africa the dissolving away of limestone by rain has gone on uninterruptedly for millions of years, resulting in a deeply fretted landscape; a man standing below the overhanging rock shows the scale.*

*nr. Fenit, Kerry. This upstanding limestone block is the stump of a high pinnacle shaped by a long period of erosion by rain, but then cut down by passing ice; two further stumps are seen in the background.*

solvents, and when further armed with carbonic acid ($H_2CO_3$), formed by the solution of carbon dioxide in the water in the atmosphere, and lesser quantities of other acids, it attacks many of the minerals of which the earth's rocks are built. These minerals were often formed under conditions of temperature and pressure different to those obtaining at the earth's surface today, and most of them, given the long period of Tertiary time when they were subjected to attack, gradually gave way and broke down into other compounds, to considerable depths. Such rocks lost their solidity, and became buried by a mantle of crumbling debris, often with a thickness of many tens of metres.

In Ireland virtually all this material disappeared during the Ice Age, either having been bodily carried away by moving ice or sludged away below sea-level by alternate freezing and thawing of its upper layers. But if we go to parts of the earth, such as Brazil, which escaped the main rigours of the last Ice Age, we can see the deep mantle still in place.

As time went on, the weathering penetrated more and more deeply, and there was often a relatively sharp horizon separating weathered rotted rock above from hard fresh rock below. The horizon was usually relatively horizontal, or at least followed the surface topography in a more subdued manner, just as the modern water-table does. Where the rotted rock has been swept away, as in Ireland, the exposed fresh rock has a very gently sloping or slightly undulating surface; if extensive, it has the appearance of a plain, and geomorphologists who study these phenomena have called it an *etch-plain*.

I consider that such etch-plains can be found in many parts of Ireland, and this is one of the more important bees in my bonnet. Much of Ireland's scenery cannot easily be explained as having been cut out by the sort of river erosion we read about in our school textbooks. I believe we can see many etch-plains, moulded by deep chemical weathering during the Tertiary, revealed by removal of their overburden during the Ice Age, and still to be seen, because the period of time that has elapsed since the Ice Age is too short for today's agents of denudation to have destroyed them. I shall point out various examples as we move along.

### Tectonic movement

We now come to the noisiest bee in my bonnet, and already an angry hum can be heard arising from my geological colleagues, who think I am merely vexatious in pushing the idea that there have been relatively recent vertical movements of the earth's crust in Ireland. One of their counter-arguments is that earthquakes do not occur in Ireland, or at least only occur very rarely.

The continents of the earth are now pictured as being built up of a mosaic of crustal plates, some of which are stationary, others are moving relative to one another. When the edge of a moving plate grates past a neighbour, vibrations which cause earthquakes occur. Absence of earthquakes in Ireland is taken to mean that the plates of the area are stable, and are not moving, either laterally or vertically.

But if the earth's crust has been stable for a long time, then differences in relief are progressively ironed out by erosion, and if the processes continue uninterruptedly and sea-level has remained stationary for a sufficiently long time, then a *peneplain* is produced. A peneplain can be defined as a land-surface of low-relief, worn down by prolonged weathering and river erosion.

High unstable cliffs have no place on the coasts of a peneplain, and we do have such cliffs in Kerry. Just west of Brandon Head cliffs rise to 400m, on Valencia Island they rise to 250m, and south of Portmagee they rise to 275m; all these cliffs are unstable, and great collapses frequently occur. When waves attack a stable sloping coastline, they cut a bench in the underlying rock, and the bench ends in a cliff against the coast. As erosion proceeds, the bench gets wider, and the cliff recedes, gradually rising in height as it does so. In soft rocks, such as occur along the west coast of France, the bench may ultimately reach a width of a kilometre or more.

But in Kerry there is no bench, and the cliffs continue down into deep water. As soon as the waves take even a nibble at the cliff-base, another collapse takes place. Here waves and cliffs are not in balance with one another, as they would be if there had been no tectonic movement for a very long time.

High cliffs also stretch up the west coast, and are to be seen in Clare Island and in Achill Island. Along the cliffed north coast of Mayo from Benwee Head to Glinsk we run into tilting. From the cliff-edge the bulk of the river-water runs south to the valley of the Glenamoy River. The tilting is most apparent on Tory Island, off north-west Donegal. From a relatively horizontal position, the island appears to have been tilted southwards, so that we have high cliffs along the north coast while the south coast slides gently under the sea.

In fact it could be argued that Ireland as a whole shows a tilt from north-west to south-east. In Wexford and Waterford the tide runs far up the estuaries of the Slaney and the Suir and its tributaries. In the north-west the Corrib cascades over rapids in Galway City as it approaches the sea. In the Leenaun Valley we have the Aasleagh Falls, and in Ballyshannon as the Erne approaches the sea, its fall is sufficient to supply a hydro-electric station at the Cathleen Falls.

I believe there was tectonic movement in Ireland about 60 million years ago, and that this continued for some time. The Mourne Mountains were created some 60 million years ago; there was a volcano in the west near Clifden at the same time; the sagging of the earth's crust which created the great basin that now holds Lough Neagh took place about 40 million years ago; and exploration for oil and gas off the south Irish coast shows that basins in which fossil fuels may lie were also in movement in Tertiary time. I see no reason why such vertical crustal movements should not also be apparent on dryland Ireland. My bees buzz happily on.

## The Quaternary Period

When we come to the Quaternary, which started about 2 million years ago, our problems with regard to evidence reverse themselves. We have far too much evidence; our difficulty is to interpret it.

During the Quaternary, there were many oscillations in climate, ranging from cold, or glacial, periods, during some of which great ice-masses formed much farther from the polar regions to which they are at present confined, to warm, or interglacial, periods when the climate of western Europe was at least as warm as, and sometimes warmer than, it is today. In some of the cold periods less ice was formed, but conditions of very severe frost prevailed. As more and more research is done in this field, still more oscillations are revealed. In Victorian days the simple single term *Ice Age* embraced this whole period, whose complexity had yet to be realised, and I tend to continue to use this short six-letter term even though it is now very old-fashioned to do so.

The last cold period, known in Ireland as the *Midlandian*, probably began about 100,000 years ago, and there were certainly great ice-masses in Ireland about 20,000 years ago, whose final collapse set in some 17,000 years ago. We can recognise the deposits laid down by this ice with some certainty, and we can picture the country north of a line from Limerick to Wexford being covered by ice, with another independent cap of ice over the mountains of south-west Ireland. The areas not covered by ice were subject to very severe frost-action. Many of these areas are themselves covered by glacial deposits which must be of still older age, but efforts to sort them out and establish some sort of chronology for them have not produced a generally acceptable scheme.

The cold of the cold periods probably exterminated all forms of life in Ireland, and when the next warm period, or *interglacial*, developed, new communities of plants and animals gradually established themselves. We used hopefully to think that the communities of the different interglacials (of which there were many) would have special characters of their own, and that close study of the fossil plants and animals contained in their deposits would establish an identifiable finger-print for each one, and so enable us to assign specific communities to specific interglacials. Such identification would lead to dating of the glacial deposits which lay above and below them.

But alas, such studies, of which there are now many, have led in the opposite direction. We now realise that recolonisation always had to start from the same area, probably southern Europe, where there was only a finite range of plants and animals to draw on, and so the same forms tended to come back in the same order in each interglacial. Also climate and soil development in each interglacial tended to repeat themselves, gradually rising to optimum activity, and then falling away. So the pattern runs—open country gives way to bushes, deciduous trees overwhelm the bushes, and then as temperatures begin to fall off and soils age, coniferous trees and heaths displace the broad-leaved trees, and gradually the plant cover breaks up as severe conditions return. Thus, although we may have made very detailed studies of the samples of peat or mud we have collected in the field, we find it very difficult to be dogmatic about their age.

In Ireland samples from about eight interglacial deposits, stretching from Antrim to Kerry, have now been looked at. None of the samples cover a complete interglacial, and most give us only vignettes of one or two of the developmental stages; so far these studies have failed to live up to earlier hopes.

Another Quaternary problem we run into is changes in sea-level. When ice-sheets form, the water they lock up in themselves has to come from the oceans, and sea-level falls; when the ice melts away it rises again. Complications arise because as a heavy weight of ice builds up on a land-mass, the land slowly sinks below it, to rise again when the weight is relieved. Where the ocean meets the land, cliffs are cut and beaches are formed. Later changes in sea- and land-level will raise the beaches up, or lower them below the water.

Raised cliffs and beaches are a common feature round much of the coasts of the north of Ireland, and occur less frequently further south. In earlier days I spent a lot of time studying these; I also went to Wales, Cornwall, the Isles of Scilly, the Channel Islands and north-west France, seeking to make comparisons with the Irish features. But more and more complications arose, and when geophysicists began to assert that the geoid, the actual shape of the earth, changes from time to time, and therefore produces changes in shore-line level quite independent of glacial events, I decided it was time to abandon my efforts.

CHAPTER 5

# Caving

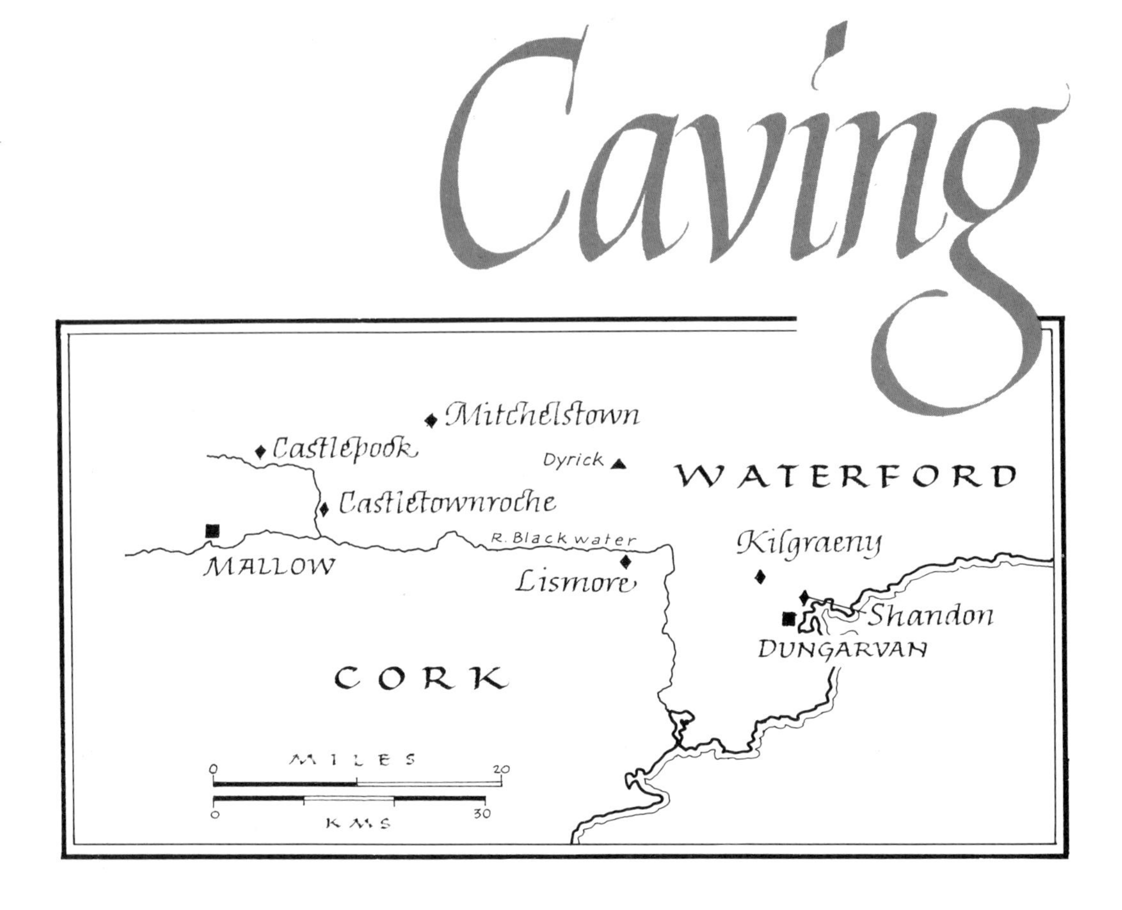


SHANDON · CASTLEPOOK · KILGRAENY

KESH, SLIGO · CASTLETOWNROCHE

Bristol lies not far from the caves of the Mendips, and in the twenties the university had an active spelaeological society, where staff and students interested in caving could meet. A member of the dental staff, T.K. Tratman, had led several parties excavating in the local caves, and found the remains of cold-loving animals. Anxious to extend his range, Tratman was attracted to the cave-ridden tract of low-lying limestone that stretches from Mallow to Dungarvan.

## SHANDON

As long ago as 1860 remains of the woolly mammoth had been found in Shandon Cave, outside Dungarvan. A Mr Edward Brenan was walking in the streets of Dungarvan when he saw 'giant's bones' being paraded through the town. He immediately realised that the bones could not be those of a human giant, but were elephant bones. Asking where they came from, he was directed to Shandon Cave on the outskirts of the town, where limestone-quarrying was in progress. He found the cave richly strewn with bones, among which woolly mammoth, bear, horse and hare were identified. I have been to the site, but nothing has survived the quarrying.

There was always doubt about the age of the horse bones. Were they of the same age as the mammoth bones—if so, they were the only horse bones of this age found in Ireland—or were they the bones of some relatively recent farm animal? The National Museum gave me some pieces of bone for age determination, and the answer was that their remaining radioactivity was so low that they must be more than 40,000 years old; a piece of mammoth bone, also from the cave, failed to give any result. We can say that the horse cannot be recent, and may go back to interglacial times.

## CASTLEPOOK

In the early years of this century R.J. Ussher excavated a big cave at Castlepook, near Doneraile, 10km north-east of Mallow. Ussher was a very distinguished naturalist, and was co-author with R. Warren of *The Birds of Ireland*, published in 1900, the first substantial book on Ireland's birds. He lived at Cappagh, between Lismore and Dungarvan, and was familiar with most of the caves in the valley. His work at Castlepook was heroic. Here there is a limestone knoll, riddled with cave passages dissolved out when the level of the ground-water was much higher than it is today. Now the same action is going on at a lower level, and the upper caves are being undermined and are almost at the point of collapse. There are gaps where the cave walls have dropped away from the roof, which they no longer support. Ussher dug away cheerfully, ignoring all this, and is reputed even to have used dynamite to open up blocked passages.

Some of the blockages were of looser material which had made its way down through holes and fissures to form cones of loose debris below. In fact, the roof was so thin that Ussher could hear reaping machines passing above, and today the bases of ESB poles run down into some of the fissures. The layers that were rich in fossil bones lay at the bottoms of the fissures, and to get at these Ussher cleaned out some fissures, and then packed the loose debris from the next group into the excavated ones. In this way he completely transformed the appearance of the interior of the cave in the parts he worked in.

Ussher discovered the abundant remains of many cold-loving animals, woolly mammoth, reindeer, lemming, arctic fox, and other animals not so strictly tied to cold, Irish giant deer and spotted hyaena. The latter is now restricted to central and southern Africa, but in former times ranged widely in Europe. Castlepook is the only cave in Ireland in which remains of this animal have been found. Unfortunately, running water had swept through the cave on more than one occasion since it had served as an animal den, and when the waters ebbed away, the bones were left indiscriminately mixed at the bottom of the passages.

Hyaena bones are relatively common in caves in England, where they chiefly date to the last interglacial period, probably more than 100,000 years ago. This dating emerged from the work of Tony Sutcliffe in the British Museum of Natural History. Many bones recovered from caves are considered to have been gnawed by hyaenas; if this is true, then the animals whose bones were gnawed must have been contemporary with the hyaena. Tony took up this idea, and not only examined bones in museums, but also went to Africa to see modern hyaenas at work. He came to see the bones in the National Museum in Dublin, and also to visit the cave.

Cavers from Cork had recently found a part of the cave that Ussher had not worked in, and they arranged to show it to us. Little did we know what we were letting ourselves in for. The entrance to the new section was via a low slit, the shape of a letter-box opening, in the cave wall. Unfortunately the wall was 3m thick. An agile caver was already inside, and so I bent forward into the slit, stretching out my arms in front of me. The inner caver seized my hands and pulled while others pushed my feet, and I shot into the inner cave like a cork out of a champagne bottle. We saw the cave as Ussher had first seen it, with cones of debris flowing down from ceiling to floor, many of them with modern animal bones protruding. We exited in the same way as we had entered, and were heartily glad to see the open air.

We could add a little to the work that Ussher and his colleagues had done. The National Museum provided samples for radiocarbon dating, and these gave an age of 34,400 years for the hyaena, and 33,500 for the woolly mammoth. The last glacial period began perhaps 75,000 years ago, but it was not a period of continuous cold, and was punctuated by warmer stages. This was a later warm stage than that in which the horse and the mammoth were wandering around Dungarvan.

## KILGRAENY

After his survey of caves in the Blackwater valley, Tratman decided to dig a cave near Kilgraeny, and I have described how I was a member of his excavating party in 1926. The party was small in number, and time was limited, so Tratman could only make a small excavation under a low cave roof. Some of the party dug inside, putting the removed material into buckets which were then carried out into daylight, where the material was examined and the contained bones collected. Praeger came to see the dig, and my first contact with the great man was not cordial. He went into the cave to inspect the deposits, and had the bright idea of putting a penny into one of the buckets to test the efficacy of the sorters outside. It was found, but I and the other sorters felt that our competence had been impugned in no small way.

As we have seen, caves in limestone are created by the acids contained in circulating water attacking the calcium carbonate of which the rock is mainly composed, and carrying it away in solution. But a slight change in conditions may cause the calcium carbonate to be precipitated on the cave floor as a sheet of stalagmite. There was a great deal of stalagmite in Kilgraeny, and in one of his trenches Tratman found in the stalagmite a human bone and a bone of the Irish giant deer in very close proximity to one another. From this it was all too easy to presume that the two bones were contemporary, and that if the fauna to which the giant deer belonged was in Ireland at the close of the Ice Age, then man must also have been in

Ireland at that time, a time of Palaeolithic or Mesolithic culture. 'Kilgraeny Man' achieved some scientific notoriety.

Hallam Movius of Harvard, whom we will meet again later on, had excavated in Ireland in the thirties. He then went on to Palestine, where he excavated Palaeolithic material from stalagmite in caves. Intrigued—like many other archaeologists—by the probability that Palaeolithic man must have reached Ireland, though convincing evidence had yet to be found, he decided to re-investigate Kilgraeny Cave. With resources much greater than Tratman's, he mounted a much bigger dig, and opened up the whole cave. His chief but very disappointing result was that, as at Castlepook, running water had been all too active, and the deposits in the cave, which ranged in age from the late-glacial to the Iron Age, had been grossly disturbed. Running water had brought the giant deer and the human bone together, and later stalagmite had surrounded them. Movius's dig preceded the development of the radiocarbon dating method, and when the human bone was later tested, it gave a Neolithic date.

## Kesh, Sligo

But if we go back to the twenties, Gwynn and Riley were very excited by the Tratman discovery, and decided to look for more evidence of early man in other Irish caves. Cold-loving animals had been found in earlier excavations in caves at Kesh, near Ballymote in Co. Sligo, and they decided to look again there. They brought me along with them, and again we camped in a field. The caves here were a parallel series of fissures running back into a cliff, and with hindsight I can see that any deposits in them must also been at the mercy of running water. All in all, they were not really a very good place to dig, but we did find reindeer and arctic lemming. Professor Bayley Butler of University College, Dublin, was digging at the same time in an adjacent cave, where he found evidence of Iron Age man, but nothing of greater antiquity.

## Castletownroche

In the late thirties, when I was a lecturer in geology in Trinity College, Dublin, I recruited a group of students to do some digging. As a leader I was kinder than my predecessors, for we had as our base the abandoned farm-buildings of a property that had been burned down during the 'Troubles'. We went to some small caves in the wall of the rock gorge of the Awbeg River at Castletownroche, Co. Cork, just above the point where the Awbeg joins the Blackwater. Further up the Awbeg, just south of Charleville, a great belt of moraine lies across the valley, and I took this, as Professor J.K. Charlesworth of the geology department in Queen's University, Belfast, had done, to mark the outer limit of the last main advance of ice in Ireland. Thus, I hoped that these caves would contain deposits of interglacial age. But again we were largely disappointed.

Lying against the mouth of the cave there was a mass of breccia, built up of angular lumps of limestone prised off the cliff-wall above by repeated freezing and thawing of water in cracks in the rock during cold periods. At the base of the breccia we found remains of cold-loving animals, including a fragment (no bigger than Praeger's penny) of a tooth of a young woolly mammoth. Further developments in radiocarbon dating have now made it possible to work with very small specimens, such as were used in the dating of the Turin Shroud, and I hope to see if the tooth fragment can be dated. A recent find of mammoth bones in England was dated to 12,700 years ago, a much later survival than had been hitherto reckoned on, and the Awbeg tooth might be equally young.

Inside the cave we found an intact stalagmite floor; we cleaned its surface carefully to avoid contamination, and broke through it, only to find a strongly smelling fresh badger-earth, accumulated by animals who were still using an alternative entry. Nothing daunted, we went on down to another floor, again a careful cleaning, but this time we came down into coarse glacial outwash gravel. When the end of the ice-sheet was lying near Charleville, vast quantities of water loaded with gravel must have flooded down the Awbeg at a level high enough to discharge gravel into the cave-mouths, thus obliterating any earlier deposits. I then retired from cave-hunting.

CHAPTER 6

# South East Corner

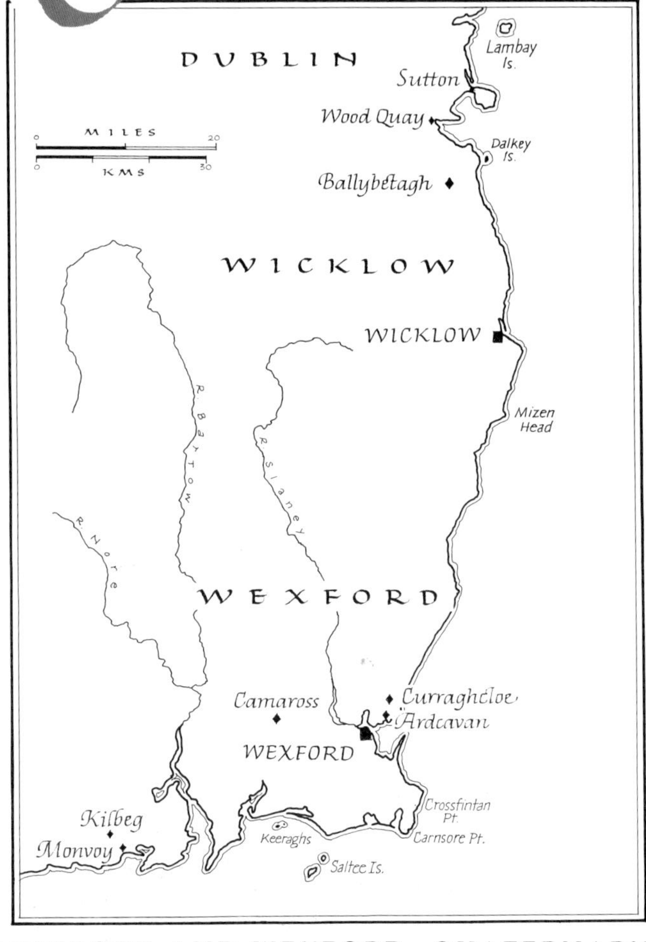


1. WATERFORD AND WEXFORD, QUATERNARY

2. SOUTH-EAST COAST, ARCHAEOLOGY

~1~
# WATERFORD AND WEXFORD, QUATERNARY

KILBEG · LATER GLACIAL HISTORY · PINGOS · GLACIO-MARINE PROCESSES

Leaving the caves behind, we start on our complex peregrination of Ireland. We move 20km to the north-east in Co. Waterford, leaving behind the Carboniferous limestone of the Blackwater valley and entering into a Caledonide area of older slates and sandstones. Here there was some contemporary volcanic activity, and lavas were interspersed through the sediments.

## KILBEG

In 1941 at Kilbeg, south-east of Kilmacthomas, a well was dug to provide more water for a small creamery. After going down through 10m of glacial deposit, the well came into 3m of peat, which rested on rotted rock. One of the Waterford county engineers knew Tony Farrington, and of his interest in glacial geology, and sent a lump of the peat up to Dublin. Tony passed it on to me, and one look at its pollen content showed that the plant fossils it contained had nothing to do with modern Irish vegetation. But they did bear a close resemblance to those in peat in an analogous position at Gort in Co. Galway. That deposit

*Bill Watts demonstrates a pollen diagram, built up from samples taken in an Irish lake.*

was found more than one hundred years ago by G.H. Kinahan, a very distinguished but also very awkward member of the Irish Geological Survey. Kinahan identified pine, hazel and spruce, and correctly surmised that such trees must have been present in Ireland 'during intra-glacial times'. Spruce is not a native tree in Ireland today, but various forms of it are widely grown in forestry plantations.

In 1955 I was lecturing in glacial geology, as well as other things, and the name of a student called William Arthur Watts appeared on my lecture-roll. Bill had taken a first-class honours degree in modern languages, but developed an interest in natural history and decided to take a qualification in that subject also. In the course of a lecture I talked about the deposit at Kilbeg, and regretted that we knew so little about it, having only small pieces of peat and a limited description of the deposit that lay on top of it. At that moment Bill was converted, like Saul on the road to Damascus, and he decided that he would find out the history of Kilbeg. In 1956 we put down a bore-hole there.

Bill produced a masterly paper on the Kilbeg deposit, studying both its microscopic pollen and its macroscopic seeds and leaves, and showed that it must have been contemporaneous with the deposit at Gort, and that its vegetational record matched well with those from comparable deposits in Britain and western Europe. From that point his research went from strength to strength, in the United States as well as in Europe, and he is now widely recognised as one of the leaders in the field of vegetational history on both sides of the Atlantic. Even though he is now serving a ten-year stint as Provost of Trinity College, he keeps his research on the move, and will return to it with redoubled energy when he is free again.

The tone of my earlier comments about Arthur Stelfox will have made it clear that I regard him as one of my fathers in science, and I am proud to say that I regard Bill Watts as my son in science. Further on we shall meet another son, this time in humanities, if that is the proper category in which to place archaeology. This son is George Eogan, Professor of Archaeology in University College, Dublin.

## Later Glacial History

We move on to the south-east coast, which for my purpose means an area centred on the town of Wexford, stretching from the Saltees on the south to Enniscorthy on the north. I wandered up and down this area for fifty years, at first generally in the company of Tony Farrington, and in later years with members of the soil survey department of the Agricultural Institute, based in Johnstown Castle. For most of the time I was chasing a will-o'-the-wisp, the outer limit of the last main ice-sheet that appeared in Ireland.

Charlesworth had laid down what he thought was the limit in Wales, and he then proceeded to do the same in Ireland, with his Southern Irish End-Moraine drawn as a tenuous line across the country. At Curraghcloe, just north of Wexford Harbour, between the Slaney and the sea, the flat ground rises into high undulating hills of sand and gravel, punctuated by steep-sided hollows, usually with small lakes. The sand and gravel were heaped up in an end-moraine at the front of a decaying ice-sheet. In the process of melting, lumps of ice were left behind in the sand and gravel, and as these thawed out the overlying material slumped down to form a hollow, known as a *kettle-hole*. I made some borings in kettle-holes and showed that although these Curraghcloe hills today have acid soils with patches of heath, in early post-glacial time they were covered with dense oak-woods.

Farrington and I accepted the Charlesworth view that this moraine was the limit of the last Midlandian glaciation, and so did Francis Synge, a younger man, then in charge of the glacial section of the Irish Geological Survey. Francis was—regrettably he died before his time—a very good field geologist, but he occasionally allowed his ideas to outrun his field observations. Wexford was the first county to have its soils surveyed in detail, and pretty soon the workers started to find patches of acid soils, very similar to those at Curraghcloe, on the west side of the Slaney, where they ought not to have been. They asked, very rightly, 'Could the ice not have passed the Charlesworth limit?' I am ashamed to say that Francis and I overruled them, with the result that the Wexford Soil Memoir, which appeared in 1964, accepted the erroneous limit.

I dropped another clanger on the north shore of Wexford Harbour. Working along the low cliffs at Ardcavan, 3km north-east of the town, Tony Farrington found what appeared to be a very plausible interglacial site—a basal layer of till deposited by ice, then peat and a layer of ochreous material, and then an upper till. Convinced that it would be washed away by the next storm, he hustled me down to see it. The storm did come, and while the deposit survived, we very nearly expired. It was November, there was a high spring tide and a south-east gale with driving rain. We worked away in fading light as the tide rose round our Wellington-boots; every time I bent down to pick up another specimen-tube, the wind lifted my coat-tails and the rain drenched my bottom. I still keep as a memento of the occasion some mud-stained pages from my field notebook.

The ochreous material was a solid mass of pollen grains, principally of the alder, a warmth-loving tree, whose presence showed that the deposit belonged to a time when the climate was as warm as today, as in a true interglacial period. I published it as such, but repeated visits to the site (the deposit survived for years, though it is now completely eroded away) suggested that the hollow in which the deposits lay was 'young', that is, of the same age as the kettle-holes a little further north at Curraghcloe, that the ochreous deposit was a weathered post-glacial mud, and that the top deposit had not been deposited by ice but by the local farmer, who had pushed earth into the hollow to level it off. In mitigation I can plead that this was the only place I ever saw post-glacial mud so altered by weathering.

Carnsore Point, Ireland's south-east corner, is built of a boss of granite, whose texture shows large red crystals of felspar, which make it easy to identify, even in small pieces. Ned Culleton, then also of the Agricultural Institute, and later creator and director of the most successful Irish National Heritage Park in Wexford, showed that quantities of the granite had been carried west of the Point, most probably by the last ice. We went to the Saltees together, and found boulders of the granite there. I nearly died of exhaustion, struggling in a very effective natural barbed-wire entanglement. We decided to take a short-cut back to the boat through some innocent-looking bracken; but as we pushed into it, it rose to shoulder-height, and then became laced through with brambles to the same level. I was almost in tears when we emerged.

Attractive as they are, the Saltees are not my lucky islands, as some years ago I was marooned there with a party from the Dublin Field Club. The morning after our arrival we threw away into a clump of nettles the excess sandwiches our wives had provided; but then the wind got up, and two days later we were beating the nettles to retrieve them. We were just bracing ourselves to a meal of roast shag, when 'ship ahoy' was heard. But the islands have splendid birds and splendid glacial geology. Ned and I subsequently went to the Keeraghs, a group of low rocks 12km north-west of the Saltees, where no Carnsore granite was to be seen, and Ned would draw the line between the Keeraghs and the Saltees.

In a further search for the limit I pushed up the road from Wexford towards New Ross to see how far kettle-holes extended in that direction. I was looking for small enclosed hollows without an exit stream. I found one basin with very deep post-glacial and late-glacial muds;

it may once have had a bog on top, but this, if it ever existed, had been completely cut away. Bill Watts and I made some preliminary borings there, and realising that it was a 'good' site, we handed it over to Alan Craig, then a research student with Bill. He produced a splendid vegetational picture, dated by radiocarbon determinations, of the return of plant-life to south-east Ireland. Alan is now Director of National Parks for the Office of Public Works.

## PINGOS

Further up the road, around Camaross, I came on the most extraordinary series of small saucer-shaped hollows with raised rims. I wandered round them, and looked at them, scratching my head, and then all at once the penny dropped—pingos. A paper had recently been published describing such features in East Anglia, and ascribing their formation to the former presence of lens-shaped masses of ice near the surface of the ground; the features are common in high latitudes today, and are called pingos by the local Eskimos.

In high latitudes the ground is permanently frozen in 'permafrost', but there will be some surface melting in summer. As winter approaches, the ground freezes again from the top downwards. On a gentle slope, water may seep in between the two frozen layers, and when winter freezing intensifies, the invading water must also freeze, expanding as it does so, and lifting up the surface of the ground into a series of pimples. In the spring the ground overlying the pimple thaws first, and slides down the flanks of the pimple, forming a rim. The ice lens then melts, and the feature is created, a hollow surrounded by a rim.

It was a revelation to me that we had had permafrost and pingos in Ireland, and I took opportunity to go to Alaska and see the processes in action. I then attempted to map their distribution in Ireland, criss-crossing the country by car, in the worst 'CWG' style. (In the United States a geologist who does most of his work through the windows of his car is dismissed as a CWG, or car-window geologist.) However, I was in good company as Charlesworth did much of his work on a bicycle. Almost all the pingos I saw lay south of his line. Other workers then took up the hunt, and on the whole pingos in Ireland are confined to the southern counties. It was fortunate that my discovery came when it did, as pingos are very susceptible to land-reclamation schemes. The farmer wants to get rid of a wet hole on his land, and it is all too easy to restore the *status quo* by pushing the rim into the hollow with a bull-dozer; many good examples have disappeared in recent years.

## GLACIO-MARINE PROCESSES

I long held to the general view that unsorted glacial materials, called tills or boulder-clays, had been fairly directly deposited by the melting of land-based ice, which accounted for their unsorted state. The ice was thought to be land-based, as it was presumed that world sea-levels were then low, because so much water had been extracted from them to form the ice-sheets. But for this explanation the complicated glacial deposits of the Wexford coasts presented many difficulties. It is now thought that water was present in the basin of the Irish Sea in sufficient quantity for the margin of the ice to float, or at least be partly supported by water. The deposits did not melt out on land, but sludged out of the ice in a turbid mixture, which had no opportunity to be sorted before it was dumped in a mass on the sea-floor. Such material is known as a *glacio-marine deposit*, which can look extremely like till deposited on land. Ice-floes, which could carry along quite big boulders, would finally melt, and the boulders would drop to the sea-floor. If the floor was of soft stone-free mud, the boulder might penetrate to some depth into it. Along much of the coast of the Irish Sea these glacio-marine deposits form cliffs, which are now being closely studied. Such studies require a whole new series of techniques, and I decided with regret that I was too old a dog to learn new tricks. But if I abandoned glacial geology, I remained with archaeology.

# ~2~
# SOUTH-EAST COAST, ARCHAEOLOGY

WICKLOW AND WEXFORD · DUBLIN · DALKEY ISLAND · SUTTON · WOOD QUAY

My active archaeology really started by chance, as with so many other features of my life. A student called Henry Rennison appeared in my classes in the late thirties and we became friends; he subsequently went on to a distinguished career as a geologist with the Burmah Oil Company. At the time I was taking exercise in the form of shooting, though I was always a hopeless shot. Henry lived on the north shore of Dundalk Bay, where he went shooting, and he suggested that I should go home with him for a weekend. In the course of our wandering, we strayed through a sand-pit, and discovered a small kitchen-midden exposed in one of its walls. I subsequently excavated it, as I will tell when our circuit brings us to that area. Looking for further clues in the fields around that site, I took to field-walking, which I found a most pleasant and rewarding occupation.

Here, although I did not know it at the time, I was following in the most distinguished footsteps of General Pitt-Rivers, one of the founders of modern archaeology. On his estate in Dorset he was surrounded by hunting-fishing-and-shooting squires, and he wrote that when they stepped into a field it was with the intention of bringing something to an end, for example the life of a pheasant. But when he stepped into a field, with his eyes glued to the ground, it was in the hope of beginning something, finding some object that would lead on to new knowledge.

In my first bout of field-walking, I had a very valuable colleague, Gwendolyn Stacpoole, one of the last of a line of Co. Clare Stacpooles. She was a keen collector of antiquarian objects, and lived alone in a house in Fitzwilliam Square, which was packed with treasures of all sorts. She was painfully shy, and possibly led a rather lonely life. Maisie Brodigan, a civil servant, shared some of her interests, and in the summer they would go away together to Donegal, where they would prowl around the coastal kitchen-middens and bring back quite a haul of material to the museum in Dublin. Miss Stacpoole's chief triumph was some Late Roman material, which she found in the sand-hills at Ballybunnion in Kerry. In the shorter days of spring and autumn she searched nearer home, chiefly in the coastal fields of north Dublin, between Portmarnock and Balbriggan. I worked north and south of her area, from Dundalk to Balbriggan, and from Sutton to Killiney.

Miss Stacpoole brought me a large quantity of material, and I soon saw that there were quite a number of Late Mesolithic implements scattered through it. David Liversage (now one of the curators in the National Museum of Denmark) was working with me at the time as a research student, and based on her material, together with what he and I had collected, he produced a valuable account of Mesolithic finds on the north Leinster coast.

## Wicklow and Wexford

After a lapse of many years I took to field-walking again on the south Leinster coast, from Greystones to Carnsore Point. I did not go beyond the Point because another group, based in Waterford, was at work there. I am afraid this group was much more systematic than I was. I contented myself with taking a zig-zag 'random walk'—as mathematicians might do--across a field; they laid out a plan of close lines on a field, and walked systematically backwards and forwards over it, thus inspecting the whole surface.

A chance discovery made me take up the threads at Wicklow, on the golf-links just south of the town. The links run down to the cliff-edge, and, below a low bluff of rock, sods had been stripped off to build up one of the tees. On the exposed surface there was a thin scatter of small pieces of flint, several of which had been struck in Late Mesolithic style, perhaps about 5000 years ago. Their makers, usually known as Larnians, because implements in this style are very common in the raised beach at Larne, Co. Antrim, started making their implements by knocking the end off a chosen block of flint, thus creating a flat platform on the block. They then struck flakes off the circumference of the platform, trying to control the shape of the flake so that it would make a useful knife or other tool. With their method of striking, the long axis of the flake made an obtuse angle with the detached part of the platform at its base. Several of the Wicklow flakes showed this characteristic feature.

I then set out to sample the coast southwards, and found quite a few small sites, usually covered by blown sand, giving material mostly rather similar to the Wicklow finds. As I approached my southern limit, I came upon flakes struck from a fine-grained volcanic rock, rhyolite. They were also found by the people working in Waterford. This type of rock occurs in the area near Tramore, and at an outcrop at Monvoy, 2km north-west of the town, there is a chipping-floor, where blocks of rock were given a preliminary dressing. The debris suggested Neolithic rather than Late Mesolithic working, but in Ireland the two groups overlapped in time. Neolithic people used polished stone axes, and several 'axe-factories' are known, situated on outcrops of rock whose properties made them suitable for the making of stone tools. Two such sites are to be found in Co. Antrim, one near Cushendun, and the other on Rathlin Island. At Ballyferriter in Co. Kerry, Late Mesolithic people also made use of a local igneous rock as raw material for tools.

One site, at Crossfintan Point, a very short distance north of Carnsore Point, provided a short-lived flurry of excitement. A knoll of till was covered in sand, with a few implements at the base of the sand. On its seaward side the waves had stripped away the sand and exposed a group of shallow trenches, about 2m long and 40cm across, in which large fires had been lit, as the floors and sides of the pits were deeply reddened by heat. Were they Mesolithic cooking-pits? There was some charcoal in the fire-debris, which gave a radiocarbon age of 1750 years, a date in the Iron Age. I brought several archaeologists to see the site, but none could make a definite suggestion for the use of the trenches. They could have been used for cooking in the style of the clambake of the Red Indians or the mumu of New Guinea. When the interior of the pit was hot, the fire could have been raked out, as in the manner of a small French bakery, and fish or shellfish wrapped in seaweed could have been put into the pit to cook by steaming.

My most prolific site was at Mizen Head, at the south end of Brittas Bay. In the field next the road there was a large ploughed-out *fulacht fiadh*, standing out as a red and black circular area from the generally grey colour of the ploughed field; there was a spring nearby. This was the ruins of a cooking-place, of a type that was used in Ireland, and elsewhere, for many thousands of years. A hole, generally lined with wooden planks or stone slabs, was dug in water-logged ground, where it filled with water. Stones were heated in a nearby fire and thrown into the water, which quickly came to the boil to be used for cooking. After use, the reddened stones in the trough were thrown aside, where they gradually accumulated in a large heap. Remains of such cooking-places are Ireland's most numerous antiquity.

Another few fields on towards the coast and near a small stream, I found the largest scatter of Larnian flint debris that I ever discovered. There probably had been an organised site here, but it also had been destroyed by ploughing. Scattered through the debris were many scrapers and blades, and also what appeared to be rough-outs for other types of implement. I brought Peter Woodman, Professor of Archaeology in University College, Cork, and Ireland's leading authority on the Mesolithic stage, to see the site, and he was suitably impressed. A little later I gave him all my east-coast material, in the hope that he might include it in a general survey.

On the coast, a short distance south of the point of the Head, I found a medieval moated site partly eroded away by the sea. These sites, which are most common in south-east Ireland, consist of a square area protected by a bank and a water-filled ditch. They are thought to have given protection to an Anglo-Norman farmhouse, and to date to the thirteenth and fourteenth centuries. Like pingos they are all too vulnerable to land-reclamation works, and require urgent investigation, as only a few have been excavated so far.

## DUBLIN

### Dalkey Island

Dalkey Island, a few hundred metres offshore at Dalkey, was the chief treasure-house of my archaeological career. Miss Stacpoole reported that she had seen pieces of flint embedded in clay near the well on the east side of the island. I went to see the island, and decided that at the point of her discovery, which lay downslope from old fields, soil had moved downslope, and the flints had got caught up in the moving soil. The small north point of the island was cut off by a bank-and-ditch, and consisted of a small flat facing west, backed by a rock-ridge. The flat ended in a low earthen cliff overlying rock. Debris of flint and shells were protruding from the cliff.

I discussed the site with David Liversage, and he applied for a licence to excavate, recruiting George Eogan as assistant. He decided to excavate the small flat, only about 40m x 20m, within the bank-and-ditch. It seemed a simple enough task, but had we realised the wealth of material of various ages that lay beneath our feet, David would have organised the expedition on a larger scale. Today, a hut to sort and label material would be regarded as *de rigueur*, but in those days a tent, or nothing, was regarded as sufficient. As it was, David was almost swamped by the rate at which objects appeared out of the ground. At the bottom there were Larnian flints—but here I must make a digression to say that not only was the deposit very rich, but it was also shallow (only about 1m thick), so that layers of different ages followed one another very quickly. Furthermore, it had been burrowed into very extensively by rabbits in pre-myxomatosis days, and this had given rise to considerable disturbance.

At the bottom there were Larnian flints, succeeded by Neolithic material which had a radiocarbon age of 5300 years ago. Early Bronze Age pottery, principally fragments of decorated Beakers, and Late Bronze Age clay moulds indicated extensive Bronze Age occupation. There was also Late Roman wheel-made pottery of a type that circulated freely in the Mediterranean in the fifth century AD. This type of pottery is widely scattered throughout western Britain and Ireland, and must indicate connection with Early Christian Europe. The Dalkey Island material contained fragments of types of vessel not known elsewhere.

There are also on the island an early church, burials perhaps dating to medieval times, because when plague invaded Dublin many of the citizens fled to the island, and also extensive anti-Napoleonic fortifications. Dalkey Island provides an epitome of Ireland's prehistory and history. Following on David's success on Dalkey Island, I dreamt of attempting a similar coup on Lambay Island. Roman and Neolithic material was found on the island when an extension was made to the harbour; there is also a promontory fort, and I had found Larnian flints when field-walking. But it would have involved an extensive campaign stretching over several years, and the necessary time never came my way. It is a project that somebody should take up, and I am sure the rewards would be much greater than those of Dalkey Island.

### Sutton

From Dalkey we jump across Dublin Bay to Sutton, where an isthmus of raised beach links the former island of Howth to the mainland. Just beside Corr Castle, I found a shell-midden resting on raised beach and covered by blown sand. This was the sort of site I liked, a site where archaeology and geology were interlinked. The bulk of the finds were flints of Larnian type, but there were also traces of Neolithic activity. At the time of my excavation in 1955 the radiocarbon method had not been fully developed, so I returned to the site in 1971 and had a limited dig to recover charcoal for dating; the answer was about 5000 years ago. Sea-level was slightly higher than that of today when the raised beach was being formed. When sea-level was highest the waves had cut away the side of the midden, but use of the midden continued, and so we can date the maximum height of sea-level as well, at 5000 years ago. Today Corr Castle has been swept away, and the whole site is covered by modern housing.

### Wood Quay

Quite early in my career I became interested in the history of the vanished buildings in Trinity College and Dublin city in general, and was surprised to find old records of peat in the vicinity of Christ Church cathedral. From what I knew of bog-formation, I thought it most unlikely that peat could have formed around the old city. In the fifties a deep sewer-trench down High Street threw up 'peat', and David Liversage and I went and looked at it. The peat turned out to be organic city refuse, and included many trimmings from a cobbler's workshop; satisfied that it was not 'peat', I am afraid I did nothing more about it.

In the sixties the area was to be re-developed, and Brendán Ó Ríordáin, later Director of the National Museum, began excavating on the south side of High Street. He quickly showed that the 'peat' contained a rich wealth of medieval material. I paid occasional visits to the site, and looked at some samples for him, but it was not until Pat Wallace, now Director of the Museum, opened up a big area on the flat ground beside the river north of High Street, that I became seriously involved. Pat laid out big parallel rectangular blocks, and as the walls of the blocks receded inwards as excavation proceeded, many interesting features, both natural and man-made, could be traced.

Pat showed that successive wooden wharves had been constructed in the fourteenth century, while I concentrated on natural features. What appeared as a small lens of sand on one face of a rectangular block, and a much larger lens on another face, were gradually revealed to be part of the same feature, a crescentic tapering sand-spit, thrown up by the river Liffey in one of its occasional flash-floods following heavy rain in the Wicklow Mountains. It became clear that the progressive silting up of the estuary by intertidal muds had been interrupted by wash-outs and deposition of sand-bars by river floods. Needless to say, such episodes gravely interfered with the stratigraphy of archaeological items that had originally been dumped on the foreshore. My work was very skeletal; a full team of various specialists following the sections in detail would have produced a great deal of valuable environmental information.

While my work was chiefly non-archaeological, I was of course fascinated by the glimpses of everyday life that many of the finds revealed. These included scattered units of the dismembered skeletons of those who had been hanged, drawn and quartered; a latrine-pit containing human faeces and wisps of moss which had served as toilet-paper; a fruit press, still packed with cherries, which had produced a cordial; half a walrus skull, imported from Scandinavia for the sake of the ivory in its teeth, and thrown away after the teeth had been extracted; a Scandinavian boulder, doubtless ballast in a Viking ship, which had been dumped overboard as the lading of the vessel progressed.

Some years later I visited the wonderful Viking ship museum at Roskilde in Denmark to see the boats that had been scuttled to block the harbour at a time of peril, and were recently raised and preserved at great difficulty and expense. Had I known that later dendrological studies would show that the framework of one of the boats, more than 50m long, had been fabricated with timber from Irish oaks which had been felled about 1050 AD, and that the boat had possibly been built in Viking Dublin, I would have examined it even more keenly than I did.

So far I have spoken only of the archaeological saga of the Wood Quay site, but there was another legal saga running parallel with it. The site had been chosen by the Dublin city authorities, who hoped to bring all their office-staffs, who were scattered up and down through the city, together on one central location. This meant clearing a very big area, and it was only after a certain amount of organic debris and its contained artefacts had been carted away and dumped, that the very great historical importance of the site began to be realised. Large-scale excavation was called for, but this would cause delay and expense to the developers. And so a running battle opened up in the seventies.

Although I was involved—if only on a relatively modest scale—events moved so rapidly that I have no clear recollection of their sequence. I can remember occupations, marches, meetings, High Court injunctions, Supreme Court appeals, and so forth. The historical cause was led by an Augustinian friar, F.X. (Frank) Martin, Professor of Medieval History in University College, Dublin. At one stage the city entered an action against him, seeking to recover many thousands of pounds they claimed to have lost over delays to the builders caused by his activities. But the sum mentioned was only a drop in the bucket compared to the extra expenses they themselves incurred due to escalation of costs, largely caused by design changes as the work progressed. In fact costs rose so rapidly that the city could not afford to proceed with the whole grandiose scheme, and ended up with only two bunker-like office blocks instead of the four that had been projected. I do not think that Frank need lose any more sleep.

But at the heart of the battle was the question—Was the archaeological deposit on the Wood Quay site a national monument in the terms of the National Monuments Act? If it was, then it enjoyed some legal protection. The Commissioners of Public Works had power to declare the site a national monument, but they refused to do so. Frank Martin raised the matter in the High Court, seeking to get the court to make the appropriate declaration. The case produced a regrettable schism in the ranks of Irish archaeologists. For most of us the site was incontestably a national monument. But Joe Raftery, the Director of the National Museum at the time, saw it only as a source of myriads of repetitive objects which would clutter up his museum. He had an unexpected ally in Brian O'Kelly, Professor of Archaeology in University College, Cork, who up to this point had for many years led strenuous efforts to get other important archaeological sites protected as national monuments, and was held in the highest esteem by me. He had recently had a dig in Cork city, and someone in Dublin had dismissed it as 'a hole in the ground'. The expression obviously rankled deeply, and so Brian regarded the Wood Quay site as just another hole in the ground. Mr Justice Hamilton sided with the majority, and made the necessary declaration.

Alas, our rejoicings were premature. A clause in the National Monuments Act, which had never previously been activated, empowered the Commissioners, provided they had the consent of the National Museum, to 'unfrock' national monuments. It became clear that the Commissioners intended to take this course. In a last throw, George Eogan, Brendán Ó Ríordáin (then Keeper of Irish Antiquities in the museum) and I succeeded in getting an interview with the late George Colley, then Minister for Finance with overall responsibility for public works. We entered the room at noon, to find him flanked by the chairman of the Commissioners and a high official from his own department. So that the interview might be programmed, I opened the ball by asking how much time he could give us, and he said about one hour. As it turned out we were there for two and a half hours, and throughout the meeting it was concealed from us that the revocation order had already been signed, and was about to be published. My chief reaction was that our time might have been expendable, but I thought that the holder of the important office of Minister for Finance ought to have had something better to do with his, rather than sit there for two and a half hours pulling the wool over the eyes of three well-meaning archaeologists.

# CHAPTER 7

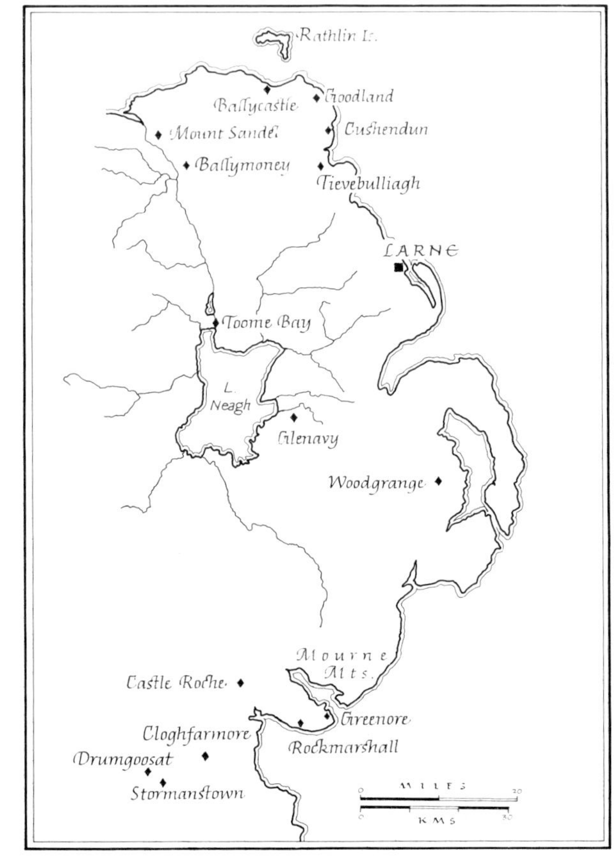


DRUMGOOSAT (KNOCKNACRAN)

RADIOCARBON DATING: HARRY GODWIN · NORTH LOUTH · COOLEY PENINSULA · ROCKMARSHALL

Resuming the trail of the giant deer, we move north to the country between Kingscourt and Carrickmacross. Here a big block of younger Mesozoic rocks has been dropped down by faulting between older Palaeozoic rocks to the west and the east, into what is known to geologists as the Kingscourt Basin. The block thus escaped the erosion that stripped these Mesozoic rocks off all the rest of the country, except the north-east corner where they were buried by still younger Tertiary volcanic rocks. These rocks had flowed over the surface of the ground as sheets of lava, which when they solidified left a protective blanket of basalt across the countryside.

## DRUMGOOSAT (KNOCKNACRAN)

In the sequence of rocks in the Kingscourt Basin there are thick beds of gypsum, which is the raw material of plaster of Paris, of great importance in the cement-making and building industries. There are several active gypsum mines in the area today. The most northern of these is at Drumgoosat, quite close to Carrickmacross. In 1942, when preparations for mining were being made, a skull of a giant deer was discovered in the neighbouring townland of Knocknacran. I went to the site with Stelfox and Hilda Parkes, who had recently joined me as research assistant. This was the beginning of a long and profitable association with Hilda, which continued until she decided to strike out on her own. With me she counted pollen, drew flint implements, and generally gave me tireless assistance in dozens of ways. At Drumgoosat we collected specimens of the mud in which the skull had been embedded to examine it for pollen, seeds and freshwater molluscs. It was remarkable that at Ballybetagh the mud did not contain any molluscs, though these were common at Knocknacran and several other sites of like age. Stelfox identified twenty-five different shells here.

### Radiocarbon dating: Harry Godwin

The late forties were exciting times for glacial geologists and archaeologists, because Willard Libby of the University of Chicago was just developing his technique of placing an age on organic materials by determining the amount of the radioactive form of the carbon atom ($C_{14}$) that still survived in them. The amount remaining was inversely proportional to the age of the material. Libby was anxious to establish that the technique was valid world-wide, and he invited leading workers in appropriate fields to submit samples to him. In this way he wrote to Harry Godwin, who was active in pollen-work in Cambridge, to say that he would date some samples for him, and Harry very generously allotted a few of his precious sample-spaces to me.

Libby announced his results in book-form in 1951, and soon scientists all over the world were trying to follow and improve on,. this revolutionary method of dating. In the physics department in Trinity Jacky Poole, Cyril Delaney and Ian McAulay took up the challenge. The carbon contained in the specimen being dated—wood, peat, charcoal or bone—had first to be transferred into another medium, where the rate of breakdown of the radioactive units it contained could be measured. Libby brought them into a gaseous form as carbon dioxide, and then recorded the rate of breakdown using Geiger counters. Such counters are used in nuclear power stations to detect the amount of radioactive breakdown or radiation to which workers in the plant are exposed.

Other workers brought the units into a liquid form, mixed that liquid into a second liquid which emitted scintillations as the radioactive carbon broke down, and then counted the flashes with a photometer. This was the route the Trinity group followed, choosing methyl alcohol, or methanol, as the liquid into which the carbon atoms were first transferred. Unfortunately this transfer was a little tricky, involving a risk of explosion, but the hurdle was successfully surmounted.

I was of course most anxious to get a regular dating-programme established under Ian's direction, and I endeavoured to raise funds for the project, which would be very expensive to maintain. In my outline, above, of the process involved, I made no reference to the complexities of the operation, which involved both highly skilled personnel and most sensitive and expensive apparatus. We did get it established on a regular basis, and produced about one hundred accurate and valuable dates, but the unit was always very small, and funds began to dry up. At the same time other laboratories were coming into the business, and it became possible to buy dates commercially at a fraction of the cost it took to do it oneself. Thus, the Trinity operation was terminated, but we withdrew from the field with our heads high.

When Harry made the sample-spaces available to me, we had already been working together for some years, and if I claim Knud Jessen as one of my fathers in science, then Harry has to be a brother in science. We first met in 1935, and I soon came to regard the Godwin house in Cambridge as my second home.

*Sir Harry Godwin*

That first meeting was on a remarkable occasion on a bog near Roundstone, in Galway, a meeting made famous by Praeger's description of it. I shall not be able to resist quoting it in full when we reach that part of the world. Harry's most important early work was as an ecologist, working closely with Arthur Tansley, often regarded as the father of that branch of botany. Harry's wife, Margaret, started to look at pollen, and it was not long before they accepted the validity of von Post's observations that studies of successions of plant assemblages, revealed by the counting of layers of pollen grains which became trapped in peat or mud as it accumulated, would throw much light on the ecology of the past. Harry later became Professor of Botany in Cambridge, and was knighted in recognition of his work for conservation.

Harry first turned to the peat deposits of the fenland near Cambridge, and soon was involved not only with changing woodlands but also with changing sea-levels. These peats had developed in fens where the ground-water was relatively rich in mineral nutrients, and were very different to the peats which built up into raised-bogs in Ireland, nourished only by the small amounts of mineral matter in rainwater. Tansley was completing his great book on the *Vegetation of the British Isles*, and before committing himself on the topic of raised-bogs, he wanted to look again at some Irish bogs, and discuss them on the spot with Hugo Osvald, the leading authority on Swedish raised-bogs. Harry wanted to widen his knowledge of bog-types by seeing Irish examples, so he was the third member of the visiting party that met up with Jessen and others in Roundstone.

That visit was in 1935, and the following year Harry proposed that we should make a raid on a Welsh raised-bog, or rather a group of three bogs, bordering on the River Teifi, near Tregaron, in mid-Wales. There would be three field-parties, each responsible for a cross-section and at least one pollen-diagram from one of the bogs. Harry would lead one group, I would lead a second, and the third would be under the charge of H.A. Hyde, from the National Museum of Wales in Cardiff. Incidentally it was Hyde who replaced the unsatisfactory term *pollen-analysis* with the new word *palynology*, which he coined with the assistance of L.J.D. Richardson, a man of very fertile brain, a Trinity graduate, then lecturing in classics in Cardiff. The word 'pollen', which implied connection with the flowering of higher plants, stemmed from the Greek verb '*paleino* — I strew'. The broad term 'palynology' thus includes other small scattered fossils, such as fern spores and scraps of insects.

As so often happens, the laboratory work started to drag badly, and it was decided that I should go to Cambridge and try to push it along. This was my first visit to Cambridge and its Botany School, and the start of a happy association that has now lasted for more than fifty years. I later worked closely with Richard West, who now holds, as Harry had done before him, the Chair of Botany in Cambridge.

I decided to allot one of my Libby dating-spaces to the mud surrounding the giant deer bones at Knocknacran, and in due course the answer came that the mud was 11,300 years old. This date is still 'good', though at that early stage of radiocarbon dating it had not been realised that some of the carbon available to water-plants was 'old' carbon which had perhaps been derived from the solution of limestone and was no longer radioactive, as opposed to 'new' carbon, recently fixed by photosynthesis from young carbon from the atmosphere. But the date gave us our first clue as to when these great animals were common in Ireland for the last time.

I returned to Drumgoosat in 1974. By that time the mine had expanded into an enormous series of underground caverns from which the gypsum had been removed, and a lot of geological information had been acquired. In one area the deposit had been intruded upon by a wall of basalt, which had solidified in a crack through which molten lava had risen and then spread out over the surrounding countryside, though it has since been stripped away by erosion. The gypsum near the hot rock had been baked to a sugary texture, and rendered valueless. Also, underground water had percolated through the gypsum in a karst-like manner, dissolving it where flow was freest, and so opening up tunnels for itself, just as caves are created in limestone. However, with the lowering of the ground-surface above by erosion, the level of ground-water has dropped also, and the gypsum tunnels are now dry.

In 1974, when a mine wall was being cut back, a hole appeared and a mass of what appeared to be small-diameter wooden poles fell out. Needless to say, near-panic ensued, because there is nothing more dangerous in underground mining than to encounter old workings, as these are often filled with water and can give rise to disastrous flooding. However, nothing drastic happened, and investigation showed that the vertical pipe was filled with a higgledy-piggledy mixture of peat, short lengths of narrow tree-trunks, and glacial gravel, which had collapsed downwards to fill an old cavity.

I learned of the discovery and asked Peter Walsh of the City University in London, a well-known authority on karstic features, to come and look at it with me. Maura Scannell of the National Botanic Gardens, who is always ready to place her expertise at the service of others, identified the 'pit-props' as short lengths of slender stems of juniper. Bill Watts and I looked at the seeds and pollen, which showed that the deposit was clearly interglacial in age.

But which interglacial? All glacial geologists agree that the 'Ice Age' was interrupted by periods when the local climate was as warm as or warmer than it is today, but there is little agreement as to when or in what sequence these interglacial periods occurred. Now radioactivity has again come to our aid. By the time 40,000 years or so have elapsed, the amount of radioactive carbon that survives in organic material has fallen to such a low level that instruments can no longer make age determinations. Interglacials are much older than 40,000 years. But uranium decays into thorium much more slowly, and dates going back to 350,000 years ago can be measured.

Libby first established the radiometric method, and it was further greatly refined by Hugo de Vries working in Groningen in Holland. Both are now dead, but de Vries's work is continued in an institute in Groningen which bears his name. The institute has launched an ambitious programme to date many European interglacial deposits by the uranium/thorium method, and it was with great pleasure that I recently forwarded some pieces of wood from Drumgoosat to the institute.

Although Bill Watts and I could not 'place' the Drumgoosat deposit in a special slot, our investigations did provide new information. Before the Ice Age the floras of Europe and North America had more in common than they have today, but this resemblance slowly ebbed as the Ice Age proceeded. Two 'amphi-Atlantic' plants, as they have been called, slender water naiad and pipewort, still have a limited distribution in small lakes in western Ireland today. Two more forms, now extinct, had already been identified in Irish interglacial deposits.

Drumgoosat produced a third, *Dulichium spathularis*, a rush-like plant of water-margins, which had quite a wide time-range in interglacial Europe, and is still very common in North America.

## NORTH LOUTH

We move on towards Dundalk Bay, where we find ourselves on the northern limit of 'The Pale'. The Pale was a rather shadowy line of defence which arose in the mid-fifteenth century to try to ensure that at least a limited area centred on Dublin was not further eroded by the growing resurgence of powerful Gaelic alliances, but remained firmly under English control. North of Dundalk the flat ground of north Leinster runs out against the broken ground of Slieve Gullion and Carlingford Mountain, country where hostile forces could be mustered, just as Dublin lay open to constant threat from the Wicklow hills. The first Norman invaders recognised the problem here, and in the mid-thirteenth century built a very strong castle, Castle Roche, 7km north-west of Dundalk. The castle ruins, which stand high on a rock-knoll, are one of Ireland's most impressive—but least known—sites. The castle continued in use for many centuries.

From Dundalk the Pale ran south-west through Ardee and Kells, both towns with buildings from this period. The northern part of Louth that lies between this line and the sea still has, in comparison with many other parts of Ireland, a sense of stability. Not of course as strong a feeling of stability as one finds in England, for example in Herefordshire, but for Ireland a feeling of stability. The stability was perhaps enforced by the many tower-houses of the area. There are no 'Great Houses'—these do not advance far north of the Boyne—but there are many well-built farmhouses with substantial land-holdings. Conditions for farming are good; compared with the rest of Ireland rain-days are few and the soil is well drained. The country is gently rolling, and the Pale essentially runs along the line that divides this flatter ground from more undulating country to the west. Such land was worth defending.

Curiously enough, traces of deserted medieval villages are almost unknown in County Louth, but there is a good example at Stormanstown, 6km north-west of Ardee. A low-lying tract is overlooked by two high points; that to the south carries a Norman motte, and that to the north an early church-site. The low ground has many banks and ditches, and a trackway and a moated manor can also be seen. Here there must have been quite an extensive village. The name is informative; an early thirteenth century deed records the granting of lands here to a Norman family called Estermyn. Time has changed the name to Storman.

The area is rich in still earlier history, for this is the region in which the well-known Cúchulainn saga 'Táin bó Cuailnge', the wild bull of Cooley, is set; the saga perhaps goes back to the Iron Age. Cúchulainn had been severely wounded in battle, but his spirit was unbroken, and he asked his followers to strap him to an upright stone so that he could continue to face the enemy. *Cloghfarmore*, the stone of the big man, near Knockbridge, 5.5km south-west of Dundalk, a splendid standing-stone almost 3m high, is traditionally identified as the stone.

## COOLEY PENINSULA

Leaving Dundalk we turn east into the Cooley Peninsula, an area of very great geological interest. Carlingford Mountain, a mass of dark gabbro rising to 590m, forms the spine of the peninsula, with Dundalk Bay to the west and Carlingford Lough to the east. Gabbro is an igneous rock, and was formed here in Tertiary time about 60 million years ago, when there was violent volcanic activity in north-east Ireland. The rock of the Mourne Mountains was formed at the same time, but with a different chemical composition. As a result we have granite, a pale-coloured rock, in the Mournes, and gabbro, a dark rock, at Carlingford. The area round Carlingford was of older Carboniferous limestone, and as the molten material pushed up through the limestone and also reacted chemically with it, it produced new minerals. There are also, as we shall soon see, many interesting glacial features.

There was thus a great deal of geological interest crammed into a small area, and in the thirties Louis Smyth used to bring student parties there, and Walter Freeman and I went along as assistant bear-leaders. Walter was one of that rare category of Englishmen, who, despite being 'very English', nevertheless establish a niche for themselves in Ireland. He came to Trinity in the early thirties, where he quickly established a very successful department of geography. He returned to Britain for war work, and never really re-settled in Ireland, leaving Trinity for a post in economic geography in Manchester. His *Geography of Ireland*, which appeared in 1948, was very successful, but the Ireland it presents was a pre-war one, an Ireland of which very little remains today. Nevertheless, the book will have an abiding value as a picture of a vanished country.

Those are far-off days; Greenore had, not a container-terminal, but a small general port with a passenger-boat to Heysham. Passengers could reach the port by train, either from Newry or Dundalk, and there was a first-class hotel—now derelict—in which they could stay. It was a hotel of character; some of the bathrooms looked down into the station, and as you wielded the towel you could watch the passengers disperse; the lounge had a huge picture-window, with a fireplace below it, which looked straight up the Lough, and so you could admire the view and warm your stomach at the same time. We would take an early train to Carlingford—the first stop, spend the day walking the mountain, and return by an evening train.

The glacial features arose from the fact that late ice moving from north to south, and hemmed in between Carlingford Mountain on the west and the Mournes on the east, played an important part in the shaping of the basin that holds the Lough; it also threw a bar of moraine across the mouth of the Lough. Ice of the same age pushed down Dundalk Bay and heaped deposit against the south side of Carlingford Mountain, giving rise to the fertile lowlands at the tip of the Cooley Peninsula. As the ice withdrew, sea-level was in a state of flux. The earth's crust, which had been depressed by the weight of the ice, was rising again as the ice thinned. The sea, whose level had been pulled down by the abstraction of water to build up the ice-masses, was also rising. If, by coincidence, both rose at the same rate for a significant time, then the waves had an opportunity both to erode cliffs in existing deposits and to build up gravelly beaches. Both features, cliffs and beaches, are well represented around Dundalk Bay.

## Rockmarshall

In the late thirties I went down to Henry Rennison for a few days' shooting, and as we walked towards the Bay we soon realised that we were crossing a series of beach ridges which had been raised above sea-level by the final upward movement of the land.

The ridges were of sand and gravel, and were pocked by small sand-pits. Near the top of one of the pits at Rockmarshall a patch of shells and charcoal was exposed, and from this we soon poked out a sliver of flint, obviously struck by human hands. The deposit had to be a kitchen-midden, but of what age?

In 1946 I returned for my first archaeological excavation, and again enjoyed the hospitality of Henry's home. Archdeacon Rennison had two parishes, one in the North and the other in the South, and on Sundays he had to remember which was the one in which he prayed for the Queen, and which was the one in which he prayed for the President; he was always delighted to have people about with whom he could argue in a gentle way. Mrs Rennison had seen her three sons depart, one to a chaplaincy in the British Army, one to Burmah, and one to Canada, and was delighted to refill her home with young people. My party ultimately rose to seven in number, but the hospitality never faltered. When the table was full, our hosts would put on their party trick. The Archdeacon presided over the bread-board (no wrapped sliced pans in those days) at one end of the table, with his wife at the other, and when Mrs Rennison called for a slice, it was sent whirling through the air to be caught with unfailing precision.

The Jenkinstown rectory is most attractive. A typical rectory, a well-built not-too-large house with rooms of good proportion, it lies on a south-facing slope overlooking the shallow tidal waters of Dundalk Bay, which change from hour to hour in splendid patterns of sand-bank and water. On a clear day the Wicklow hills can be seen in the distance. Two of the rooms, the study and the drawingroom, look out on this view. They are separated by sunny steps, which invite one to laze. There are trees with a rookery at the back of the house, and to sit on the steps, looking out over the bay, lulled by the cries of the rooks, is relaxation indeed. I should have loved to retire there. I like to have not a passive but a dynamic landscape, if possible with the sea prominently in view. We will meet my ideal at Greencastle in Donegal.

My excavations at Rockmarshall in 1946 and 1948 were very limited in extent, but I was fortunate enough to retrieve, although in small quantities, implements of flint, stone and bone which showed clearly that those who built up the middens were of Mesolithic status, with close affinities to the Larnian folk of the Antrim coast. Fortunately I retained some of the charcoal we discovered, and after the development of the radiocarbon dating method in the fifties, it was possible to have this examined. The answer was an age of 5500 years, a date that corresponded with the dates I had obtained at Dalkey Island and Sutton.

The beach ridges had been separated by narrow lagoons, and these originally held fresh water. The still-rising sea then flooded into the lagoons, and brackish-water deposits were laid down. Occasionally layers of freshwater mud interrupted the estuarine deposits. It was obviously a complicated story, and I made some pollen-studies in an effort to decipher it.

*Knud Jessen, Frank Mitchell and Johannes Iversen stand on an Irish raised-bog in 1949. Iversen was the Danish worker who revolutionised our ideas about past vegetation, by showing that man's influence on the landscape was recorded in fossil weed-pollen trapped in bogs and lakes.*

But I was overtaken by events. During the war workers in Denmark were very isolated, and they turned their attention to looking at local deposits in greater detail. Led by Johannes Iversen, of the Danish Geological Survey, they made their microscopy very much more sophisticated, and they tried to identify not only the tree pollen, but all the pollens they encountered in their preparations. Pollen of weeds associated with agriculture came under special notice, and Iversen soon realised that there was a relationship between values for tree pollen and for weed pollen—when one went down the other went up—and this could only mean man-made clearances in the woodlands for farming purposes. Neolithic objects were associated with the earliest interferences noted, and so he produced evidence for Neolithic farming.

Soon many workers were seeking similar evidence. I returned to Copenhagen to be trained by Iversen.

Because of the war, news of these developments was slow to leak out of Denmark, but when it did it made many pollen-studies then in progress utterly archaic; my Jenkinstown work was one of the victims. However, something was rescued; the freshwater muds yielded seeds of *Naias flexilis* and *Naias marina*. I have already mentioned the slender naiad (*flexilis*), a small, inconspicuous, totally submerged water-plant, that still lives in a few lakes along Ireland's western seaboard. An amphi-Atlantic plant, it is common in eastern North America. Jessen found it fossil at a few localities, chiefly west and north, and I found it here in Louth, thus showing it had been widespread in Ireland, probably about 7000 years ago. Why its modern range should be so restricted is rather a mystery. *marina* is another problem; it is totally extinct in Ireland, and survives in Britain only at one locality in the Norfolk Broads. These discoveries delighted Praeger, who saw his collection of Irish seeds in the National Museum coming into its own at last. Jessen and I used it on many occasions, and blessed his foresight.

*Knud Jessen*

The general decay of international contacts brought about by the war also very much delayed the publication of Knud's work in Ireland. He had staggered back to Denmark in 1935, laden with thousands of samples of various sizes, all of which had to be patiently worked through. The work was proceeding well when war broke out. 1945 came, the diagrams were ready for the draughtsman, but the final text had yet to be completed. So it was arranged that Knud and his wife, Ingrid, would come to Dublin in the summer of 1945 and stay with us in Merrion Square. Knud and I would sit down at my typewriter, he would dictate and I would type, and we would more or less sit there till the job was finished. Meanwhile my wife and Doreen Farrington, Tony's wife, would entertain Ingrid. We did the job, the paper was read to the Academy in the spring of the following year, and was finally published in the summer of 1949. It had 290 pages of text and 13 plates of illustration, and its publication immediately put Irish quaternary studies in the forefront of European knowledge.

It was this close working together over stretches of several hours that built the intimate relationship between Knud and myself, a relationship that never subsequently faltered. I went to Copenhagen many times, staying with the Jessens and working over unidentified material with him. Just before lunch he would look at my problem seeds; we would eat, each with a flora before him, turning over the pages and saying, 'it can't be this; it might be that.' I would then go to the herbarium and collect reference seeds; in the late afternoon we would look over them together, and quite often make further identifications.

In Ireland we only saw Knud as the tireless field-worker. In Denmark, where he had been honoured by the Crown, he had high standing. He was university professor of botany, member of many important conservation projects, and a director of the Carlsberg Foundation, which both managed a brewery and dispensed its profits on scientific research. Knud was above all a family man, and, as well as having many grandchildren of his own, adopted our two daughters into his clan.

CHAPTER 8

# North East Corner

1. COUNTY DOWN AND BELFAST · 2. LOUGH NEAGH

3. LARNE · 4. GOODLAND · 5. NORTH COAST

# ~1~
# COUNTY DOWN AND BELFAST

MOURNE MOUNTAINS · STRANGFORD LOUGH · WOODGRANGE · THE PALAEOECOLOGY CENTRE · THE BRITISH ASSOCIATION FOR THE ADVANCEMENT OF SCIENCE

## MOURNE MOUNTAINS

South county Down centres on the Mourne Mountains, but my contacts with these hills are all too slender. I have walked across them, I have driven through them, but never for long enough to sense their real feeling. I should like to have seen them in the company of Estyn Evans, who savoured them to the full and distilled off much of their flavour into his splendid book, *Mourne Country*. Estyn was the founder of modern geographical studies in the north of Ireland, and the inspiration of many advances in other fields.

One of the most striking features of the area are the massive drystone granite walls around small fields on the lower slopes which encircle the hills. The walls are built of rounded boulders, rather smaller than a football, with a few larger boulders here and there. At first one thinks that the stones have been rounded by being rolled along by running water, but there are far too many of them for that. Lifting one's eyes to the hills immediately makes their origin clear; they are core-stones, produced by chemical weathering.

Granite tends to be cut up by fractures, often at right angles to one another, and so the rock can be likened to a mass of giant sugar-cubes. When chemically active water passes through the rock-mass, its effect is most severe on the corners of the cubes, which could be attacked from three directions. The centres of the cubes often survive as spherical masses of solid rock, known as core-stones.

The Mournes were not overrun by ice during the last glaciation but were subject to severe freeze-thaw action. As a result, the rotted rock sludged away downslope, carrying the core-stones along with it. Some core-stones were left behind in sheets on the upper slopes, where we can still see them today. Many reached lower ground, and here, in order to clear the ground, they have been built into massive walls surrounding small fields. An immense amount of labour was also built into the walls.

On the hill-tops the depth of weathering was irregular, and when the rotted material was sludged away, jagged spikes of solid rock were left behind as tors. This feature was dramatically developed on Slieve Bignian, whose resultant cockscomb crest can be seen for many miles.

## Strangford Lough

My main interest was in Strangford Lough and the lower ground around it. This is *drumlin* country, aptly named 'basket of eggs' landscape. Everybody agrees that drumlins, elongated hills of glacial deposit, in shape remarkably like eggs cut in half longitudinally, were moulded below ice-sheets. They may be packed together in serried ranks, as in Down, or occur in scattered isolation. Nobody, least of all myself, fully understands the complex processes involved. The west shore of the lough is studded with half-drowned drumlin islands, whose flanks carry raised beaches which record post-glacial changes of sea-level. The sheltered beaches were favourite haunts of Larnian hunters, who found—just as today—abundant fish, shellfish and water-birds around the islands. The Lough is now protected by the Wildlife Scheme.

## Woodgrange

West of the lough itself, higher sea-level flooded in between the drumlins, and at one place, Woodgrange, 5km north of Downpatrick, late-glacial muds were discovered below later brackish-water deposits. These muds were deposited between 13,000 and 10,500 years ago, and their pollen content gave a clear picture of the grassy landscape through which the Irish giant deer wandered. Remains of giant deer are quite common in the area, and records of finds go back as far as 1725. East of the lough, muds of the same age occur below sea-level on the shore at Roddanstown.

## The Palaeoecology Centre

To me, Belfast means the Queen's University of Belfast. When in the early thirties I first became interested in glacial geology, J.K. Charlesworth, the Professor of Geology, a Yorkshire man of enormous energy, was the leading figure in the subject in Ireland. Estyn Evans was gradually building up the Department of Geography, which he headed for many years with great distinction. Oliver Davies, nominally in the Department of Classics, was making archaeological forays round the province, and carrying out with Estyn a series of excavations in megalithic tombs, which were to revolutionise our views of the Neolithic in the north of Ireland.

As time went on Alan Smith, who had learned about pollen with Harry Godwin in Cambridge, arrived in Belfast, and in the early 1950s he and others in Queen's persuaded the Nuffield

Foundation to set up what grew into a most successful multi-disciplinary Palaeoecology Centre. Smith led the way with palynology, a radiocarbon laboratory with Gordon Pearson followed, and then Mike Baillie opened up the field of dendrochronology.

Smith first proceeded to follow up Iversen's methods of extracting evidence of prehistoric agriculture from lakes and bogs. In the early sixties he combined pollen with radiocarbon to show that the vegetational disturbances associated with the making of a clearance in the woods for short-lived fields could reverberate for about 350 years. His original demonstration in Londonderry has since been replicated by Mick O'Connell in Connemara, and Pete Coxon in Kerry.

As radiocarbon dating became more sophisticated, anomalies began to cause difficulties, and it became clear that the radiocarbon reckoning of years did not entirely correspond with the historical record of calendar years, and further that the degree of correspondence, or divergence, between the two records was not constant. Pearson embarked on a most ambitious programme of dating individual tree-rings in wood—which also provide an annual record—and emerged with a remarkable graph which enables radiocarbon datings to be calibrated against calendar years.

But this method presupposes that the ages of the tree-rings are known, and this is where dendrochronology comes in. It has long been understood that in countries with seasonal rainfall the size of the ring of wood that is added to the tree by annual growth is directly related to the amount of rainfall. A simple count of the rings will tell the length of life of the tree, and detailed study of their widths will reveal the sequence of good and bad growth-years. The sequence can be extended by studying trees whose growth-periods overlapped.

Does the method work in Ireland, where we do not have seasonal rains and the annual growth period is long? The answer seemed to be 'No', until Mike Baillie took up the challenge. Travelling Ireland with a chain-saw and a trailer, he collected oak samples of all ages, from trunks buried in bogs to rafters in old buildings, and ended up with a continuous record 7200 years long, which carries us back to the Neolithic period. Others were at work in England and Germany, and to everyone's surprise the areas showed mutually consistent ring-patterns, and so north-west Europe is linked in a common chronology.

Baillie provided wood samples of known calendar age, and Pearson determined the number of radiocarbon years that attached to each sample, and so it became possible to evolve an elegant calibration-curve. As long ago as 1932 Hugh Hencken realised the possibilities of the method, and when he was excavating the big crannog at Ballinderry in Offaly, he had the rings in some of the oak-posts that surrounded the crannog examined. A pattern was recognised, but it was only possible to say that some long trunks had been cut, and the pieces used separately in different parts of the crannog. If Hencken was digging now, Baillie would be able to tell him the calendar year in which the oak trees were cut down. The centre flourishes today under the leadership of Jon Pilcher; long may it continue to do so.

## The British Association for the Advancement of Science

The British Association for the Advancement of Science held its annual meeting in Belfast in 1952, and a number of Dublin people were involved; Charlesworth, Farrington and I spoke at a discussion on glacial geology. A lot of preliminary publicity material was distributed before the meeting, including one pamphlet with a strongly 'Orange' tinge. Tom Wheeler, Professor of Chemistry in University College, Dublin, took exception to this, and wrote in complaint to the president of the Association, A.V. Hill. Hill was a remarkable man, who had three high points in a very distinguished career.

His lifetime work was in experimental physiology; in the thirties he did pioneer work on radar with Tizard and Blackett; during the war he was responsible for the organisation of scientific personnel. Hill replied that if he had objections to the way things were run in Belfast, Wheeler should invite the Association to Dublin, which it had not visited since 1908. Wheeler wrote back to say it was not possible for him to do so, as by its constitution the Association could only meet in the United Kingdom or associated countries. Hill replied, 'Ask us, and see what happens.'

A Dublin committee was set up with Wheeler as chairman and myself as vice-chairman, an invitation was sent, and it was promptly accepted. A very successful meeting was held in 1957. I had been a regular attender at BA meetings for some years, and could see that the annual jamboree rolled like a juggernaut through the various cities it visited, crushing the local scientists as it passed. Eric Ashby, then Vice-Chancellor of Queen's, had been the chairman of the Belfast committee, and, hearing that he would be in Dublin, Tom and I waylaid him for dinner, to pick his brains. Like Winston Churchill, he jotted down on half a sheet of notepaper twelve points which we would have to watch closely if the situation was not to get out of hand. Every one of them surfaced in due course, and those jotted notes were the foundation of my admiration for Eric Ashby. We met again in Cambridge when he was Master of Clare College, but after that he rose to the House of Lords and beyond my ken.

Lord Fleck, chairman of ICI, was president at the Dublin meeting, but the president-elect was Patrick Blackett, another intellectual giant. If Hill had three areas to which he made distinguished contributions, Blackett had at least five, ranging from naval strategy to continental drift. When in Dublin he was concerned that one of the radiocarbon labs in England was painfully slow at getting into commission, and we had several discussions about the organisation of the Trinity laboratory which was then running smoothly. As with Ashby, during our talks I got a deep impression of the keenness of his brain. He disappeared as far as I was concerned after the Dublin meeting, but in Cardiff the following year when we were assembling for a BA excursion, our steps happened to coincide, and he immediately said without introduction 'You will be glad to hear that problem has sorted itself out'. As I envisaged all the meetings and discussions he must have had during the preceding twelve months I was staggered by this instant recall.

## ~ 2 ~
## LOUGH NEAGH

LIGNITE DEPOSITS · GLENAVY · LIFE IN THE LAKE

Lough Neagh, which is the oldest and largest, as well as the scenically dullest, lake in Ireland has recently created a furore. It owes its origin to the Tertiary volcanic upheavals that took place in north-west Europe between 65 and 50 million years ago. Successive outflows of lava followed one another only slowly, and there was a sufficient time interval for the surface of the basalt to weather to soil, which became invaded by plant growth before the next flow scorched but did not completely remove all traces of the soil and plant debris. Study of these remains tells us that the climate at the time was warm and wet.

This outflow of molten rock had to be compensated for by crustal movement, and by about 35 million years ago a great depression, in which water could accumulate as the first Lough Neagh, had developed in south-west Antrim. This depression formed a focal point for the local rivers, and they began to carry clay, sand, and plant debris out into it; under the weight of this introduced material the floor of the basin continued to sag until the debris reached a thickness of 350m. The temperature remained warm, and the local forests included redwoods and palms as well as trees still growing in Ireland today.

## Lignite Deposits

As the sediment thickened, pressure on the plant debris gradually transformed it into lignite or brown coal, a very useful fuel intermediate in calorific value between typical black coal and peat. For a long time it was thought that the beds of lignite lay at too great a depth for their working to be economical. But a recent drilling programme by the Geological Survey of Northern Ireland showed that along much of the east shore of the modern lough great thicknesses of lignite lie almost at the surface, covered only by a few metres of much younger glacial deposit. Commercial interests rushed to the lake to follow up this discovery, and now it is shown that enormous quantities of lignite at shallow depth surround much of the lake. Furore indeed; there is so much lignite under the town of Ballymoney that it would be profitable to move the whole town so as to gain free access to it. An application to allow mining in the vicinity of the town was lodged in 1990.

What to do? The north of Ireland already has excess generating capacity at Ballylumford and Whitehead, but these power-stations use expensive imported fuel. Lignite is a less efficient fuel, but around Lough Neagh it is easily accessible to cheap open-cast mining in almost inexhaustible quantities. To transfer it to an existing power-station would be very expensive, and to make economic sense it would have to be burned in a new power-station immediately adjacent to the excavations. There is no doubt that power would be cheaply produced, but the effect on the local environment would be disastrous. Also, the works would be on waterlogged ground near the lake-shore, and foundation stability might be a problem.

## Glenavy

If the Ice Age had not intervened, the primary lake might have continued to accumulate fossiliferous sediment, and so give us a wonderful picture of the development of Ireland's vegetation over many millions of years. But unfortunately ice swept across the basin on several occasions, and substituted its own sediments for the upper layers of those already there. In order to open up trial pits in the lignite, it was necessary to remove the glacial deposits, and in the vicinity of Glenavy on the east side of the lake this process created a further minor furore. A layer of gravel yielded tusks and teeth of the woolly mammoth, and while these fossils were not in primary position, they indicated that in some cold phase of the Ice Age these animals must have been common in the vicinity. Sands above the gravel were rich in vegetable debris, and while this again was not in primary position, it indicated totally different climatic conditions. Spruce and pine were most common, but there were also fruits of hazel and yew; these latter trees cannot stand severe frost. Beetle remains were common, and these suggested that at the time the debris was deposited, the climate of the area was much the same as it is today.

I have had a semantic quarrel with most of my glacial geology colleagues over the status of this warm phase. We know that throughout the Ice Age there were many oscillations from cold to warm. Some scientists think that the Ice Age is not yet over, and that we are living in a warm phase which will come to an end, perhaps quite soon. Glacial studies started in north-west Europe, and illogically we define a warm phase as one like that in western Europe today, where climatic conditions favour the growth of broad-leaved, deciduous trees, and such vegetation is the mark of an *interglacial*. But the cold and warm oscillations were not equal in strength or length, and sometimes a modest return of warmth for a short period only allowed the growth of hardier trees, such as the pine and birch. Such were the conditions when the giant deer was last wandering in Ireland, and such a phase is called an *interstadial*. I think that the presence of hazel and yew on the shores of Lough Neagh indicate interglacial conditions with temperate woodlands; my colleagues say no, the conditions were interstadial.

## Life in the Lake

The modern freshwater lake stands about 15m above current sea-level, but it contains several animals more generally at home in salt water. Most notable are the pollan, a version of the herring, and a shrimp, generally found in sea-water. How and when did they get into the lake, or were they trapped there from a time when the lower Bann and the lake were an estuary? They are unlikely to have survived the Ice Age in the lake. We know that in early post-glacial time, north-east Ireland was still recovering in height from the level to which it had been pushed down by the weight of overlying ice, and we know that sea-level was oscillating, but most workers cannot picture a combination of circumstances that would have allowed these animals to reach the lake at that time. For the present, the mystery must remain.

Over-fishing of pollan in the past has made it an endangered species. The whole lake is now endangered. Over its total area it is remarkably shallow, generally not exceeding 15m in depth. Light can penetrate its waters almost to the bottom, and this means that algal growth is vigorous. A number of towns—Antrim, Lurgan, Portadown and Dungannon—lie on the gentle surrounding slopes, and their effluents, both domestic and industrial, inevitably make their way into the lake, where the additives promote algal growth. Phosphorus from domestic detergents is especially active. Normally wind movement keeps the upper layers of the water in slight motion, and this deters the growth of algae. But should a substantial number of calm days succeed one another in summer, then algal growth might froth up, and in doing so consume all the available oxygen in the water, with fatal results for all other forms of aquatic life. However, an increased awareness of the problem, ably promoted by Palmer Newbold, who moved from his professorship in the university in Coleraine to head the Council for Nature Conservation and the Countryside, will probably enable this doomsday situation to be averted.

In the opening sentence of this section I described Lough Neagh as 'scenically dull'. This is because it lies in a depression in a generally featureless landscape; there are no nearby hills to be reflected in its waters. The hedges which surround it make it difficult to see, except from the lake shores themselves. My favourite viewpoint is at Ardboe on the west side of the lake where the ground rises in an isolated knoll to 30m, and a well-carved scripture-cross forms an added attraction. This is very isolated country, where old ways die hard, as beautifully told by Polly Devlin in her book *All of Us Here,* published in 1983. Lignite underlies Ardboe also, but the locals will have none of it. At a symposium in Belfast which discussed the implications of the lignite find, one speaker from Germany described how a community of 50,000 people had been successfully moved to allow lignite deposits to be worked; a film of the development had been made and he was sure that if people in Ireland could see the film, their objections would be lessened. A man from Ardboe rose at the back of the hall and said they had seen the film, and that their objections had been redoubled thereby.

## ~3~
## LARNE

RAISED BEACH GRAVELS · THE BROIGHTER HOARD · HALLAM MOVIUS'S EXCAVATIONS

### RAISED BEACH GRAVELS

To most people Larne means a car-ferry *en route* to Stranraer, but although now heavily built over there are extensive areas of raised beach gravels in the harbour area, and for more than a hundred years it has been known that these gravels contain abundant flint implements. Praeger started life as an engineer, and his first assignment was to dock-excavation in raised beach and estuarine clay deposits in Belfast. Characteristically he was more interested in the fossils the deposits contained than in the excavations themselves, and he soon noted that the assemblage of shells indicated water temperatures slightly higher than those in Belfast Lough today. It is now widely accepted that we did have higher temperature values for a short time early in the post-glacial—a time often referred to as the 'climatic optimum'—but it has proved very difficult to define 'the optimum' precisely in terms of warmth and duration. Praeger did find animal bones, including those of the wild boar, in Belfast, but he did not find any evidence of human presence.

## The Broighter Hoard

Praeger started to look at the gravels in Larne about a hundred years ago, first with the Belfast Field Club, to see whether flint implements occurred only on the surface of the gravels or whether they also occurred at depths throughout the gravels; the latter was the case. But he had to sharpen his interest when he was called as a witness in an absurd law case over the ownership of some very important gold ornaments that had come to light in a field at Broighter, near Limavady, Co. Londonderry, in 1896. The finest item, a magnificent gold collar, was certainly fabricated somewhere in north-west Europe during the Iron Age; some of the other items sit uneasily with it, and for them Mediterranean, and even Indian, parallels have been suggested.

The British Museum, which had acquired the objects, wanted to prove that they had been discarded, in which case the museum would have them on the principle of 'finders, keepers', and it alleged that the objects had been thrown overboard from a boat as a votive offering to some god. The Crown, which had called Praeger, wanted on the other hand to establish that the area was dry land about the time of the birth of Christ, the period to which the objects could be assigned. The objects had not been discarded, but had been deliberately concealed by someone who intended to reclaim them, in which case the Crown had a right to them as treasure-trove.

Praeger joined forces with George Coffey who had also been subpoenaed. George Coffey, who has the right to be called the father of Irish archaeology, was then organising the collections in the new National Museum (opened in 1890). Coffey and Praeger measured sections in the deposits at Larne, and also visited many exposures of raised beach deposits around the north coast of Ireland, and were able to show convincingly that, just as they are today, these deposits were above sea-level at the time of the birth of Christ. The Crown won, the objects were treasure-trove, King Edward VII presented them to the Royal Irish Academy, the Academy deposited them in the Museum, and Coffey had the pleasure of setting them out as one of the chief displays in his new arrangements. Fortunately the geological content of their evidence was not left to moulder in the pages of some law report, but was published by the Academy in an important joint paper in 1904.

To his account of these proceedings in *The Way That I Went*, Praeger added a cryptic footnote: 'There is a sequel to the story, but it cannot be told yet.' In 1940 Françoise Henry, the founder of modern studies of Early Christian art in Ireland, added to the mystery by stating that the objects had not been dug up but were found in a ditch, rolled up inside an old umbrella. The late Dr Michael Quane, administrator of the Museum during Adolph Mahr's enforced wartime absence, showed me an affidavit (which Mahr had seen) sworn by a respected professional man, which stated that he was brought up near Broighter, and it was then widely believed that the objects had been stolen from a display case in a house in the neighbourhood some years before the discovery. Like Mahr and Quane, I accept the affidavit which provides a logical explanation for the heterogeneous nature of the hoard.

## Hallam Movius's Excavations

My first visit to the Larne gravels was in 1936 to see the extensive excavations that Hallam Movius was making in the raised beach gravels. Hallam, whom we have already met at Kilgraeny, was Hugh Hencken's chief lieutenant during the Harvard programme of excavation in Ireland, and as well as digging with Hugh, whose chief interests lay in the Early Christian period, he also excavated older sites, caves and raised beaches independently. Hallam was built on a generous scale—an asset to any tug-of-war team—and Bill Riley used to tell of an occasion when this caused a problem. Bill was conducting Hallam round some caves in the Blackwater valley on the look-out for excavation sites, and at one point it was necessary to squeeze through quite a small hole. Hallam did get through, but the effort was temporarily too much and he fainted at the far side. Poor Bill was frantically worrying as to how he could possibly push this inert lump back through the hole, when Hallam recovered as promptly as he had fainted.

Hallam and I met at Cushendun in 1934, and we became life-long friends; in the fifties I went to the Peabody Museum in Harvard and worked through the material he had excavated at Larne with him. The results of his Irish work ultimately appeared in a handsome book of some 350 pages—*The Irish Stone Age*—published by the Cambridge University Press in 1942. Unfortunately it was war time, and the bulk of the edition was torpedoed on its way to the States, with the result that the book became rather a collector's item.

Much of the coast of Antrim is built up of chalk which contains nodules of flint, very suitable for the making of stone implements. Erosion, both by ice in the Ice Age and by waves more recently, broke up the chalk and set free masses of flint nodules. There was thus abundant material available for tool-making by human hands. In the Larne gravels Hallam opened up a pit 5m square and 5m deep, and from it he obtained over 15,000 pieces of humanly struck flint, but unfortunately relatively few finished implements. Flint knapping probably took place on the open beach, unwanted flakes were discarded and the more promising pieces were carried away to be worked up into finished tools elsewhere. Sea-level was rising at the time, and the discarded flakes were incorporated into the accumulating gravels. Most of the finished implements, axes, flakes and scrapers, were rather coarse and heavy, and it is thought that they were probably carpenters' tools. The people who made these tools were obviously very active around Larne, and so they and their culture have come to be known as Larnian. They probably lived at Larne about 7500 years ago. They do not seem to have had domestic animals, and their lifestyle was Mesolithic, with fish and shellfish playing an important part in their economy. Praeger and Coffey—lacking of course any help from radiocarbon—placed them in the Neolithic, because of the presence of stone axes which at that time were thought not to occur before the Neolithic period.

# ~ 4 ~
# GOODLAND

CHALK DOWNLAND · ESTYN EVANS · EVIDENCE OF EARLY AGRICULTURE

## CHALK DOWNLAND

The very name of this townland, Goodland, tells us to expect something, and we are not disappointed. Wide areas in England are covered by chalk downland, and at Goodland we had, until it was smothered by peat, a very small area of such downland, much exploited by early farmers. And yet the parallel is not exact. In England the chalk was not greatly disturbed by later geological events, although it was gently flexed into downs and wolds. But in the north of Ireland the chalk had great masses of molten basalt poured out over it, and while it is due to the cover of basalt that we owe the survival of chalk in this area, in the process the chalk got baked and hardened. In England the chalk is soft and porous, while in Antrim it is hard and impermeable, but its fertility for plant life remains unaltered.

When the pure, fine-grained limy debris that later consolidated into chalk was being deposited, the geography of Europe bore little resemblance to that of today. About 100 million years ago, in late Mesozoic time, a great sea stretched from Ireland to the Caucasus, and limy ooze which also contained small amounts of siliceous debris accumulated on its floor; the silica gradually coagulated into nodules of flint and the ooze became chalk. Later earth upheavals raised areas of chalk above sea-level, and these were immediately attacked by erosion. Under this attack all the chalk in Ireland disappeared, except that in the north-east which was protected by its cover of Tertiary basalt.

Goodland stands on the edge of a cliff, looking out to Scotland across the North Channel. Here erosion has, as it were, cut a window in the basalt, and exposed chalk at the surface over a limited area at an altitude of about 250m. Ice swept over the area on several occasions, but left only thin sandy deposits with a patchy distribution. Soil evidence indicates that there was woodland here early in the post-glacial, but this was cleared away by early Neolithic farmers. After a time soil conditions deteriorated, and blanket-bog began to cover the area.

## ESTYN EVANS

My first visit to Goodland was in 1945 with Estyn Evans. He brought me to a place where the removal of peat was creating a field whose surface was strewn with worked flints and fragments of polished stone axes. Estyn also knew that there was Neolithic pottery to be found in the area. Samples we took at the base of the peat—where we found a worked flint *in situ*—subsequently showed weedy grassland being replaced by bog. At the time I did not realise that the pollen indicated Neolithic grazing land giving way to bog, and the diagram was never published.

Having collected our samples, we wandered across the downland, and Estyn pointed out to me old field-banks and outlines of medieval booley huts that he had noted from time to time. In summer, upland areas carried a lush growth of grass, and the herds were driven up there to feast on the grass, a practice known as 'booleying'. The herdsmen camped out with the animals, living in flimsy huts. We dropped down below the edge of the cliff overlooking the complicated geology of Murlough Bay, and we sat down to eat our sandwiches with our backs to the white chalk cliff, and our legs almost touching bright red Mesozoic sandstone below the chalk. Lunch over, Estyn got out his sketch-book and began to draw the Scottish coast, which was set out in the sunlight before us. I alternately looked through my binoculars at the diving gannets which had wandered down from Ailsa Craig—a small isolated island in the Firth of Clyde—or at the primitive coal-mining going on in Carboniferous rocks at the base of the cliff. We lazily discussed the circumstances of peat growth, and the first arrival of people in the vicinity. It was one of those rare but perfect moments when one feels at one with one's companion, and that God is in his heaven, and that all is well with the world.

## Evidence of Early Agriculture

Excited by accounts of early pottery to be found at Goodland, Humphrey Case of the Ashmolean Museum in Oxford started excavating here in the early 1950s, and as he soon found Neolithic objects and structures underneath the peat, he asked me to come and look at the peat in detail. The site was of such great interest that it had many visitors. Bruce Proudfoot from St Andrews looked at the soils, Geoff Dimbleby from the London Institute of Archaeology looked at the pollen in the soils, Michael Morrison from Queen's also made some pollen counts, and Jack Heslop Harrison, then Professor of Botany in Queen's, and his wife Yvonne, looked at the modern plant communities for me. Jack then went on, first to be Director of the Kew Botanic Gardens, and then a Royal Society Professor in Wales.

Even before Humphrey's arrival, Jean Sidebottom from Queen's had, at Estyn's suggestion, excavated some booley hut-sites that could be seen in areas not buried by peat. In fact there were so many cooks that it looked as if the Goodland broth would never get to the table. In 1967 I was fortunate enough to have a year in Cambridge as a Visiting Fellow at the newly-founded Clare Hall, and after a round-table conference with the others who had worked at Goodland, I undertook to draw the various threads together, in a joint paper.

As a result, when I walk around Goodland today, or failing that, look at an aerial photograph, I see a mixture of bog and grassland. The picture opposite has the cliff-top running along its

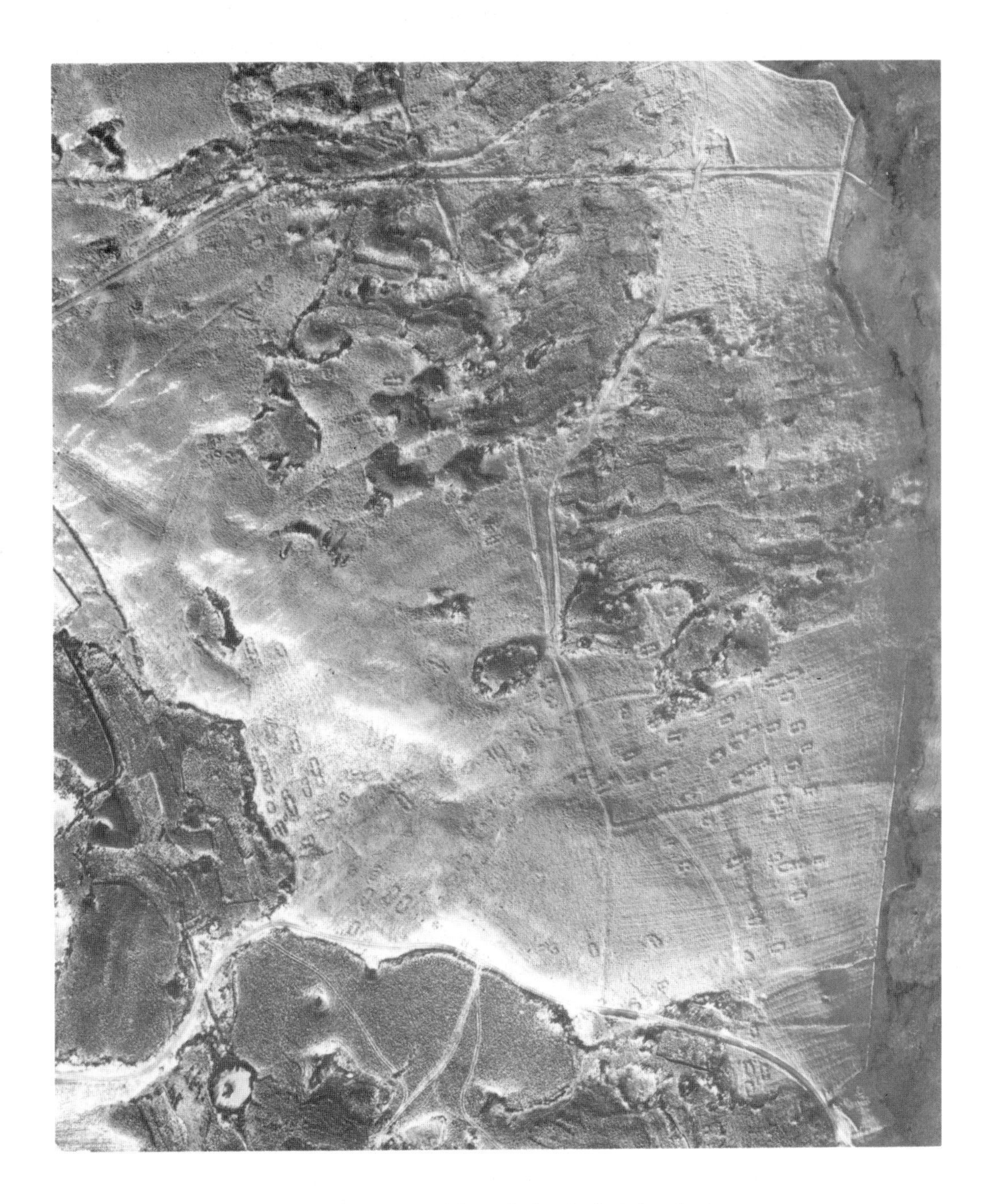

*Goodland, Antrim. The peat-buried chalk grassland at Goodland, from the air.*

right margin; white chalk debris can be seen. The lower left-hand corner is largely occupied by bog, and it was through this peat that Humphrey made his excavations. In the middle we see grassland on chalk, and a long bank, running north–south, and still partly buried by peat, divides the picture. From the southern end of the bank, other banks run out at right angles to the cliff-edge, enclosing rectangular fields with former cultivation-ridges.

Above the upper field a lobster-claw of surviving peat stretches out and buries some field-banks, showing that the banks precede the formation of the peat. Inside the field we see small ghostly rectangles, and many others occur outside the field. These are the foundations of small huts, and if we look at the main bank on the left of the field, we can see that it is straddled by hut bases, which must be younger than the bank. If we look inside the lobster-claw we see a hut-base as well as a bank, showing that late peat-growth also buried some huts. Jean Sidebottom found a sixteenth-century silver brooch in one of the huts, and fragments of pottery of the same age were found high up in the peat. Estyn interpreted the huts as a temporary summer settlement (a booley) used by dairy farmers in the milking season.

Huts near the bog edge in the bottom of the picture produced scraps of prehistoric pottery, and starting here Humphrey traced the pottery out under the bottom of the peat, where he soon came on a complex of pits, ditches and holes, which contained masses of Neolithic pottery and flint implements, and also a few stray Mesolithic implements. The pollen-diagrams showed the settlement was in weedy grassland with some cereal plots.

But then a dramatic change set in. While higher ground remained dry, and went over to heath, on lower ground the soil deteriorated and became waterlogged; sheets of rushes expanded, and vegetable debris, the precursor of peat, began to cover the ground. As I wander, I speculate on the cause of the change from fertile farmland to rushy slopes. Did the climate become wetter, and did the rushes invade the waterlogged soil? Did soil exhaustion, brought about by continued farming, favour the growth of heath on dry soil and rushes on wet, and was it the development of a matted layer of roots of rush that checked the downward movement of water? Early farmers made great use of fire to keep vegetation open; did the ash from their fires get washed downwards to clog up the pores in the soil, and so make it retain water? Today these questions are the subject of much debate.

True bog then began to develop where vegetable debris sealed the soil surface, but the debris had a patchy distribution, forming first in hollows and then creeping upslope. It did not form on the top of hillocks, and some of these remain free of peat to this day. As it expanded the bog reduced the amount of land available for farming, but its surface also provided a convenient rubbish-dump, and later farmers threw field-stones, earth and domestic refuse onto its surface. The amount of domestic refuse was all too scanty, but as he dug down through the successive layers of peat Humphrey did find some scraps, and these together with pollen-studies enabled a skeletal agricultural history of the area to be built up.

Goodland's fascination for me lies in the fact that we have here, more clearly than anywhere else in Ireland, a kaleidoscope of landscapes, stretching back at least six thousand years to the time when Mesolithic hunters were wandering through its woodlands. Neolithic farmers arrived about five thousand years ago, cleared away the trees and set up meadows and cereal plots, which survived into the Early Bronze Age. There is then a big gap, and after a long period when the area went over to heath, we again see farming, probably with the aid of ploughs, in the Early Christian period. The old field-banks are perhaps thirteenth-century Norman, when there was also grazing on the downs and on the expanding bog. The booley huts are probably fifteenth to sixteenth century in date, associated with seasonal communal grazing, the fields having been abandoned. As land use intensified, the bog was in part drained, in part cut away for fuel, and its active growth probably stopped towards the end of the eighteenth century. Today the area is peaceful and lonely.

# ~ 5 ~
# NORTH COAST

BALLYCASTLE · RATHLIN ISLAND · COLERAINE

## BALLYCASTLE

In 1945 the Evans family were holidaying in Ballycastle, just round the corner from Fair Head, and I joined them there. They were staying in a terraced house overlooking the harbour, and the name of the terrace was Railway Houses. Ballycastle was at one time reachable by rail, and an enterprising developer had offered a permanent season ticket to Belfast to anyone who bought one of the houses. 'Permanent' in this case meant seventy years, as the line finally folded up in 1950.

Ballycastle has a warm place in my memories, because for many years in the thirties Louis Smyth had brought parties of students there, as there is so much geological variety and so much splendid scenery easily at hand. From some outings we walked back in the rain, but there was a special pub in the village where a 'hot colie' was always to hand. All the whiskey from the Coleraine distillery has long been drunk, but then the pub had a kettle sitting perpetually on a little oil heater, and there was never long delay. The resultant drink would, as the man told Praeger in Killarney, 'go down your throat like a torch-light procession, and warm the nails in your boots'.

## Rathlin Island

We took the opportunity to spend a few days on Rathlin, bringing one of Estyn's younger boys, David, with us. A budding ornithologist, he had just been promoted to a pair of binoculars, through which he was determined to see every bird on the Irish list. Some farmyard geese were promoted to greylags. Remembering the kindness I had received from Mr Brunker, I found it hard to decide what attitude to adopt. Was I to correct, and so perhaps discourage the boy, or to agree and allow him to wander further astray? I think I preserved silence as far as possible. Today David is a distinguished artist, producing beautiful water-colours.

The weather was not kind, as there was dense fog throughout our stay, so dense as to keep the island's two lighthouses uninterruptedly at work. One had a fog-horn, the other detonated maroons. For the picnic lunch one had to make a decision; was it to be near the fog-horn, and jump each time it sounded, or near the maroon where one could watch the little cartridge slide up a lanyard, and know exactly when it would detonate? We chose the latter.

The main purpose of our visit was to see the Neolithic quarry and axe-factory at Brockley. A rock has to have very special qualities to be suitable as a raw material for the fabrication of axes and other implements. It has to be dense and tough, and at the same time it has to be capable of splitting readily when struck by a skilled craftsman. Flint is an ideal material, but it is followed closely by *porcellanite*, a rock which as its name implies has the fine-grained texture of china. When Antrim basalt was weathering under the tropical conditions of long ago, it sometimes broke down into a clay rich in iron and aluminium; if such a clay was baked by a succeeding lava flow it became lithified into porcellanite.

Only two outcrops of such rock are known in Antrim, one at Brockley and the other on the slopes of Tievebulliagh, high up above the village of Cushendall. There is an axe-factory at each outcrop. That Neolithic peoples found these sites is an indication of the detailed searches that must have been made for suitable rocks for axe-making. At Tievebulliagh a quarry was opened up, and the rock was broken down into blanks, suitable in size and shape to be worked by flaking and polishing into finished axes. Most of the material was probably exported from the site as blanks, as the quarries are littered with blocks of rock and rough flakes, but with few signs of polishing activities.

## COLERAINE

I place the western limit of my north-east corner at Coleraine, where the Bann draining out of Lough Neagh reaches the sea. All along the course of the river from the lake to the sea we find evidence of Mesolithic peoples. In 1951 I carried out a very small excavation at Toome Bay, near the lake exit. It produced some scraps of flint in Mesolithic style, and more excitingly a few pieces of worked wood; these had been broken and used as firewood, but it was still possible to say that the charred fragments came from pieces of carpentry; radiocarbon later showed that the site had been occupied about 7700 years ago, the earliest date then recorded.

At the lower end of the river, just south of Coleraine, a high gravel-bank overlooks the river. Local slumping took place from time to time, and it was often possible to pick up from the exposed gravel surface worked implements in various styles, Mesolithic, Neolithic and even Early Bronze Age. Amongst these were very small points of neatly worked flint of a style well known in Britain and in north-west Europe, and there named *microliths*. In the 1970s Peter Woodman, who was then in the Ulster Museum, had an opportunity to dig at Mount Sandel, a knoll in the gravel area, with surprising results.

His excavations revealed the foundations of several circular huts, with the bones of pigs, fish and birds, and also charred hazelnuts and water-lily seeds. He found thousands of stone implements, the most common being microliths, and there were also some small axes. The site seemed to have been a base-camp, from which parties of hunters would have set out on expeditions. The radiocarbon date was about 8700 years ago, making it the earliest site known in Ireland, much older than the coastal Mesolithic sites such as Larne, where the microlith was virtually unknown.

Irish Mesolithic material appears to fall into two groups, an earlier one, running from perhaps 9000 to 8250 years ago, which I have ventured to name as *Sandelian*, characterised by small implements centred on the microlith, and the later *Larnian*, which ran from about 8000 years ago to about 5000 years ago, when the Larnian hunters were overrun by, or perhaps merged with, the first farmers. The Larnian is characterised by large implements and an absence of microliths. The implement types of the two groups are strikingly different, with no suggestion of overlap, and are different again from cultures of the same age in Britain. Where these first Irish hunters came from is an enigma.

I am afraid that when I go field-walking I have a blind-spot as far as microliths are concerned. When I was in Cambridge in 1936, more than fifty years ago, Grahame Clark, later Disney Professor of Archaeology there, and a most distinguished archaeologist, said to me, 'Look, one day you are going to find microliths in Ireland; they must be there; and so that you will know what you are looking for, here is a small representative collection.' I studied them, I handed them round in my lectures for years, but neither I nor any of my students ever found one. I showed them to Miss Stacpoole, and she wore herself out on the north Leinster coast looking for them; she brought me masses of tiny pieces of flint, but never a microlith. And yet they were there; Don Hodgers walked the fields around Dundalk and found them. Peter Woodman has picked them up in the Blackwater valley, and they also occur in the Shannon Basin, as we will see when we reach those parts. So about 8500 years ago there must have been small scattered parties of Sandelian hunters in Ireland. The Larnian people were more numerous, as we have many records of them, chiefly down the east coast.

In addition to my memories of its whiskey, I have other pleasant recollections of Coleraine, where I was external examiner in environmental studies for a period in the seventies. I was very impressed by the keenness of the staff in the department, and much enjoyed my stays with Palmer and Joe Newbould at their home outside the town. To the great benefit of environmental protection in the north of Ireland Palmer took the opportunity of early retirement offered by the university, and turned his full-time attention to conservation. His decision may have been partly prompted by the inevitable upsets that followed the shotgun marriage between the Coleraine New University and the Jordanstown Technical College to form the University of Ulster. The university at Coleraine seems to have been born under a cloud. It had a long legal battle with its architect, whose plan is alleged to have been a design that was a runner-up in an English competition. My chief recollection of the campus buildings is of the all-too-central central-heating system ejecting tarry blobs like a volcano, blobs which created dark stains all over the central podium.

CHAPTER 9

# North Donegal

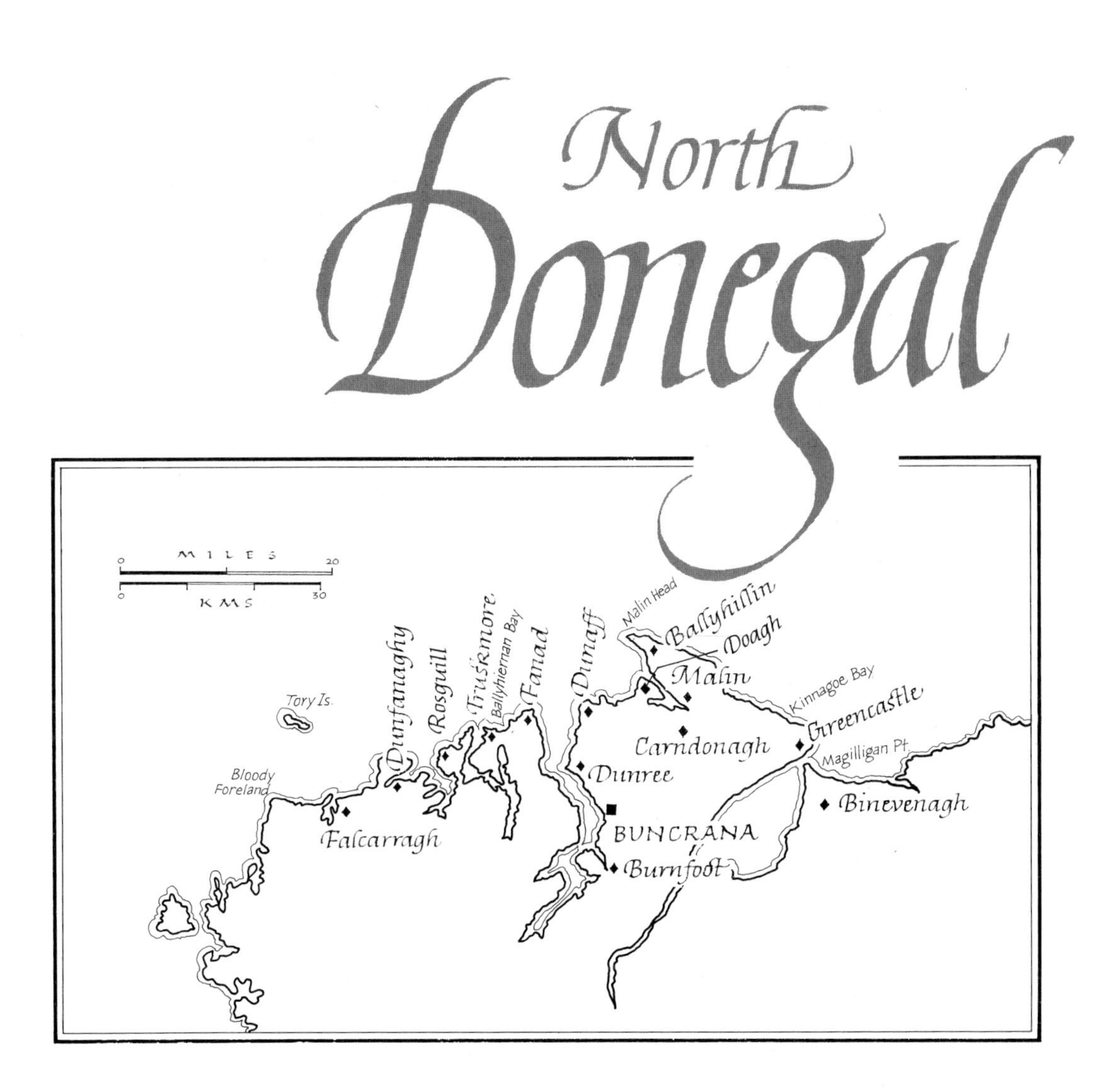


INISHOWEN · MULROY BAY · SHEEP HAVEN

TORY ISLAND · BLOODY FORELAND

## INISHOWEN

Without intending to cast any aspersion on the scenery of Donegal, it always seems to me like Scotland on a smaller scale. And within Donegal, the Inishowen peninsula is an epitome of the county, with its splendid scenic variety, rocky ridges, lonely valleys, cliffs, inlets and sandy beaches. A diamond-shaped piece of country, 40km across, all areas are easily accessible.

I start with Buncrana, as it was from there I first got to know the peninsula. A relative had married an Englishman who had a passion for fishing. A wealthy man, he had fishing rights on rivers in Norway, as well as England and Ireland. At one time he owned the rights both on the Drowse which flows out of Lough Melvin and on the Mill River at Buncrana. After his death his widow, Nellie Beart, lived on at the Mill House just outside Buncrana, with a superb view down the full length of Lough Swilly. Mrs Beart was very hospitable, and as my brother and I had been given an old car by another aunt, we used to go up to Buncrana when odd gaps appeared in our college terms. Most days we would start out with thermos flasks and a cold chicken, and drift lazily round Inishowen.

I find it hard to realise that Praeger never owned or drove a car, but treated such a means of transport with contempt. I can barely remember a time when I did not have access to a mechanically propelled vehicle. I started on motor-bikes at fourteen, and when I became eligible for a car licence at seventeen, I already had half a car. But then Praeger's work was essentially walking and looking, pausing to make notes or place a specimen in a vasculum. I was usually encumbered by heavy steel rods, which could be assembled to make a drill with which one could take specimens from deep in a bog, together with a levelling staff and other gear.

My brother has a passion for fishing, but I am afraid it passed me by. However, one time in Buncrana, as I was lodging beside a good river in a house that was full of expensive fishing-tackle, I decided to give it a try. I succeeded in assembling a splendid Hardy split-cane rod and appropriate tackle. Moving along the river bank I jumped down into a field, failing to observe in my excitement that the field held a solitary large bull. I threw the rod back over the hedge, and followed it without delay, and that was the end of my fishing career.

Nowadays I take Inishowen the other way round, starting at Greencastle on Lough Foyle, and moving anti-clockwise. Greencastle is a historic spot, with a fourteenth-century Anglo-Norman castle cheek by jowl with anti-Napoleonic fortifications. I go for the scenery, and the scene from the lawn below the Manor House is, to my taste, one of the finest views in Ireland. Immediately below are tidal rocks, a perch for gulls, cormorants and herons, and at the right season eider ducks. Then there are the tidal currents of the Lough, pinched up here by Magilligan Point, a tremendous spit which stretches out from the opposite shore; on the water there is an almost constant stream of curiously shaped and coloured small ships moving to and from the chemical plants of Londonderry. Behind all are the black basaltic crags of Binevenagh, their outline made jagged by enormous landslips in the past. These slopes were a happy hunting ground for Praeger, as mountain avens (*Dryas*), saxifrages and other alpines still linger there.

Kinnagoe Bay, just round the corner of Inishowen Head, is the next stop. A steep twisting track runs down the cliff-face to the sands below. This is a romantic as well as a beautiful spot, as only a few hundred metres away the remains of the *Trinidad Valencera* lie below the waves; much of her treasure is now safely in the Ulster Museum. We move on round Glengad Head, to Malin Head, where we find splendid cliffs and birds. Just as we approach the Head we swing around Ballyhillin Bay, where we see the most convincing evidence for the ability of thick sheets of ice to depress the land on which they rest, the land rising again as the ice melts. About 18,000 years ago north Donegal was covered by thick ice, and as the ice retreated, beach gravels quickly filled the bay at Ballyhillin, and these early gravels were subsequently carried up about 20m above modern sea-level. The road and the village lie on the crest of the beach-ridge. These early gravels were cut into when sea-levels changed again about 5000 years ago, and a low wave-cut cliff lies between the village and the sea.

Our road takes us on through Malin—a very pretty village which was laid out in the seventeenth century and which still retains its triangular village-green—to Carndonagh. Here on the outskirts of the town, in the grounds of the Protestant church, we find one of Ireland's Early Christian enigmas. There is a large cross-shaped slab, with small carved standing-stones to each side; there are other decorated pieces in the churchyard. The slab carries an incised cross, worked in ribbon interlace, with Christ and some of the apostles below. The ribbon interlace is very like that in the Book of Durrow, which is reasonably dated to the seventh century; Françoise Henry claimed the same date for the Carndonagh cross. But tucked in among the main decorative features are smaller details, some of which have a very Viking look; Robert Stephenson, formerly Director of the Scottish Museum of Antiquities, would place it in the ninth or tenth century. I have looked at the cross many times and failed to make up my mind.

The foundation of the site is undoubtedly early, and I would like to go along with Françoise Henry; but looking at the detail, I have to feel that Robert has a point. There is a rather similar cross at Fahan, south of Buncrana.

From Carndonagh we run along the south side of Trawbreaga Bay and turn out across a stretch of sandy, grassy machair to Doagh Isle, an enchanted spot. If we follow the road that runs due north across the isle to its end, we find ourselves beside the tidal race through which the bay fills and empties. Here we see old common-fields still in use, and at the water's edge a group of Donegal long-houses scattered in a clachan. A *clachan*, as defined by Estyn Evans, is a rural cluster of small dwellings, not organised in streets, and without any services, such as a church or a shop. Most of the houses are occupied, and some show signs of gentrification; one even has a lily-pond with gnomes. At the south end of the isle there are low rock-surfaces, and on these are carved a rich assemblage of Early Bronze Age designs, concentric circles and cup-marks. There must have been a substantial population here, perhaps 3500 years ago.

Through Clonmany we swing round the north-east end of the Urris Hills and enter the magical area of Dunaff. The hills to the south and Dunaff Head to the north are of quartzite, and stand up high. In between there is a band of granite which succumbed to tropical weathering and now floors a lowland between the two highs. Mesolithic peoples were the first to find this fertile area, which still carries a dense, if scattered, population. Much of the land shows the old-fashioned open-field layout, even if the strips are now separated by barbed wire. The fishing-clachan at Lenankeel is still closely occupied, though a mobile home and some abandoned tractors make its appearance less picturesque than it was forty years ago. We turn back through the Urris Hills at the Gap of Mamore, where on its upper slopes we can still find the dwarf willow (*Salix herbacea*), a survivor from the end of the Ice Age. As we turn south down the shores of Lough Swilly, we look down on the old fort at Dunree Head, and are amazed that as recently as fifty years ago it was thought to be a military site of great strategic importance. When I first visited Buncrana, British officers still had a cachet in certain social circles in the peninsula. Now occupied by Irish soldiers, the fort is essentially a museum. Looking across the lough we see Knockalla Mountain, the geological continuation of the Urris Hills.

Returning through Buncrana we need only look at the mouth of the Cranagh River, where an old bridge leads first to the ruins of the fifteenth-century O'Doherty castle, and then to a very pretty early eighteenth-century house built by the Vaughan family. Our peregrination ends at Burnfoot, where we are on the edge of the ambitious nineteenth-century intake of land between the mainland and Inch Island. Because of design mistakes and lack of capital, the work was never successfully completed, but nonetheless this is the most Dutch view that we can obtain anywhere in Ireland.

## MULROY BAY

Mulroy Bay lies sandwiched between the peninsulas of Fanad on the east, and Rosguill on the west. The bay has a very complicated outline, rather like a miniature Lough Swilly to which a north-stretching subsidiary extension has been added. It looks rather like a distorted Y in which the left-hand arm opens to the sea, while the tip of the right-hand arm is blocked by a narrow cross-bar. Before the last advance of ice there may have been two separate small islands here. The one on the east, Fanad, was dumb-bell shaped, with an extension to the west, Trusk More, linked to it only by a narrow thread of rock at Kindrum. Rosguill lay to the west.

When the ice retreated, Trusk More was joined to the mainland on its south side by a group of drumlins. Complicated post-glacial movements of sand and gravel and changes in sea-level then linked Fanad and Rosguill to the mainland, and the sea flooded in in a narrow channel between the drumlins and cut off Trusk More on the south, leaving Mulroy Bay with today's many confusing tidal flows. There are numerous small sheltered bays, heavily used for fish-farming. Driving in this area is very confusing as one seems to be confronted by the sea at every turn. The migrations of sand and gravel have left stretches of beach and expanses of machair on all sides.

We enter the Fanad peninsula at Rathmelton, and move up the west side of Lough Swilly. As we round the corner of Knockalla Mountain, we see the great strand of Ballymackstocker Bay, which links us to the hills of Fanad ahead. At Fanad Head, we are on granite again, and at Rinmore Point we come to vast stretches of sand around Ballyhiernan Bay. Our road rounds a low rock knoll, and immediately on our right we see what looks like a row of upside-down curraghs transformed into sand. In the curragh, the utility boat of the west of Ireland, canvas is stretched over a light wooden frame. There is no keel, the stern is square, but the bow rises high like a pointed spoon; turn the curragh over, and it looks like a dolphin with a pointed snout. At Ballyhiernan the snouts are the abrupt ends of wide cultivation-ridges which spread over an enormous sand-dune, several hectares in extent. The whole dune is covered by organised ridges, so the layout cannot be the work of land-hungry peasants; it seems to be a scheme launched into by some well-meaning landlord. In the early nineteenth century there must have been a large population here, as there are several deserted clachans scattered around. The entire layout is in loose sand, and I should have thought that the local gales would soon have played havoc with its symmetry. I did not see similar features anywhere else in the vicinity, and feel that it must have been some local scheme that went wrong. I should love to know more about it. If we continue west, we enter the Trusk More peninsula.

To get to the Rosguill side of the bay we must retrace our steps 20km to Millford, and then turn north again. At Carrickart, on the sand and gravel that links Rosguill to the mainland, there is one of the largest stretches of machair in Ireland, but here I did not see evidence of former cultivation. On the east side of the high ground in the centre of Rosguill, on a low rock-ridge which rises through a field near the sea at Mevagh, there are splendid Bronze Age cup and circle carvings. In the graveyard surrounding a ruined church a little farther to the north, a prostrate slab has twenty-three clearly defined cup-marks cut into it, again Bronze Age in feeling. As at Doagh in Inishowen, there must have been a Bronze Age population in these parts.

North-east of the high ground lies Tranarossan Bay. As I moved out towards the strand and looked down on the dunes, the name suddenly rang a bell. I remembered that thirty years previously Miss Stacpoole used to bring in brown paper bags full of decorated pottery and labelled 'Tranarossan'. One largely blown-out dune had a flattish area remaining, a sure sign that the sand there had been bound by fragments of charcoal and other organic debris, and had so survived wind attack. A short walk to it and I was filling a plastic bag with more of the same pottery, probably medieval in age.

## Sheep Haven

The Sheep Haven is more open, but on its south-west inner end it has several lesser bays, which reflect the general north-east/south-west trend which was impressed on Donegal scenery by the Caledonide phase of folding. It is bounded by Horn Head on the west, and Rosguill on the east. Dunfanaghy lies at the base of Horn Head.

Dunfanaghy always reminds me of July 1927. On twenty-eight of the days of our family holiday, heavy rain fell; on the other three there were showers. We were in lodgings in the upper end of the street, of which I only remember two things. The small sittingroom with its primitive gramophone and limited store of records which we ground out over and over again till we knew them all by heart. *Oklahoma* tells us that in Kansas City you could 'walk to privies in the rain and never wet your feet'; that was impossible at our lodgings where there was a damp earth closet at the bottom of the garden, armed only with an elderly copy of the catalogue from the London Army Navy Stores. But there was fascinating reading on each page as it was detached, because the Stores offered a remarkable range of goods suitable for every climate.

In despair we would change into our swimming togs in the house and put on our raincoats, and then our father would drive us to the pier at Portnablagh where we would swim—in the sea the rain did not matter—and then have a damp drive back. When the rain ceased we would try, with a few clubs and rather battered balls, to play golf on the links east of the village. Our Dublin next-door-neighbours, the Millards, who were motoring through Donegal, joined us for a few days. The son, Jim, and I thrashed at the balls, but my chief recollection is of the black rabbits which ran around the links in great numbers. Rather to our envy, the Millards were enjoying the benefits of Arnold's Hotel, and on recent visits to the area I have followed their example. It is a splendid family-run hotel, with comfort but no ostentation, the latter being the curse of many Irish hotels.

For me Horn Head and corncrakes are the chief features of Dunfanaghy. The Head has splendid bird-cliffs, many old walls, some of which must be of considerable age, and fine examples of long houses. On a recent visit another placename, just as in Rosguill, rang a bell—Muntermellan. I set out for the dunes at the edge of the bay below, and was promptly bitten by a dog. Some men were shearing sheep in a farmyard with two collie puppies running around. I stopped for a few words with the shearers, and the mother of the puppies walked up behind me and quietly sank her teeth in the calf of my leg; bursts of laughter were the only sympathy I got. However, I staggered on and was rewarded by a rich haul of decorated pottery, which had been revealed since the two ladies made their collection.

The Muntermellan site would repay examination, because the sand-dune in which the midden of burnt stones, shells and pottery is buried is seated on peat. A radiocarbon date for the top of the peat would ante-date the midden, and pollen-studies in the peat would throw light on the environment of the time.

Falcarragh lies 10km south-west of Dunfanaghy, and the hay-meadows in between are the last stronghold of the corncrake in Ireland. Hearing them in such numbers reminded me of 'ringing days' with Alec Mason in the 1930s. Then they were abundant in south County Dublin; today one or two birds may turn up there, but they move on after at most a few nights' calling. In the last ten years their numbers in Ireland have fallen by a further 30 per cent, and there are less than a thousand calling birds in the whole country. We must try to persuade farmers in the areas where corncrakes are still to be found to keep to old-fashioned hay-making and not make silage, if necessary paying them compensation for doing so. This is already happening in Fermanagh.

In this field the Irish Wildbird Conservancy is doing remarkable work. The Conservancy is an efficient body of some considerable strength, and I have to smile when I think of its predecessor, The Irish Society for the Protection of Birds (annual subscription two shillings and sixpence). After a lifetime of committees, I look back to my first and second. The first was the Leinster Branch of the Irish Amateur Swimming Association, where I was a schoolboy representative; we met in some solicitor's office on the quays. The second was the bird committee which met in C.B. Moffatt's room in a lodging-house in Lower Baggot Street. Father Kennedy, Peter Dunne and Mr Brunker would be there. I found the proceedings rather embarrassing, as Moffatt was by then a very feeble old man, and the meetings were really held as an act of courtesy and kindness to him. Still I was very glad to meet him in the flesh, as the preliminary work he did many years ago on the behaviour of robins never really met the acknowledgement it deserved.

## Tory Island

With my younger daughter, Rosamond, I left Drogheda around midday in the summer of 1976 for Gortahork, intending to sleep there, but she was driving and made such good time that we arrived in the late afternoon. The thought struck us that we might get a boat to Tory that evening. We went down to the pier and there was a boat ready to set off. We enquired where the crew were, and were told they were up in the pub. We went up to the pub, passing a group of revellers on the way. The pub said the crew had just started down, and we then realised who the revellers were.

We were not long at sea before we discovered that we and two schoolgirls were the only sober persons on board. Fortunately the sea was calm, and there was no roll on the boat, because on a previous trip not long before, one of the inebriate crewmen lying on the deck had rolled overboard and not been missed till the boat arrived at Tory.

One of the crew became convinced that I was a long-lost friend and kept offering me a swig from a bottle of whiskey. The repeated offerings led to a point where I had either to hit him or accept the drink. I took the latter course and was delighted to find that the whiskey was well diluted with water, and was in fact quite a pleasant drink. On arrival my friend produced lodgings where we could stay.

The island certainly is an extraordinary place, but I made no social investigations. My daughter, who has excellent Inisheer Irish, was surprised that she found it so difficult to follow the local dialect. I looked for, but failed to see, any of the primitive farming implements that Tommy Mason illustrated in *The Islands of Ireland*. I did see some hen-houses built of large stones, which gave them a strangely megalithic appearance.

My main interest was two aspects of the geomorphology. As I have already mentioned, I am convinced that in some parts of Ireland the only explanation for the landscape as we see it today is that there have been movements in the earth's crust in the fairly recent geological past. Such movements are well known in other countries, where they are studied under the name of neotectonics. But in modern science everything must be quantified, and I am no mathematician. In any case geomorphological change, either by removal of material by erosion or relative change in position, usually proceeds almost infinitely slowly and is extremely difficult to measure. How is one to know that the reference-point on which one bases one's measurements is not itself in motion? Like Archimedes, where are we to stand? I recognise that my observations are purely subjective, without any quantitative basis, no more than ephemeral bees, but nonetheless I am convinced that there has been crustal movement in Ireland, some places being raised, some lowered, others tilted in relatively recent times.

I believe that Tory has been tilted, and in independent support for my belief I reproduce Derek Hill's splendid painting *Tory Island from Tor More* (Pl.2). Derek Hill has long made Tory a special stamping-ground of his own, and indeed I met him on the island where he was lodging in his bothy. The previous evening my daughter and I had been wandering around the west end of the island, and passed a curious structure which looked like a container that had been washed high ashore by some prodigious wave; on enquiry we were told that that was where the painter lived. Doubtless it was luxuriously appointed within, but from the outside it looked a most appropriate home for a man who had founded a school of primitive painting on the island.

The painting shows clearly what was for me the most dramatic feature of the island—high cliffs reaching almost to 100m along its north-east side, with the ground sloping steadily away to the south-west and gliding gently below modern sea-level. In the Channel Islands we can see similar tilting on a much grander scale; Jersey slopes southwards from 150m on the north coast to about 60m; a late Tertiary age has been suggested for the tilting. Again in Brittany, the north coast is cliffed, but the south slips gently below sea-level. This is best seen near Vannes, where the Gulf of Morbihan, studded with small islands, suggests relatively recent subsidence. There are even megalithic tombs which are submerged at high tide, but here we cannot rule out the possibility of post-glacial changes in sea-level. Immediately to the east of the Gulf we have the drowned mouth of the River Vilaine; I use the word 'drowned' because the tides run far up the river channel, in exactly the same way as they run up the Suir estuary in Ireland.

The bulk of Tory is of granite, but the east tip is of quartzite, which forms the eastern headland. Ice moving out from the mainland once crossed the island, as I saw erratics and some ice-moulded rock. The quartzite, which is traversed by many fractures, has been dissected by the sea into narrow pinnacles or *tors*, hence the name of the island. The quartzite headland has also been cut into laterally, so that it has three successive 'waists'. Each of the waists is protected by one or more ditches, and there are also about twenty hut-sites and some wells, so at some time, probably during the Iron Age, there must have been a substantial settlement keen on self-defence, despite the windiness and bleakness of the site. We are reminded of Dun Aengus on the Aran Islands. This settlement probably had no connection with the Early Christian monastery complete with round tower that was sited near the harbour.

The second aspect of my curiosity was deep rock weathering. I have already spoken of the warm, wet climate of Tertiary times, when decaying tropical vegetation was built up into lignite. Warm water sank deeply into the surface rocks, leaching out some of the elements that built up their minerals, and reducing many rocks to a mush, 100m or more in depth. Granite, which is important on Tory, is particularly susceptible to such attack.

When the cold conditions of the Ice Age came along, with alternate freezing and thawing, the mush was sludged away, leaving the core-stones high and dry on less weathered granite beneath. Tory shows splendid examples of this phenomenon. The granite of the Wicklow Mountains was similarly weathered, but here during the Ice Age the mountains were high enough to build up their own cap of ice. As a result, most of the core-stones were carried radially away from the hills to be deposited in the surrounding countryside. Donard in Co. Wicklow lies on slate, west of the granite, but so many core-stones of granite were deposited there when the ice melted that the original geological surveyors thought there must be solid granite below, and entered granite on their field-maps. On Tory, low stacks of core-stones, still in their original position, protrude through the finer materials on the surface of some slopes; such features on a much grander scale can be seen in the Isles of Scilly, especially in those parts that were not overrun by ice.

## Bloody Foreland

There are further suggestions of deep weathering at the Bloody Foreland, so-called because of the red-stained rock. The Foreland itself is a mass of granite, threaded through by reefs of quartzite. The staining is very well seen in Altawinny Bay, where spikes of red quartzite perforate the granite. Again there is controversy; is the colour due to warm chemical weathering which often forms red soils, or had the quartzite a small content of some iron mineral which oxidised to a red colour, not necessarily under the influence of warmth?

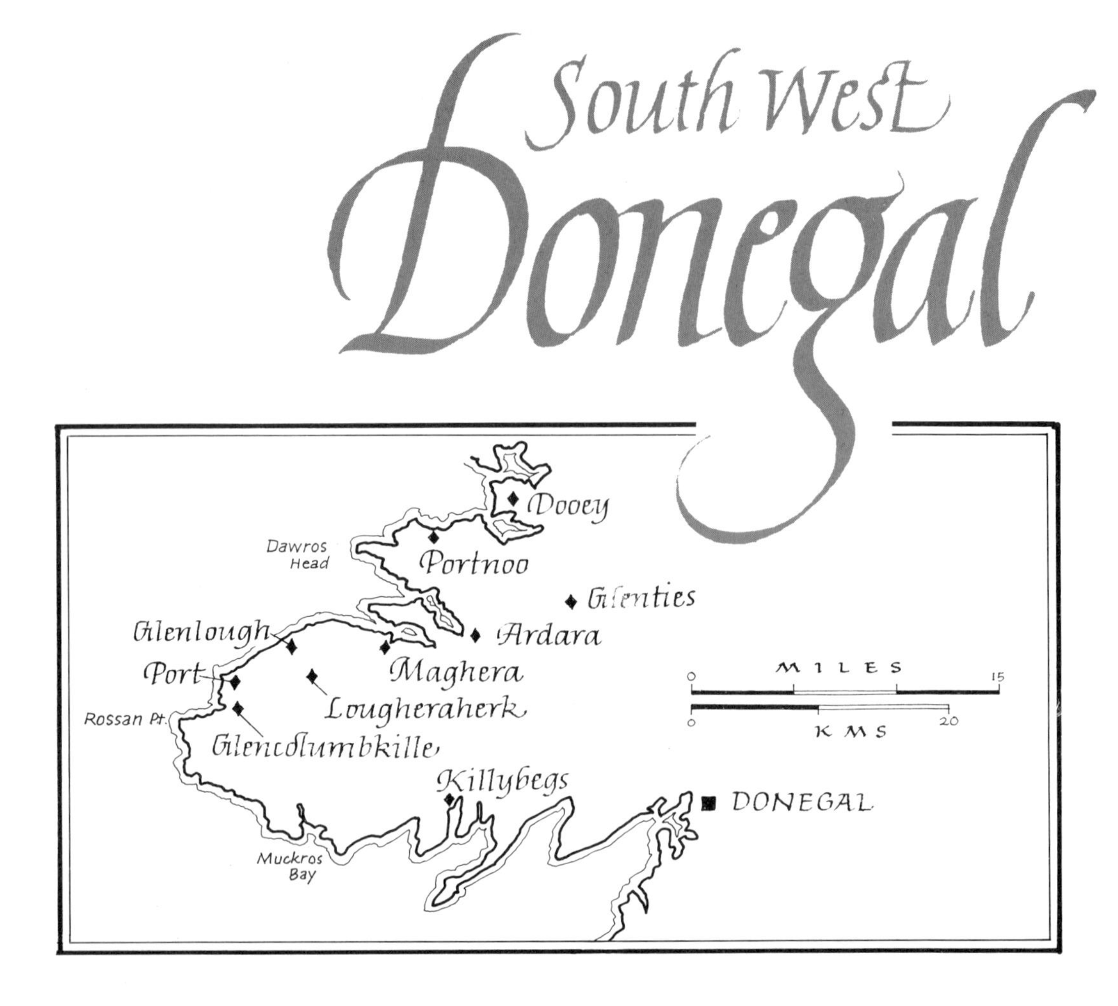


# CHAPTER 10

DAWROS PENINSULA

PORTNOO · ROSSAN PENINSULA

There are splendid mountains and much of interest in central Donegal, but I was more interested in the two promontories of south-west Donegal. The Dawros peninsula, the smaller northern headland, lies west of Glenties, and the Rossan peninsula, the larger southern one, lies west of a line from Ardara to Killybegs, and ends in Rossan Point.

## DAWROS PENINSULA

The Dawros peninsula centres on an eroded mass of granite, circular in outline and low-lying, surrounded by a low rim of the rocks into which it has intruded. Dubliners, living with the Wicklow Mountains constantly in view, think of granite as a hard upstanding rock. But its complex mineral nature makes it very sensitive to chemical weathering, particularly, if the climate is warm. And the core-stones which are spread over the surface of the Ardara granite (taking its name from the nearby town) make it clear that the granite here has been subjected to severe chemical weathering.

One might imagine that core-stones would form fairly rapidly, relative to the great age of the earth. But in one remarkable area in Sweden it has been recently shown that some core-stones may have been in existence for at least 70 million years. There some core-stones have been undercut at their edges, so that they are mushroom-like in form. A Swedish geologist, wandering through a group of such undercut core-stones, looked underneath the mushroom caps and was astonished to see in some cases remains of an entirely different rock, chalk, adhering below. Just as in Ireland, this part of Sweden had been covered by the chalk-depositing seas at least 70 million years ago, and the core-stones were already standing there with their mushroom caps. They were entombed in chalk, and have since been exhumed, but not altered in size in any way. So here at least the erosional process was slow. I have wandered through the Ardara core-stones hunting for chalk in their cracks and hollows, so far without success, but there is no reason why it should not be there. We shall return to this question of erosional rates when we get to Galway.

## PORTNOO

On the north side of the promontory at Portnoo is another of my special Irish beauty-spots. In the background we see the high Donegal mountains. Nearer are the sand-hills around

Dooey Point, where very dramatic archaeological discoveries were made a few years ago. Normally such sand-hill sites produce medieval pottery or Iron Age material, but here an Early Christian jeweller's workshop was found. There were ingots, crucibles and moulds, and a number of pieces of jewellery, still in the course of fabrication. Except for a fallen pillar-stone, there was no evidence of a nearby settlement, and the reason for siting the workshop in lonely sand-hills remains to be explained.

But the special charm of my view lies in the immediate foreground. We look down on Inishkeel, a small islet with a ruined church and important early crosses. Joined to the mainland by a sandy bar at low tide, it slowly separates itself as the waves rise. Having passed the island on both sides, the waves meet in gentle collision in an ever-changing pattern. They rise over one another, they pass through one another, and I could sit there for ever, fascinated by this simple kaleidoscope.

Alas another site nearby, also high on my list, has been defiled. Doon Lough takes its name from the great stone fort that rises on an island in the lake. In character like Staigue Fort in Kerry and the Grianán of Aileach near Londonderry, but unlike them not 'restored', and probably of Iron Age date. The whole setting had a special charm, but when I was last there about four years ago the space between the access road and the lake was being used as a rubbish-dump, and I turned back rather than push through herring-gulls raking among refuse.

## Rossan Peninsula

When, in the southern peninsula, we look at the great cliffs of Slieve League, rising 600m into the air, it is hard not to think of recent tectonic uplift. And the same is true of the whole peninsula, which is bounded by four high rock-ridges, arranged like the edges of the diamond on the playing-card, surrounding central lower ground which is drained by the Glen River. A great fault running from Killybegs to the vicinity of Ardara separates the Crocknapeast ridge from the lower country to the east. Another fault runs west from Ardara and separates the Slieve Tooey cliffs, some of the finest in Ireland, from the lower Dawros peninsula to the north. Cliffs also form the western edges of the diamond. The whole diamond is a stony mass of quartzites and micaschists, metamorphic rocks created from earlier rock material by Caledonide heat and pressure. There are many rocky headlands and small sandy bays, in which the Atlantic swell rises into rolling waves which break on the shore.

The north-west face of the diamond is cut by three valleys, which decrease in size as we go north. The largest, Glencolumbkille, and the Malin coastal area south-west of it, were occupied as early as Neolithic times, as there are many early megalithic tombs in the vicinity. Christian hermits perhaps reached the valley in the seventh century, and the valley takes its name from these followers of St Columba who created their 'desert' in this remote and beautiful place. A very impressive number of decorated slabs and pillars still survive, and are formally visited on an annual pilgrimage.

The Port valley a few kilometres to the north is smaller and still more remote. Here among the infertile quartzites and schists there are small beds of limestone. Much of this has been removed by erosion, with the consequent creation of small basins, but enough has been left to give some fertility to an area of otherwise barren soils. Surrounded by an area deeply covered by bog, one small fertile basin is still farmed, but there is only one active home, though several ruined houses lie nearby. A mosaic of small fields is cultivated by hand, with small meadows, with potatoes in lazy-beds, and with oats in broader rows, but grown on the ridge-and-furrow principle. We saw such ridges abandoned in Fanad, and abandoned ridges are common throughout Ireland, but Lougheraherk is the only place in Ireland where I have seen this method of growing cereals still surviving.

Lougheraherk is also the only place in Ireland where I have seen the evidence for earlier Ice Ages, many millions of years ago. The till, that is, unsorted glacial debris, from the last Ice Age has not yet been consolidated into rock, but till from Ice Ages millions of years ago has usually been lithified into a rock known as *tillite*. It is now recognised that in the geological past, ice such as is now found in Antarctica formed in many other parts of the world, Brazil, North Africa and Ireland, to name only a few. At Lougheraherk layers of tillite can be seen interbedded among rocks we know to be many millions of years old; tillites do also occur at other localities in Ireland, but this is the only place I ever saw them.

Still further north the little valley of Glenlough, which holds Lough Anaffrin, is even more remote. Although there is no road into the valley, there are a few house ruins, and until recently a lonely hermit lived there, emerging only occasionally to draw his pension and buy his provender; today the valley is left to birds and sheep.

Loughros Bay Beg lies at the foot of the high Slievetooey cliffs, and there are interesting dune systems here. I visited the dunes at Maghera on the south side of the bay with Palmer

Newbould, Bill Carter and a group of students from the university in Coleraine. Parts of the dunes are mobile and aligned under the influence of north-west winds; elsewhere they are stable, and where not all the calcium from sea-shell debris has been leached out, hazel grows freely. Where all the calcium has gone we get heath dominated by ling (*Calluna*). In places, iron washed down from the upper layers of the sand has formed a continuous sheet or iron pan, which holds up water. If the side of the dune is cut away to expose the pan, then the trapped water flows away freely in a small spring, which seems quite out of place in a dry sand-dune.

On the north, Dawros, side of the bay, opposite Maghera, are fossil dunes, buried by blanket-bog, and the alignments of these dunes show that when they were forming, the wind was coming from a south-westerly direction. We all talk about post-glacial changes in climate, but here there was clear evidence of a change in general wind direction at some time in the past. I took a sample for radiocarbon determination from the base of the peat, and the answer was an age of 4200 years. This sample killed two birds with one stone; first it said the wind change took place more than 4000 years ago; and second it said that by that date the surface of the dune had become sufficiently water-logged for peat to start to form on it. This is one of Ireland's oldest dates for the beginning of blanket-bog formation.

CHAPTER 11

# Sligo

LIMESTONE COUNTRY · CARROWKEEL

KNOCKNAREA · CARROWMORE · SKREEN

## LIMESTONE COUNTRY

As we have seen, before the chalk sea covered Ireland, the country had suffered an earlier inundation—about 300 million years ago—when equatorial seas with corals submerged almost the whole of the country. The sea was generally shallow, and limy muds, now transformed into grey limestones, accumulated on its floor. Some geographical change then took place, and rivers from the surrounding lands carried sediments, which are now transformed to shales and sandstones, into it. There were some wide estuaries, and here great tropical forests grew on the sandbanks, and their vegetable debris was later turned into coal. Extensive coal deposits of this age still survive in many parts of north-west Europe—though not in Ireland—and deposits of this age have the geological name *Carboniferous*.

If no sediment reached the sea, then the shelly debris of marine animals accumulated on the sea-bed. These animals built up their shells by combining the calcium (lime), carbon and oxygen present in the sea-water into calcite (calcium carbonate), and the debris on the sea-floor was later transformed into limestone.

Although rocks of Carboniferous age still cover more than half of Ireland, so far in our peregrination we have largely avoided them. We crossed a narrow band between Dublin and Drogheda without comment, but the caves we looked at in Cork and Waterford were excavated in Carboniferous limestone.

Cave scenery often provides dramatic examples of the power of rainwater to dissolve and to re-precipitate calcite, but these examples are puny compared with the general karstic effect on wide areas of landscape, as for example the Burren in Co. Clare. Even before we left Donegal we could have seen a mini-karst near Ballintra, while in Sligo itself the whole landscape is a tribute to the solutional power of rainwater.

At the surface the limestone is full of cracks, created when the rock was uplifted, and through these the surface water drops downwards. The cracks widen into fissures or *grikes*; areas where water-movement is easy are lowered to form hollows (if small, they are *dolines*, if large, *poljes*); areas where water-movement is difficult survive and begin to stand up as *pinnacles*, or if on a larger scale, as blocks of higher rock or *hums*. We can see all these features in many parts of the world, China, Jamaica, Africa, and they are present also in the Carboniferous limestone areas of Ireland. But because Ireland was glaciated in the relatively recent past, moving ice cut away many of the features that are so conspicuous in non-glaciated karst areas, and the main skyline of the Burren is one of glacial rounding rather than karst irregularity. In western Ireland, Galway and Roscommon in particular, the low-lying dolines are often flooded by standing-water in winter, and are known as *turloughs*. In summer grass grows freely on their dried-out floors, and they provide useful grazing.

The development of karst can continue to such a degree that the pre-existing topography is completely destroyed, and we are left with a tumbled mass of rock which drops into hollows separated by irregular pyramids; such an arrangement is 'cockpit karst', well-developed in Jamaica; such scenery can be seen on a small scale around Colgagh, just north of Lough Gill, Co. Sligo. If we move north from Colgagh, we scramble up rough limestone slopes to the limestone tableland at 500m south of Glencar. The country is cut into wide grikes and scattered deep dolines; blanket-bog developed here about 4000 years ago, and many of the hollows are treacherously bridged by peat. Sheep wander here and there. Unattractive country for the farmer one would say, but Michael Gibbons and his colleagues in the National Archaeological Survey have recently shown that the area has many megalithic tombs, some of very considerable size, erected by Neolithic farmers some 4500 years ago, before the peat had formed.

## CARROWKEEL

These new discoveries add to the already considerable number of such monuments on the Sligo limestone upland. If we move 30km south we find Carrowkeel, a large isolated block or hum of limestone at 300m, just west of Lough Arrow. Again we find dissected limestone, peat and tombs. These were discovered by Praeger at the end of the nineteenth century, and he returned there in 1910 with R.A.S. Macalister, Professor of Archaeology in University College, Dublin, and E.C.R. Armstrong, of the National Museum, to do some excavation. Macalister had dug extensively in the Middle East, where fast excavation was the rule of the day, and by modern standards the digging at Carrowkeel went far too fast. However, they made spectacular discoveries; several of the cairns contained small tombs with central chamber and entrance passage—passage-graves—like Newgrange, but on a much smaller scale. They found coarse, roughly decorated pottery—later dubbed Carrowkeel ware—and beads of a type now known to be standard for such tombs, and above all, Praeger, with his engineering skill, produced splendid plans. They also found a group of about fifty hut-circles, presumably an associated village.

Armed with the new technique of pollen-counts, I went to the area during the second world war. One could get to Boyle by train, and then cycle, complete with drill-rods, over the Curlew Mountains to Lough Arrow, where there was a friendly guest-house. From there the hills were within walking distance, and the drill could be hidden under heather, rather than carried back each evening. I found the peat on the cairns rather thin and dry, with a low content of tree pollen, and beyond confirming that the peat was post-cairn, did nothing further. Today I would of course look eagerly for non-tree-pollens in the peat for information about early agriculture, and get a radiocarbon date for the peat base.

But I did do a lot of other work. The Carrowkeel Hills are not a solid block, but are cut into four slices by narrow rifts which run north–south. In pre-glacial times the rifts would have been narrower, but ice pushed through them and gouged them out. The retreating ice left bars of morainic debris across the rifts, and lakes, which eventually turned into bogs, were formed. I set to work on the bog in the western rift, and had 10.5m of rod screwed together before I hit rock at the bottom. I had a full record of the vegetational history of the valley from late-glacial times (including the three-fold sequence of deposition originally recorded by Jessen at Ballybetagh) to the present day, because the top peat layers had pine pollen from trees planted in the past two hundred years. Where I worked this bog was intact, but peat in a neighbouring valley had been much cut away.

At my first site the formation of the initial lake was only possible because impermeable glacial deposits had sealed the cracks in the underlying limestone. The bog, as it grew, sealed more cracks with vegetable debris. But the peat-cutters had easy drainage where they were working, because all they had to do was to make a channel leading to a crack in the nearby limestone, and the water drained away like water running out of a bath. As a result they had the highest peat-faces I have ever seen in an Irish bog, standing vertically to a height of 3m. Near the base of the peat they had cut through a lens of charcoal and stone, and I was able to get a radiocarbon age of 3670 years for the charcoal, placing it in the Early Bronze Age.

## KNOCKNAREA

Knocknarea, about 7km west of Sligo town, is another isolated limestone knoll which rises to a height of over 300m. Crowned by a great cairn, popularly supposed to be the grave of Queen Maeve of Connaught, as a landmark it commands a wide area. Wandering over it in 1947, I discovered some hut-circles tucked into a hollow on its eastern slopes, and scattered on the ground about them many small hollow scrapers made of chert.

When limy ooze on the sea-floor was consolidating into chalk, the small quantities of silica it contained clotted, as it were, into nodules of pale flint, eagerly sought by early people for the making of implements; the shelly debris on the floor of the earlier Carboniferous seas also contained silica, and this clotted into masses of chert, black in colour, and rather more difficult to fabricate into tools, though used of necessity where flint was scarce. A hollow scraper is a small flake of chert or flint into one side of which a concave notch has been cut by the systematic removal of small flakes; it could be used as a saw for cutting small bones or twigs.

I did not want to excavate the site myself, as I tried to confine any digging I did to places where the material was embedded in a geological deposit; but I told many people about it, and discovered that the hut-circles could be clearly seen in an aerial photograph of the hillside taken by Kenneth St Joseph of Cambridge University in 1964. Kenneth was then engaged in an aerial survey of archaeological sites in the United Kingdom, and this was generously extended to include the south of Ireland. His very large collection of aerial photographs, now in the National Museum, has been and continues to be of enormous value to Irish archaeologists.

Thus I was somewhat wryly amused when in 1984 I opened a Swedish archaeological publication to see Kenneth's photograph appear with the claim that it had been taken by a recent special survey. However, the site had been dug, had produced almost 400 hollow scrapers along with other implements and pieces of pottery, and had been given a radiocarbon age of 4250 years, a late Neolithic date. So one of my loose ends was tied up at last.

## CARROWMORE

Between Knocknarea to the west, and to the east another limestone knoll which rises to 120m beside Lough Gill, there is a considerable area of low-lying morainic gravel and sand, laid down by retreating ice, at Carrowmore. This glacial debris offers a complete physiographic contrast to the nearby limestone table-lands, but it seems to have been equally attractive to Neolithic peoples, who must have had a very extensive range of farming skills. A century ago about a hundred prehistoric monuments could be recognised here, but today, because of farming and gravel extraction only half that number survives. Two-thirds of the survivors are megalithic tombs, made of large boulders, all sited on natural mounds occurring on the surface of the gravel. One of the tombs is clearly a passage-grave.

Over the years one gravel pit grew to a very large size, and two monuments which lay within its perimeter completely disappeared. Such an enormous hole is a great disfigurement to one of the finest prehistoric cemeteries in Europe, and all archaeologists would like to see it filled in, and the setting of the monuments improved. In the early 1980s neither Sligo Corporation nor the County Council had suitable sites for the disposal of refuse, and a proposal was made to use the hole as a land-fill site and restore the landscape. Most archaeologists were horrified at the idea; some local residents, screaming 'rubbish-dump', secured a court-injunction restraining the Council from using the pit, and so the matter came before Mr Justice McWilliam in the High Court. Mine was one of the very few archaeological voices raised in support of the Council.

Everyone agreed that the filling-in of the hole was most desirable. Some proposed that gravel from elsewhere should be brought in, but this would have to be purchased as well as lorried in. It became clear that the only material which could be considered as fill was something you got for nothing, that is, refuse. The protesters made great play about traffic on narrow roads; but there was going to be traffic whatever substance was used, and it was not noted that the area's roads had survived the gravel being carted out. It was estimated that the filling of the pit would take about thirty years, and there was no doubt that during this period, despite any effort that the Council might make to the contrary, there would be considerable nuisance from far-flying plastic bags—but no part of Ireland is free from this menace.

My point was that we were dealing with a landscape that had been there for 6000 years, and that a period of local nuisance lasting perhaps thirty years was a small price to pay for the restoration. Of course there would be some local hardship: people spoke of pollution of wells from seepage, but almost all the local houses had piped water; methane gas might be generated as the refuse decayed, but because the restored land was going to be part of an archaeological landscape there were never going to be any buildings below which gas might be trapped; there would be traffic, but traffic removing gravel had been going on for at least thirty years. The judge dealt with the matter on a pragmatic basis, and found in favour of the Council.

The objectors appealed the matter to the Supreme Court, where there was considerable argument as to the extent of the Carrowmore passage-grave cemetery; was the gravel-pit inside or outside it? Before launching on the project the County Council had had opinions from two distinguished archaeologists that the pit lay outside the area deserving special protection. The question of a 'fallow area' around a monument was raised, as one surviving monument was in close proximity to the pit. Fallow areas have long been a bone of contention; some of the surviving monuments at Carrowmore are in a perilous state because the protection given to them as national monuments ends at the perimeter of the ring of stones that defines them, with no fallow area. Gravel extraction in some cases has crept up to the stones themselves, leaving them perched on low cliff-tops, ready to fall at any moment. Some of the monuments have no legal protection. The court upheld the appeal on what appeared to be archaeological grounds.

In my opinion Sligo County Council was hard done by. If they caused temporary nuisance to local residents at Carrowmore, nuisance would have ceased for much larger numbers of people at other sites in the county, and at the end of thirty years the Carrowmore eyesore would have been obliterated. The Supreme Court judgment underlines a 'grey area' which will continue until it is legally recognised that in some archaeologically important areas the haphazard protection of individual monuments must cease. Whole areas must be protected as archaeological parks, within whose confines all development must be controlled.

## SKREEN

From Sligo we run south to Ballysodare, where we brush against the metamorphic rocks of the Ox Mountains, which rise through the limestone running in a diagonal Caledonide ridge from Manorhamilton to Westport. We head out on the road to Ballina, so that we can visit the churchyard in Skreen, about 20km west of the town. The main road now by-passes the village, so we must turn aside. In the eastern part of the churchyard, there is a large box-tomb with a carved panel on its north face, which shows a farm worker with all the tools of his trade. The man is shown as ploughing, with spades and forks arranged around him. The most remarkable feature is that, although he is driving a two-horse plough, he is dressed in a tailed coat and wears a top hat.

*Skreen, Sligo. This carved slab on the side of a 19th-century tomb shows a farmer, dressed in top-hat and tailed coat, driving a horse-plough; other agricultural implements surround him.*

The design was long a mystery to me, till by chance I hit on a most interesting book *South Westmeath Farm and Folk* by Jeremiah Sheehan, at one time Chief Agricultural Officer of the county. Today a few agricultural shows still survive, but in the early nineteenth century there were a great many, run by the local agricultural societies. Various contests were held, with medals going to the owners of the farm, and prizes, often in the form of clothes, to the workmen involved. The book lists a ploughing competition in which the prizes were, first, a coat, second, a hat, and third, 'a pair of leggins'. So the ploughman at Skreen must have won some prizes, and was shown arrayed in them on his tombstone.

## CHAPTER 12

# Mayo

EARLY AGRICULTURAL PRACTICES · BEHY
BELDERG · GLENAMOY · BELMULLET · INISHKEA
BLANKET-BOG · ACHILL ISLAND · LETTERKEEN
BURREN (MAYO) · KILLADANGAN · CLARE ISLAND

## Early Agricultural Practices

From Skreen the road turns south-west along the lower slopes of the Ox Mountains; as we pass from Co. Sligo into Co. Mayo, we can see that their lower slopes are deeply covered by blanket-bog. On these slopes at Carrownaglogh, near the village of Bunnyconnellan, Professor Michael Herity of University College, Dublin, dug away a considerable area of bog, and revealed a field-system with cultivation-ridges and a small round house, with a radiocarbon age of 2750 years, placing the agricultural phase in the Late Bronze Age. Pollen-studies by Mick O'Connell of University College, Galway, have shown that the settlers cleared away the local trees, and practised both arable and pastoral farming. Infield/outfield agriculture may have been carried on. An 'infield' close to the settlement was intensively cultivated, while the peripheral 'outfield' was used more for grazing. At Carrownaglogh the outfield could be extended almost indefinitely over the surrounding slopes. But these Late Bronze Age people cannot have been the first farmers in the area, as there are also megalithic tombs deeply embedded in peat nearby.

We move on from Ballina along the coast road to Belmullet; at Killala we leave the limestone behind and progress to older, less fertile rocks; west of Ballycastle we enter an area almost entirely covered by blanket-bog. But it was not always so. In many places we can see tree-stumps at the base of the bog, and Seamas Caulfield of University College, Dublin, has brilliantly shown that prehistoric peoples were also here in pre-bog days. Had we been here 4000 years ago we would have seen a farmed landscape, not a dreary expanse of blanket-bog. We shall find items of interest all the way to Belmullet.

## Behy

At Behy, a few kilometres west of Ballycastle, Seamas revealed below the peat a large series of parallel stone walls, spaced about 150m apart, with cross-walls at intervals of about 200m, a field system clearly designed for the management of stock rather than cultivation. The walls continued up the peat-covered hillside, and as there had to be a limit to the area excavated, Seamas decided to continue exploration by probing. Seamas is a man after my own heart; no costly apparatus for him if some simpler method will suffice. He armed himself with stout bamboo rods of equal length, and graduated at regular intervals. These could be easily pushed down into the bog (and equally easily withdrawn). If a wall was encountered, obviously the rod could not go down below the top of the wall. Pushing in rods at equal intervals at right angles to the hidden wall made its height and width clearly visible. If it was a bank of earth, and not a stone wall, there would be a ditch from which the earth came beside it, and the alignment of the tops of the rods soon showed the relative heights of ditch and bank. In Valencia Island I also had to deal with walls below peat, and Seamas very kindly came down and demonstrated his method to me. I am afraid I did not practise it to the same detail, but the use of one graduated probe enabled me to make at least a skeleton map of the sub-bog walls.

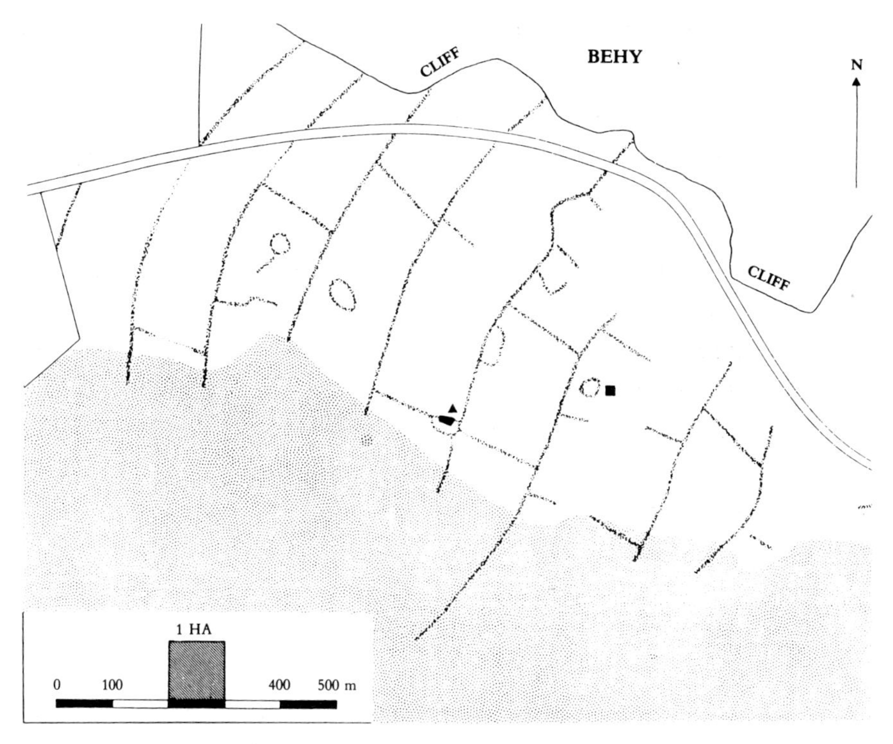


*Behy, Mayo. An old field-system is being revealed as blanket-bog is cut away.*

Inside one field at Behy there was an oval enclosure, whose excavation produced Neolithic material and a radiocarbon age of 4500 years. On the top of a hillock nearby, also buried by peat, there was a court-grave, a type of megalithic tomb where a stone-roofed passage in a cairn opens onto an oval space defined by large stones. Excavated by the late Rory de Valera, and Seán Ó Nualláin, Archaeological Officer with the Ordnance Survey, it produced Neolithic material, and the base of the overlying peat was dated to shortly after 4000 years ago. Still farther west at Ballyglass, Seán later excavated another court-grave, and to his delight found that it had been erected on top of an earlier rectangular house built around 4700 years ago. Thus there was extensive Neolithic activity throughout north Mayo.

## BELDERG

Seamas had earlier excavated at Belderg, about 6km west of Behy, where he was on his home ground. His father was the schoolmaster there, and had noted walls under peat long before Seamas came of archaeological age. Here the story was more complicated than at Behy. The soil surface below the peat had isolated tree stumps and a scatter of Neolithic material; peat then started to form, but after a time trees were able to invade its surface, and pine and oak stumps had radiocarbon ages of about 4000 years. Agricultural activity was then resumed; some peat was removed, but not all, for a wall that started on mineral soil continued out on to peat, where it had been strengthened by the insertion of oak stakes with a radiocarbon age of 3200 years. A piece of charred oak found in a round house nearby had the same age; there were cultivation-ridges and possible plough-marks in the area. This phase of activity must lie early in the Bronze Age.

If before we leave Belderg we exchange our archaeological hat for a quaternary one and go down to the harbour, we can see sections in a till full of marine shells, presumably collected by ice moving from the north across the floor of Donegal Bay. The age of this till has long been in dispute, but a solution to the problem is perhaps edging nearer. Amino acids, which occur in all organic tissue, including marine shells, gradually change in composition with age. If the rate of change is constant, then an estimate of the amount of time that has elapsed since the organism died can be calculated. But it seems that the rate of change is susceptible to temperature changes, and if there have been such fluctuations, then an age estimate may be suspect. Much work is going on in this field at the moment; it may be that the technique can only be used to establish gross differences in age, but it could be of great help in sorting out the deposits of different interglacials, which lie thousands of years apart.

Before we leave the harbour, we can change our hat yet again for a geomorphological one. I have spoken of tilting in connection with Tory Island. Continuous cliffs run from Belderg to Benwee Head, and from the cliff-edge the ground slopes to the south. This is most dramatically seen at Portacloy and in the three valleys to the east, where the streams flowing south start almost at the cliff-edge. The river pattern here must go back to a period far older than the cutting of the cliffs by wave erosion.

## GLENAMOY

From Belderg to Belmullet a botanical hat will be the most appropriate headgear. At Glenamoy we pass the site of the agricultural research station, set up by the Agricultural Institute with funds from an international research organisation to try to make two blades of grass grow where only blanket-bog was growing. Despite a lot of hard work under the leadership of P.J. O'Hare it ultimately had to be recognised that attempts to carry out any normal type of agriculture in the *milieu* of extensive blanket-bog would be utterly uneconomical. At one point Paddy had located a hollow beneath the blanket-bog, and he directed Bill Watts and myself to this in 1955, as we wanted to find out what the area looked like before the bog had started to form. We went through blanket-bog peat to a depth of 6m, and after that 50cm of fen-peat. The fen-peat showed open vegetation similar to that which covered most of Ireland about 10,000 years ago. Working upwards through our pollen-diagram we could follow the typical development of dense woodlands, until at 3m we found evidence of agriculture in the vicinity, accompanied by very high values for pine pollen. Here we were probably at the Belderg 4000-year-old level, with Bronze Age activity. Tree pollen (with the exception of pine) was still present in relatively high values up to 2m, but above that level it faded away, and the countryside must have taken on its present treeless aspect.

At least one very surprising plant, the Mediterranean heath (*Erica erigena*), survived this dramatic change from forest to blanket-bog. Restricted in Ireland to the great Mayo/Galway blanket-bog area, and not found in Britain, this heather also grows only in the Pyrenees, where it occurs on damp ground. Setting aside for the moment the question of why it is in Ireland at all, it showed remarkable adaptability in being able to exchange the damp soil of sheltered Lusitania for the water-logged nutrient-poor windswept surface of the Mayo blanket-bog.

A short distance further on we come to Bellonaboy Bridge. Here in the river bank a section through the shallow blanket-bog can be seen. There are two superimposed layers of pine stumps, one at the base of the peat, the other 20cm higher. A basal stump gave a radiocarbon age of 7100 years, and a higher stump an age of 4350 years. The lower stump may be of the same generation as the lower stumps at Belderg, but the higher stump parallels the higher stump at Belderg which is 4300 years, and probably also ties in with the high pine values in the Glenamoy boring. Around 4000 years ago is probably the age of the great expansion of the pine on bog surfaces in western and central Ireland. In Connemara Mick O'Connell has noted a phase of bog-woodland lasting for about 500 years centred on 4000 years ago. Pine also flourished on raised-bogs in the midlands between 4000 and 3500 years ago. Increased wetness after that time may have prevented the pine seedlings from establishing themselves on the bog surface.

On the western sea-board pine stumps are widely seen deep down in peat, and as sea-level was perhaps rather lower at this time, the peat can be followed down below the highwater-mark, as we shall see if the tide is out as we approach Belmullet.

Bellonaboy Bridge is north of Carrowmore Lake. At Muinhin Bridge, where the water drains away at the south end of the lake, there is again a shallow peat section, in which Knud Jessen recorded a prominent horizon of charred pine stumps near the base. His pollen-diagram, though short, tells the same story as Glenamoy, and the pine stumps probably correspond with the upper layer at Bellonaboy. Charred pine stumps are also known elsewhere, and the unsolved question is 'Were the fires due to natural causes, or were they clearance fires of Bronze Age peoples?'. In 1931 two stone moulds, one for a looped spearhead and the second for a spearhead and a knife, possibly dating to about 3000 years ago, were found below peat not far from Carrowmore, so Bronze Age people were certainly in the area.

## BELMULLET

On our 1955 visit Bill Watts and I teamed up with some people from the Agricultural Institute, and we spent the night in a guesthouse in Belmullet. It was a Thursday evening, and the landlady came round to ask, 'Who would like a fry for their breakfast in the morning?'; this was the opening gambit for members of the party to ask what time Mass would be. Bill and I decided to support Martin Luther, so we opted for the fry. When breakfast was served, a pile of plates separated by metal rings appeared. Bill's plate and mine showed what has since come to be known as 'A full Irish breakfast', but, as the other rings were removed, splendid salmon steaks were revealed. We felt our effort on Luther's behalf had been parried.

My first visit to Belmullet was in 1948. I was then secretary of the Dublin Zoo, and during one annual meeting we had James Fisher, the famous ornithologist, to lecture on one of his favourite birds, the fulmar petrel. James and I were born in the same year, 1912, and we soon became friends, though we met too rarely. James was then editor of the Collins *New Naturalist* series, and he asked me to do a volume on Ireland. Collins had earlier made the same request to Praeger, but when they received his text it was considered not altogether suitable for the series, and it was published independently in 1950 as a *Natural History of Ireland*, a most valuable compendium.

So later in 1948 I acquired a Goerz quarter-plate camera, and Eric Hosking, the famous bird photographer, secured a supply of Ektachrome for me. Colour illustration of books was just coming in, and the early volumes of the *New Naturalist* series were packed with colour plates. Eric gave me a piece of good advice. If the picture was worth taking, it was worth the trouble of putting the camera on a tripod to take it. I decided that a colour-photograph of the red-necked phalarope, whose only Irish station was near Belmullet, was a must for the book, and so I went to Belmullet with Alec Mason and Rex Dick, another very sound bird-man.

*nr. Belmullet, Mayo. The guardian of the reserve is driving the absurdly tame red-necked phalaropes towards the photographer; eight birds can be seen.*

At that time I was the owner of the phalarope location, where a local farmer acted as occasional guardian. The Irish Society for the Protection of Birds had purchased the piece of ground where the birds nested, in the names of Fr Kennedy, Peter Dunne and myself. In due course Fr Kennedy and Peter passed on, leaving me as the sole trustee. I was later approached, perhaps at the time the Irish Wildbird Conservancy was being formed, and asked to yield up my trusteeship, which I did, though I was sorry to break a sentimental link with the past. It was a very dry June, and the lake was small and low in level. I set up my tripod in the water, and Rex and Alec were able to drive the absurdly tame birds past me.

At the time I had a Volcano kettle, another vanished form, put out of business by the buta-gas stove. The kettle had a conical central cavity, surrounded by a thin water-jacket with a hole at the top through which one dropped small pieces of any inflammable material; the kettle sat on a base with holes to admit air. If there was a breeze, it would bring the small amount of contained water to the boil remarkably rapidly. This June had been very dry, and the cow-pats which were lying around were quite desiccated. So on that occasion only I used cow-dung as a fuel, and as the pungent fumes emerged I felt the equal of a bedouin in a desert. But the kettle could cause embarrassment, especially on French camp-sites where such a thing had never been seen before. I would get out of the car with the kettle in one hand, and the petrol-can in which I carried the water-supply in the other. To an onlooker I appeared first to stuff the object with paper, and dowse it with petrol, and then set fire to the lot, despite large notices prohibiting the use of open fires.

A suffix to the *New Naturalist* story. By 1948 several volumes, full of colour, had appeared. The colour plates were very expensive, and Collins were trying to reduce the number of plates in the books. I intended to write my book around the illustrations, and I had to know how many colour plates I was going to be allowed. I could get no definite answer, and in the end I forced an interview with Sir William Collins, then head of the family firm; James was there too. I came away satisfied that there were going to be not *less* than twenty-four colour plates, but when I got the contract it said 'not *more* than', and so I threw it in the fire. But twenty-five years later Collins came back to me, and the book, without any colour plates, eventually appeared in 1976 as *The Irish Landscape*.

## INISHKEA

On a 1978 visit I went south from Belmullet down the Mullet itself, a curious peninsula rarely more than 30m above sea-level, till it rises into a boss of granite at its southern end. It is essentially a chain of skerries or former rocky islets, linked together by glacial deposits and storm beaches, the whole copiously plastered over by sand-dunes, which tend to advance from the west, driven by the prevailing winds. So the western side has 'machair', sweet grassland on calcareous sand, while the east has poor soil on glacial deposits, only partly ameliorated by an addition of wind-blown sand.

My purpose was a trip to Inishkea with David Cabot, of Greenland goose fame, and Roger Goodwillie, then an environmental officer with the now defunct Foras Forbartha, and co-director with his wife Olivia of the Lavinstown Nature Centre in Kilkenny. David visits the islands annually to make a census of the white-fronted geese that spend their winters there, and on a recent visit he had seen peat lying below stones, and he wanted my opinion on the age of the deposit.

I had innocently foreseen an uneventful trip in a stout boat under the charge of a local master mariner. But the salmon season was on, and no boatman could be expected to accept whatever fee we could offer. So I found myself on the quay at Blacksod, helping to inflate a rubber boat in a strong wind with poor visibility. We set out, and then it emerged that the intrepid David had never navigated a boat to the island before, and indeed it was almost the first time he had ever been in such a boat. There were only two life-jackets, and so for the only time in my life I had the opportunity to do the Captain Oates act. My children were reared, but David and Roger had young families, so they had the jackets; I sat on the gunwale of the boat and held on tight to the lifelines. Somehow we made it, and the interest of the island quickly banished all fears.

I found myself on a mini-Mullet. There had been a short chain of skerries, and there still is one permanent gap between Inishkea North and Inishkea South. The south island has several low east–west gullies, and these are crossed by winter storms. On the west are some of the biggest storm beaches I have ever seen. The highest are richly covered by lichens, and are obviously only occasionally reached by modern gales. The frequency with which environmental extremes, like the hurricane that devastated the trees in south-east England in 1986, occur is a matter which is being debated more and more. We used to speak of 'the storm of the century', like Ireland's 'night of the big wind' in 1839. It is now being realised that the cycle may be longer, and a period of one thousand years is being discussed.

On Inishkea South some improving landlord had built, perhaps early in the nineteenth century, a long high stone wall running north–south not far to the east of the highest storm beach. The wall gave some protection to the strip-fields which ran down from it to the village on the eastern shore. Near its northern end the wall spanned one of the gullies already referred to, and the peat we had come to see was a little to the east. There was a well-defined gap in the wall, and to the east a thick scatter of wall-stones, many of which lay on the peat. Thus my reading of the situation was that there had been, some time since the wall was built,a gale of the century which had breached the wall and hurled its stones eastwards on top of the peat. We can even attempt to pinpoint the date. Françoise Henry, who did so much to expand our knowledge of Early Christian Ireland, was quite intrepid. In 1938 she camped with a few workmen on the north island, and carried out some excavation. While there, she was told of a great storm some thirty years earlier which had cut off a piece of the north island and completely removed a sand-hill. The Irish meteorological record tells of a very severe storm on the night of 26/27 February 1903, and this may have been the storm that breached the wall.

There were also splendid areas of abandoned cultivation-ridges, divided by low lynchets, showing that cultivation must have gone on for a considerable time. If a slope is cultivated, soil will move downslope from the top to the bottom of the field, creating a low cliff or lynchet at the margin of the field. The island was abandoned in the early thirties.

We then paid a fleeting visit to the north island, as I was most anxious to see the remarkable crucifixion slabs that Françoise had studied during her excavations. There must have been sand-dunes among which lay a large Early Christian settlement. A small church, a graveyard with slabs, and the remains of two sand-dunes which had carried buildings can be seen. The smaller dune is rich in slabs, and the larger one must originally have carried quite extensive structures. Winnowing away of the sand by the wind has caused almost everything to collapse and slide, but there are still some house foundations and a decorated slab on the top. This feature is called *An Bailey Mor,* and is remarkably similar to an isolated mound, now surrounded at high tide, that stands on the shore at Killadoon, south-west of Louisburgh. There wind is also removing sand, and causing slabs and human bones to slide down the flanks of the mound. The sand-dunes of the Irish west coast are very unstable features, though they do appear to have 'static' periods, when they become covered with soils. Radiocarbon dating of some soils on the Mullet suggests that there were periods of dune stability about 1000, 1500 and 2300 years ago.

## BLANKET-BOG

From Belmullet we turn south to Achill Sound and cross what Gordon Davies and Nick Stephens have described in their book on Irish geomorphology as 'kilometre after kilometre of sodden blanket-bog, studded with the boles of ancient trees, and spreading across the landscape like some malignant fungus'. Well—one man's meat is another man's poison. To botanists this is one of Ireland's most dramatic, as well as most fragile, landscapes. An area of bog is a seamless garment; cut it, and you may create irreparable changes. We still do not know what factors initiated the formation of blanket-bog, but they resulted in the creation of an impermeable membrane on the earth's surface. With no nutrient matter available from the soil, only a limited number of plants could sustain themselves on the small quantities of nutrient salts that the rain carried down from the atmosphere; but enough could grow, and their partly-decayed remains slowly built up peat, which, provided the atmosphere remained moist and the slope of the terrain was not too great, gradually covered the whole landscape with blanket-bog. Conditions near to the Atlantic seaboard were especially favourable because the nearby ocean kept the air moist, and spray whipped up from the sea was incorporated in the rain, which came to have an augmented mineral content.

Peat has been used as a source of fuel at least from the beginning of the Christian era. But it is a bulky fuel, and so is expensive to transport over long distances. Until recently exploitation of the Mayo bogs was limited to providing fuel for the few local inhabitants, who pecked away at the bog-edges, but did not develop large drainage-schemes. The first major attack on the bogs came about 1960, when the Electricity Supply Board set up a peat-fired power-station at Bellacorick. Soon large quantities of peat were being burned, and the tentacles of bog-drains extended further and further. Such drains change the water-balance of the peat over a wide area, the natural way-of-life is destroyed, and changes in vegetation quickly follow.

Until 1980 the coastal bogs remained uncut, but then an ambitious project arose, which involved spending 7 million pounds on the erection of a peat briquette plant in the vicinity of Belmullet, and preparing thousands of hectares of the surrounding bog to produce the peat to feed it.

With specialised machines, the cutting of drains in the bog was all too easy, and that went ahead. But the cost of erecting the plant and getting it into commission far outran the capital available, and in 1989 the project collapsed, leaving unpaid debts and a great blot on the landscape. Ireland's large areas of blanket-bog are environmentally unique, and must be protected against attack.

## Achill Island

I have driven round, and holidayed in Achill, but I only did one piece of work there. Francis Synge wrote a paper on the glacial history of the island, and he thought that the last advance of ice had left some low-lying parts uncovered. A French worker, Armand Coudé, visited Ireland in the mid-seventies, and he considered that the whole of Achill, except for the higher hill-tops which protruded as nunataks, had been covered by ice. Among the sections he recorded was a cliff-face in a gully at Ashleam Bay on the west side of the island near its southern tip. At the rocky bottom of the gully there was a beach gravel (a little higher than the modern beach) buried by glacial deposit which Coudé considered was deposited during the last glacial episode. As the beach section had not been previously recorded, I went to see it.

The coast road runs round the bay, and crosses the deposit. On the seaward side Coudé's section ended upwards in laminated clays laid down in water at the final dissolution of the ice; they had a flat surface. I followed what appeared to be the same surface inland from the road, and found, in the wall of the cutting which had been made by the stream running down to the bay, a further series of silts and sands. In these there were, about 1m from the top, sheets of horizontally lying leaves of the dwarf willow (*Salix herbacea*), which we have already met at Ballybetagh near Dublin. I foolishly leapt to the conclusion that the whole deposit had been laid down without interruption, and that in age the leaves should belong to the period of ice melting. A sample weighing 5gm was then necessary for a radiocarbon age determination, and as a dried fossil leaf weighed 1mg, this meant that 5000 leaves had to be procured, and I had to wash 6kg of the material through a fine sieve to obtain the required number. I made my washings in 1980; since then a new technique of dating has been developed at the Oxford University Radiocarbon Accelerator Unit, which requires only very small samples. The unit recently dated a fragment of the Turin Shroud, and five leaves would have been sufficient for their test.

I had hoped for a date of say 16,000 years, the approximate period of ice decay, but the answer was 11,200 years, the same order of age as the upper clay at Ballybetagh. The deposits in fact were not a continuous series, but there was a hiatus during the first period of warming after the ice-retreat. When cold returned again, snow-beds formed in Achill. A snow-bed forms where suitable conditions, a hollow in the ground, or a north-east facing aspect which gives shelter from the sun, mean that snow is late to melt in spring. Only a few plants can tolerate such conditions, first surviving under the snow, and then being able to make adequate growth in a short growing season. The dwarf willow is such a plant *par excellence,* and it will completely floor a snow-bed. In Norway, when road-planners are proposing a high-level route near the snow-line, they look out for such willow patches and avoid them, for they know that if the road runs through such a patch, much clearing work will be required in winter. When the melting snow finally sludges away it carries enormous quantities of small leaves with it.

At Ashleam, as the snow sludged down it picked up deposits from the preceding warm period, and so, as well as willow leaves, I made a collection of beetle debris, moss fragments and seeds. The insect debris went to Russell Coope in Birmingham, who has carried the art of identifying beetle scraps to such a high level that he knew, even before the radiocarbon date came along, that the material was young, rather than of the age I wished for. The mosses went to Jim Dickson in Glasgow, who has specialised in late-glacial fossils. The seeds went to Gina Hannon for stereoscan photography, to see if identifications could be carried to species level. There were six varieties of beetle, mostly northern in modern range, lots of caddis-fly and midge larvae, and many water animalcules. There were twelve mosses, again northern and well-known in other late-glacial deposits in the British Isles. There were at least fourteen flowering plants, but it was not possible to carry the identification to the species level in every case. The most interesting plant was the mountain sorrel (*Oxyria digyna*), very common in the Arctic today, but in Ireland only found on a few mountain-tops. As with so many of my excursions, a trip that set out to look at a fossil beach ended up by producing another late-glacial locality and another late-glacial date.

## LETTERKEEN

Leaving Achill, we follow the north shore of Clew Bay as far as Furnace Lough. Here we turn north up a minor road, which we follow for 10km to reach the rath at Letterkeen, which was excavated by Seán Ó Ríordáin: we will meet Seán again at Lough Gur.

The rath is one of the commonest of Irish antiquities, probably because of its essential durability. The simplest type is a circular bank of earth about 20m in diameter, the earth being obtained by digging a ditch encircling the bank on the outside. When in use the bank was often added to by a timber palisade or a stone revetment. Today it is thought that they were most commonly constructed in Early Christian times, between the fourth and the eighth centuries. When the rath was abandoned, some earth from the bank would slip down into the ditch, but little else could happen, and so the monument would remain unless it was interfered with by people. For a long time the raths were believed to be points where fairies would assemble, and superstition protected them. But as this form of defence crumbled, many of the raths were swept away, especially in recent years when such destruction was made all too easy by the advent of earth-moving machinery.

Forty years ago our ideas on the age of raths were less clear, and some saw them going back to the Bronze Age, as a few raths had yielded antiquities of this period. A splendid cluster of field monuments, including raths and old fields, occurs at Cush in Co. Limerick, where there were Bronze Age finds also. Seán Ó Ríordáin dug there in the late thirties, but his results were rather ambiguous. A somewhat similar site occurred at Letterkeen, and in the forties he and Máire de Paor excavated it.

As we drove up the side road, we were following a north–south valley. Ice came down the valley, and as it retreated it left an interrupted series of moraines, behind which water accumulated in lakes; Furnace Lough is the nearest to the main road. We then passed the much larger Lough Feeagh, and arrived at the headwaters of the Attamoney River among the Nephin Beg Mountains. Here the valley is choked by a spread of glacial gravel to a height of 100m, and this is where Ó Ríordáin's site lies. Today the area is covered by planted conifers growing on blanket-bog, and there is no human occupation, but in prehistoric times the area was a Shangri-La with an oasis of well-drained fertile soil, sheltered by a ring of high ground.

On a low rise there was a rath, and casual digging in its interior had produced a Bronze Age cist and pottery. Hence Seán's interest, which was well-rewarded because he found both Bronze Age and Early Christian material. The surrounding ditch was almost 1.5m deep, and was filled with peat, some of which also occurred in the interior of the rath. I did not visit the site during the excavation, but Seán sent me a series of pollen-samples from the ditch, and examination of these showed that the site must have belonged to two periods. The Bronze

Age people had dug a ditch around their burial site, and the basal peat in the ditch showed traces of agricultural pollen, but pollen of pine was completely missing. As we have already seen, the pine disappeared from Mayo about 4000 years ago, so the Bronze Age material must be younger than that time, a dating with which the archaeological evidence from the site concurs. Wood then appeared in the peat in the ditch, and values for birch, willow and hazel rose, showing that the site had been abandoned and become covered with scrub. Above this level pollens of cultivation, including cereal pollen, became very common, and shrub pollens disappeared. Here we see the arrival of the Early Christian farmers who must have taken advantage of the still-existing ditch when they were building their rath. When we come to the upper peat, probably part of the blanket-bog which ultimately buried the whole rath as well as the surrounding countryside, evidence of agriculture in the vicinity virtually disappears.

Seán discovered masses of charcoal at different horizons, but when he was digging, radiocarbon dating was not available. I should love to see the site re-examined so that the two phases of agricultural activity could be more closely dated. We can see similar sites elsewhere in Ireland, where areas that were fertile farmland as recently as Early Christian times are now deeply buried by blanket-bog, but the small area at Letterkeen, surrounded by barren mountains, is particularly impressive.

## BURREN (MAYO)

We return to the coast, and at Newport make a diversion to Castlebar, and from there a shorter diversion north for 10km to Burren. The Irish word *boireann* means a rocky or a stony place, and so there are several burrens in Ireland in addition to the famous Clare example. This Burren lies on the south-east slopes of Croaghmoyle, a hill 400m high that marks the south-west end of the Ox Mountains. A complex and tortuous system of streams drains the slopes, and in many places the streams have cut through the glacial deposits that are plastered against the hillside. At the village of Burren a massive bridge spans the stream; it seems out of proportion, but heavy rainstorms can beat against the hill, so that the stream quickly swells to a raging torrent. At one point on its south side, about 1km above the bridge, the stream has cut through the glacial deposit into a mass of peat, rich in wood and other plant debris.

Francis Synge discovered the peat here (and also another exposure in a neighbouring valley) in the late sixties, and since then various people, myself, Bill Watts, Pete Coxon and Gina

Hannon, have looked at it and taken samples. Bill has suggested that what we are looking at is much the same as we could have seen in the area about 4000 years ago, that is, dense coniferous forest growing on blanket-bog. But the fossil forest at Burren was not of pine only, there were also fir (*Abies*) and spruce (*Picea*), and growing round the base of the trees were rhododendron and several varieties of heather, most of which are very rare in Ireland today. This was another Irish locality for this type of fossil forest, first seen more than a hundred years ago near Gort in Co. Galway, and seen again at Kilbeg. Similar forest assemblages in corresponding situations are also known in Britain and on the Continent.

Here at Burren, Gina found rhododendron seed capsules, proving that the plant had been growing at the site. Some interglacial plants, killed off by the next phase of cold, failed to return when the climate warmed up again. The rhododendron is a very good example of this; it was widely distributed in early interglacials in Europe, but after the last bout of cold it survived only in the Caucasus and in Spain and Portugal, and was not able to expand from those refuges. It was introduced into gardens in Ireland in the eighteenth century, from which it escaped to become a woodland pest, especially near the west coast. But its pollen is abundant in the interglacial deposits at Burren, Gort, Kilbeg and elsewhere in Ireland. Until recently the surviving populations of rhododendron in Europe were lumped into one species, *ponticum*. But pollen studies are being revolutionised by the use of the scanning electron microscope which can produce images of many thousands of times magnificatiom. We can now see that the surfaces of many pollen grains are not smooth, as our earlier poorer magnification suggested, but in fact are ornamented with very detailed patterns. The patterns vary with the species, making it possible to make pollen identifications down to species level. We tended to assume that our fossil rhododendron would be allied to the forms still growing in Spain and Portugal, but electron microscope studies now suggest that our pollen more closely resembles the Turkish form.

As we leave we stop our car at Burren and look up the valley from the bridge. Today we see bare rock and blanket-bog. If we had been here in an interglacial many thousands of years ago, we would have been pardoned for thinking that we were somewhere in the Black Forest in Germany.

## KILLADANGAN

Returning to Castlebar, we continue on through Westport, pausing only to note that it is one of Ireland's more elegant 'landlord' towns, laid out by James Wyatt for the Marquis of

Westport in the late eighteenth century. There is a tree-lined mall with water flowing down its centre, and a neat octagon which held a hotel and a theatre.

We turn out along the south side of the bay, and draw up at Killadangan, 6km west of the town. Parallel with the shore we have a strip of very old, highly metamorphosed rocks, and erosion has produced a rugged topography. In 1983 John Jackson was on a geological trip here to see these rocks, under the leadership of Adrian Phillips, who did a great deal of work in the area trying to sort out the rock structures. John, who will crop up several times in my story, is a colleague of long-standing; his career has been in geology, as university teacher, National Museum officer and consultant geologist. We met when he came to Trinity after war service, and have been close friends ever since. His unrivalled knowledge of geology in the field in Ireland has guided me to many interesting sites. Adrian has since moved on to the interpretation of satellite images of the earth's surface, seeking to identify geological deposits and patterns of acid-rain attack on forests. As the group passed a knob of rock John noted marine shells and a scrap of flint banked against it; for a short time he defaulted from the group, but he had to move on to join it again. John told me about the site and I went to see it. I soon realised that the shells were not belonging to a raised beach, but were part of a cone of midden debris (including bones) that had been discarded from above. I went up the little knob, which had a sloping ramp of rock on the east, and found that it had been used as a defended house-site. A bank and ditch had been made across the ramp, and there was the outline of a rectangular house on the top.

The bones I collected from the debris were identified by the National Museum as coming from pig and calf; there was also one mistle thrush bone. The shells were of common food species, oyster, cockle, mussel, limpet and periwinkle. I sent two bags of shells, one oyster, the other periwinkle, to my friend Kim Donner in the University of Helsinki. Kim and I have been colleagues for many years, and his geology department and also the Finnish Geological Survey have specialised in the radiocarbon dating of shells. Shell material is not as good as wood or charcoal for this purpose, but does give a reliable approximation. The answer in each case was about eleven hundred years ago, so the occupation of the site can be placed in the Early Christian period. There may well be other similar sites in the vicinity, and I hope to get the opportunity to go back and look for them.

A short distance farther on, on the right-hand side of the road, a tongue of low-lying ground, covered by high spring tides, stretches seawards. It carries a complex arrangement of monuments, a small stone circle, stone alignments, two low mounds which might be barrows, numerous scattered standing-stones, and near the roadside a suggestion of a bank-and-ditch. I have looked at the site in puzzlement many times. Comparable assemblages occur in mid-Ulster, usually on upper hill-slopes, and often covered by blanket-bog. The most dramatic of such sites is at Beaghmore, 12km north of Pomeroy in Tyrone, where there is a complex of stone circles, cairns and alignments, all formerly buried by peat. Peat-cutting during the war began to bring this site to light, and it was first noted in the mid-forties by Alec May. Alec was the local bee-keeping instructor, and as such criss-crossed the area and met all sorts of people. He took some samples for me, but my short pollen-diagram was not very informative. George Eogan and a team from Queen's returned to the site in the late sixties, and much excavation and environmental work was done. The site was then very well conserved, and is now an important national monument. The bulk of the activity probably took place during the Middle Bronze Age, and the Killadangan features may well be of comparable age.

If people with wandering countryside jobs, such as Alec May had, are also interested in archaeology, they are in a position to gather a great deal of very valuable information that would otherwise go unrecorded. Patrick Tohall in Sligo was such a man; a local valuer for the Land Commission, he was passionately interested in archaeology and folk-ways. Through his contacts he came to know of temporary exposures, such as a bog-section revealing a trackway, and the records of the National Museum were considerably added to as a result of his efforts.

## Clare Island

We continue on through Louisburgh to Roonah Quay, where we take the boat for Clare Island, and its famous survey. During the early years of this century, Praeger organised, with the support of the Dublin Naturalists' Field Club, a relatively modest survey of the natural history of Lambay Island off the Dublin coast. This proved to be very rewarding, and he immediately set out to find a larger island for still closer scrutiny; the choice fell on Clare Island in the middle of Clew Bay. Clare Island's western position counterbalanced the eastern Lambay; it was larger, being about 5km long, and it had greater relief, rising to 475m. It can perhaps be regarded as a detached part of Achill Island, as its landscape is rather similar.

Under the auspices of the Royal Irish Academy Praeger now mustered 100 scientists from a very wide range of disciplines, field-work extended over a period of three years (1909–11), and more than 8500 organisms were identified, of which over one hundred were new to science. It took six years of Praeger's spare time to edit the sixty-seven reports, which were published in three large volumes at a cost of £1000. After an interval of eighty years the Academy is now proposing to repeat the survey, to estimate change and make further discoveries. The toll of inflation can be readily seen, as it is reckoned that the preliminary feasibility study alone will cost £9000. Praeger's industry receives a continuing tribute from the islanders, who still describe wandering naturalists as 'praegers'.

Only one scientist let Praeger down, F.J. Lewis, who had undertaken to study the peat deposits of the island. But one cannot be too hard on Lewis, who at the time was engaged in a systematic survey of the peatlands of Scotland and the Isles. He tried to trace out a chronological sequence in the layers of peat in Scottish bogs, particularly relying on layers rich in wood, which he recognised as Lower and Upper Forestian. But as he had neither palynology nor radiocarbon dating to assist him, his was an uphill struggle. Much of his work was in press at the time of the Clare Island Survey. He had probably said Yes to Praeger without realising the extent of the work he was asked to commit himself to; it may be that some of his manuscript notes still survive.

Just as at one time I had dreams of doing archaeological work on Lambay Island, so I also dreamt of repairing Lewis's omission by making a survey of the bogs of the island, but I'm afraid it was 1977 before I got to the island, and by then my days of ambitious long-term projects were over. However, I was sufficiently stirred up by what I saw to get the members of the Irish Association for Quaternary Studies (IQUA) to visit the island for their annual field-trip. Some John the Baptist had to be found to make a preliminary survey, and Pete Coxon of the TCD Department of Geography, who is interested both in pollen-work and in geomorphology, came forward. He visited the island, looked at the glacial deposits and the peat, and produced a preliminary field-guide for the excursion. So far its circulation has been limited, but its notes on the bogs of the island must have enabled Praeger to settle more easily in his grave.

At the time of the first census in 1841, the island had 1600 inhabitants, all of whom were using peat as fuel, and so the area originally covered by peat has been greatly reduced. As the peat cover shrank, cultivation-ridges expanded to take its place, and great areas of such ridges are to be found. One pollen-sample from the soil buried below a ridge showed that while the bulk of the pollen was of heathers, grasses and weeds, there was still some birch and hazel scrub in the vicinity. At another point, where the ridge had been built on a thin layer of surviving peat, the peat showed clear evidence of extensive cultivation nearby.

Before gross human interference, blanket-bog covered the upper slopes. At the end of the Ice Age, on lower ground, there were many small lakes and ponds lying in depressions in either solid rock or glacial deposits. These hollows first accumulated mud and then fen-peat, until peat akin to blanket-bog peat finally blotted them out. In one such hollow Pete Coxon located 5m of deposit, even though some of the top had been cut away. Here he traced the vegetational succession from late-glacial times almost to the present day. About half-way down the boring he met very high values for pine pollen, and the trees that produced this pollen were probably contemporaneous with the pine stumps that are widely distributed in the cutaway bogs in the east of the island, and also with those of Mayo generally. Today we date this layer to about 4000 years ago. Immediately above the high pine values, pollen typical of agriculture appeared, so we can say that people have been on Clare Island at least since the beginning of the Bronze Age.

In one area the new surveyors will notice change, and that not for the better. With sheep numbers very greatly increased by over-generous headage-grants from the European Commission, the upper slopes of the island are now heavily over-grazed. What soil cover there is is being exposed to the rain, and will be progressively washed away, till only bare rock is left. This problem is not confined to Clare Island, but will arise anywhere in Ireland where slopes are steep, and sheep numbers are too high. It will be sad indeed if over-grazing reduces substantial areas of the Irish landscape to the same level as many parts of Spain and Greece, where past over-grazing and burning have left only bare rock.

CHAPTER 13

# Galway

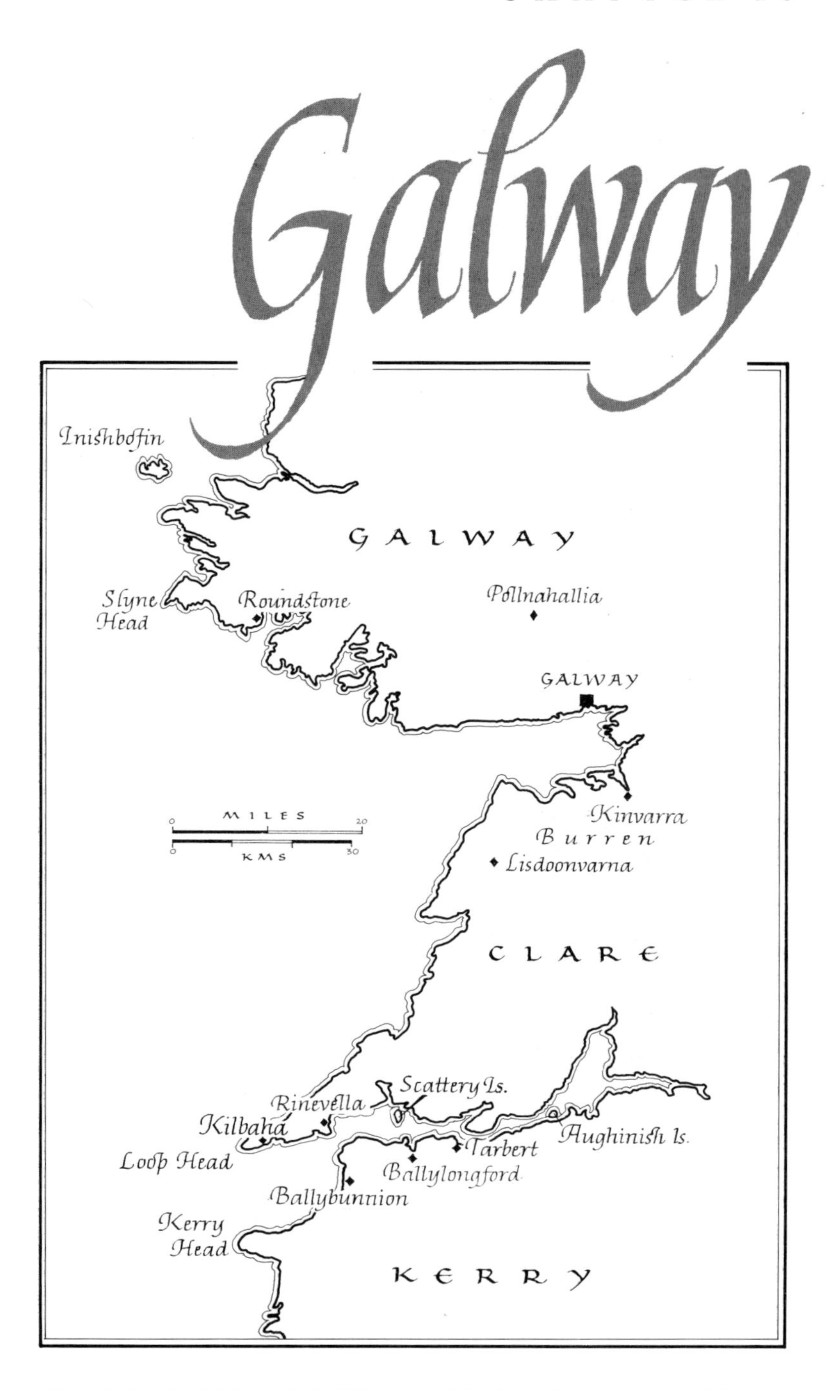


INISHBOFIN · ROUNDSTONE · POLLNAHALLIA

## INISHBOFIN

I had long wished to visit Inishbofin, but I did not succeed in getting there until 1986. Stirred by my interest in Early Christian Art in Ireland, I had visited Iona where Colmcille had founded his monastery in 563, and from there followed Aidan to Lindisfarne where, in 635, he began the conversion of the Saxons. The date of Easter was changed at the Synod of Whitby in 664, but a small group of monks at Lindisfarne, both Irish and Saxon, refused to accept the change. Led by Colman they returned to Iona, but after a short stay they moved on to Inishbofin. There the Irish monks tended to slip back into the local community, while the Saxons found it hard to acclimatise themselves, and Colman finally moved with the latter group to the mainland of Mayo, where he died about 675.

The setting for the monastery was well chosen, but nothing contemporary with Colman survives. There are the ruins of a later church set in a graveyard which is still in use; only a grave slab with a simple cross incised on it, and two bullauns (small boulders with excavated hollows, thought to have been used in pounding), suggest antiquity. The ruined site lies in a small valley, guarded by sand-dunes from the sea. A stream from a small lake further up the valley flows past it. In clear weather there is a splendid view of the mountains of Connemara. Mick O'Connell and his colleagues from Galway have recently taken samples from the muds in the lake, and when these have been examined we should have a fine record of man's activities in the vicinity.

Though almost as large as Clare Island, Inishbofin provides a strong contrast. It is rather low-lying, with no point on the island more than 100m high, whereas Clare Island reaches up to almost 500m. On its eastern side there is a beautiful sandy bay studded with small islands, and here I got a very strong impression that I was on one of the Isles of Scilly, which had in some mysterious way been towed about 500km to the north-west. There was the same membership of a small archipelago, the same low undulating topography, the same wide sky, and the same extensive sandy beach. In the early years of this century the Congested Districts Board covered Inishbofin with a network of narrow roads, and thus as in Scilly there is ample opportunity for almost traffic-free walking, and the island is the same small size, so that all parts of it can be quickly reached on foot.

I have said almost traffic-free, but that is because most of the cars there are immobile. The widespread distribution of dead cars is the island's only objectionable feature. Apparently old 'bangers' are bought, shipped to the island, and run till they expire. As soon as one dies, you buy another, and it seems to be almost a status symbol to have several dead cars outside your house, indicating sufficient means to buy another without delay.

If we take a wider basis for comparison, both island groups have the same exposure to Atlantic storms, and the same almost frost-free climate. But a closer look at the landscape quickly dispels the comparison. There is fuchsia in the hedges, but very few of the other exotic plants that run riot in the hedgerows of Scilly. Beyond the hedges areas of bog quickly make it clear that we are more than three degrees of latitude further north. Most of the island was probably once covered by peat, with blanket-bog on the slopes, and deeper peat with pine stumps in the hollows; a few small open-water lakes still survive.

Today the island has less than 200 inhabitants, but in 1841 there were 1400, and at that time of high population peat-cutting would have been heavy. Much of the peat has been cut away, and the curious practice of paring sods of grass off rough pasture and burning them still continues. C.R. Browne, who wrote an anthropological account of the island in 1893, writes that they use ' "scraws" of the thin peaty layer which covers the rocky surface of the higher and wilder parts of the islands, cut into blocks the size of peats, and dried in the sun. The substance thus obtained can be burned and will throw out considerable heat, but is extremely dirty and wasteful, as it contains a large proportion of earth and small pebbles, which are left in the ash'. Browne does not comment that such a practice leaves the subsoil virtually barren, and unfit for agriculture. Considerable areas of land have been, and are still being 'desertified' in this way; the same practice also continues on Tory Island.

Agriculture has been virtually abandoned on the island, and I did not see 'serious' farming anywhere. The island now depends on fishing and tourism. For the visitor who wants sea and sky it has a great deal to offer in the way of walking, sea-fishing and swimming; there are two good hotels and a cafe beside the sandy beach. For the historian there are the church ruins and a splendid seventeenth-century star-shaped fort in a good state of preservation; for the archaeologist there are promontory forts, a curious cashel and old hut-sites and walls, some of which are part-buried by peat. The north side of the island has two deep bays, and on the east side of the western bay a promontory, Fawnmore, carries a series of banks and ditches; there appear also to be hut-circles, but as the local people build rings of stones on which to dry their peat, only excavation could establish the age of the circles.

A constant stream of boats from Cleggan provides easy access to the island, and at the right time of year you can hear the corncrake.

## ROUNDSTONE

I first came to Roundstone, which lies on the shore of a sheltered bay at the foot of Errisbeg, in the summer of 1933, on holiday with my mother and sister, and had my first view of the white sand of Dog's Bay. Praeger was later to describe the bay as 'one of the greatest attractions that Roundstone offers. A narrow mile-long granite island set half a mile off shore has got joined to the mainland by a sand-spit, which forms two curving bays—Dog's Bay and Gorteen Bay—set back to back, and filled with the clearest of Atlantic water'. The setting is an enlarged version of the island and tidal sand-spit I have already described at Portnoo.

We had happened to hit on a heat-wave, with extremely calm air, and the Atlantic swells had died away to nothing. The tide advanced and retreated over the white sand, but not a ripple disturbed the water. I suddenly saw that the inshore water had thousands of little translucent purple thimbles suspended in it. As a second-year student in zoology I had done the Hydrozoa, and I realised that these must be one of the forms, related to the jelly-fishes, that the textbooks described as a 'helmet-shaped swimming bell up to 2cm long, rare in Irish waters'. I was unable to get specimens, as the weather broke before a supply of fixative which I had ordered could be delivered. I have never seen the animal since. Nor have I ever seen its larger cousin, the Portuguese man o' war, which has a large purple float and many painfully stinging tentacles, though I have often looked out for it. Nor has my search of beaches ever been rewarded by the finding of a large nut, floated across the Atlantic from the West Indies; I have seen such nuts sent to the TCD Botany School for identification, but I have never been lucky enough to find one myself.

I little thought when, as a student of zoology, I lay sunning myself on the beach in Roundstone in 1933, that in two years time I would be back in the area as a fledgling quaternary botanist in pouring rain, or that the occasion would be enshrined in *The Way that I Went,* published in 1937. Praeger's account is well known, but I cannot resist repeating it:

> That great bogland behind Urrisbeg recalls a quaint scene on a very wet day in August, 1935. A number of botanists had foregathered at Roundstone, and the particular occasion

> was a kind of symposium on bogs, held in the middle of one of the wettest of them. There were A.G. Tansley from Oxford, H.E. Godwin from Cambridge, Hugo Osvald from Stockholm, Knud Jessen and H. Jonassen from Copenhagen, G.F. Mitchell from Dublin, Margaret Dunlop from Manchester. We stood in a ring in that shelterless expanse while discussion raged on the application of the terms soligenous, topogenous and ombrogenous; the rain and the wind, like the discussion, waxed in intensity, and under the unusual superincumbent weight, whether of mere flesh and bone (including my own 16½ stone) or of intellect, the floating surface of the bog slowly sank till we were all half-way up to our knees in brown water. The only pause in the flow of argument was when Jessen or Osvald, in an endeavour to solve the question of the origin of the peat, would chew some of the mud brought up by the boring tool from the bottom of the bog, to test the presence or absence of gritty material in the vegetable mass.

I propose to give some background to the story, and also add a postscript. Arthur Tansley, Professor of Botany in Oxford, was one of the founders of the science of ecology. In 1911 he published a book, *Types of British Vegetation*, which immediately became the bible of ecology in Britain. It was a long time out of print, and Tansley started working on its successor, which appeared in 1939 as *The British Islands and their Vegetation*, a book with 1000 pages and 400 illustrations. In order to prepare himself for writing the section on bogs, Tansley asked Hugo Osvald from Uppsala, who had done a great deal of work on the vegetation and growth of raised-bogs in Sweden, to visit the bogs of Ireland with him. Harry Godwin, who had already studied the low-lying peats in the English fens, was anxious to extend his experience by seeing bogs in Ireland. There was a very close relationship between Arthur and Harry, somewhat similar to the relationship between Knud Jessen and myself, except that Harry was an established botanist when he met Tansley, whereas I was an undergraduate when I met Knud. If I have described Knud as my father in science, I think one could say that Arthur was Harry's uncle. An additional attraction for coming was that Jessen was on his second field-season in Ireland, and had already amassed a vast amount of information about both the vegetation and the history of its bogs. It was agreed that Tansley's group would catch up with Jessen somewhere, and it was purely by chance that Roundstone was the meeting-point. The Praegers were holidaying in Roundstone, and Margaret Dunlop, a botanist from Manchester, was staying with them.

Hugo Osvald returned to Ireland in 1936 to look at Irish bogs more closely, and I drove him round the country. It was a very timely visit, because it just preceded the massive mechanical attack on the Irish boglands. Hugo wrote a most important paper on the vegetation of the boglands, then still undisturbed, a paper that could not be written today because so much has been destroyed. I well remember driving south from Portlaoise, and passing a bog at which Hugo said 'Stop'. So we walked onto it and spent a few hours listing its plant associations. Today the bog is reduced to a dusty surface of milled peat, awaiting transport to a power-station.

I mentioned earlier that at Ballybetagh Jessen had found, sandwiched in the basal muds, a gritty layer with arctic plants. He was particularly elated when he struck the same sequence at the bottom of the Roundstone bog, as it showed that an open vegetation of cold-loving plants had once covered the area. Today the Roundstone district is the home of rare heathers which have their modern homelands in the Pyrenees; they cannot have been growing in the area during the cold phase, and must have immigrated subsequently. But when, and from where? Two North American plants, the naiad and the pipewort, also grow in the Roundstone area, and their late-glacial history is a similar mystery. It is good that a substantial part of the great bog area between Roundstone and the Twelve Pins has already been purchased by the State. This whole area ought to be a National Park, where the still puzzling history of these rare plants could be further studied. Airports should not be allowed to proliferate in the area.

The postscript. Our lodgings in Roundstone were directly opposite the harbour pier. When we got back from the bog I was soaked from head to foot; water ran down the back of my neck and out from my boots. Despite the still pouring rain, I decided that a swim would freshen me up, so I threw off my clothes, put on my togs and plunged in. The local dispensary doctor, who was very keen on fishing, thought that the local seals were too many in number, and hearing my splash, and not conceiving that anyone could be swimming on such a day, seized up his gun and rushed down the pier. So I surfaced from one plunge to find myself looking up the barrel of a gun. Mercifully the doctor recognised a human head.

## POLLNAHALLIA

Soon after we crossed the River Moy at Ballina we left behind us the Carboniferous limestone which we had looked at in Co. Sligo. All through Mayo and Galway we were on older, harder and more disturbed rock formations, whose irregular dissection by erosion has given rise to the mountains and valleys of that scenic area. From Roundstone we move north-east to

Maam Cross, and then north to the north-east corner of Lough Corrib, to take a last look at this splendid landscape. We follow the north shore of the lake as far as Cong, where we find ourselves on limestone once more.

At Cong we turn south and until we reach Kinvarra in Co.Clare, the gateway to the Burren proper, our road never leaves the limestone and nowhere rises above 75m in level. Here, as elsewhere in Ireland, the limestone is riddled with karstic channels, resulting in a countryside of disappearing streams, and of 'turloughs', low-lying areas, grassy and dry in summer, but changing to shallow lakes when the rising winter water-table floods them. At Carran in the Burren, a very large karstic depression has been described as 'a true polje'.

Just before we reach Headford, a short length of lane to the west brings us to Ross Abbey, one of the best preserved of Ireland's many Franciscan abbeys. Founded in 1357, most of what we see today belongs to the fifteenth century; church, cloister and conventual buildings all show very interesting detail.

In Headford itself we must make another detour, taking the road to Tuam. Ahead we soon see an isolated limestone knoll, which rises to 170m. Though only half the height of Knocknarea in Sligo, it is a sister knoll. Knocknarea is crowned by a great stone mound, the legendary grave of Queen Maeve, while here the smaller knoll is called Knockmaa, again recalling the queen; it also carries a stone mound.

But the reason for our visit lies on its lower southern slope. Here at Pollnahallia, 2km south-west of Knockmaa, limestone with a patchy cover of glacial deposit forms the surface of the ground. In the late seventies a local farmer was somewhat surprised to see white sand thrown up out of rabbit-burrows. Investigation showed that the sands, which were extensive if patchy, consisted almost entirely of small grains of quartz or silica, free from contaminants such as iron oxides. Deposits of such 'pure' sand are rare, and are desirable for certain industrial purposes, such as glass, special cements and sand-textured paints. The land-owner opened up a pit to exploit the deposit. The Geological Survey was anxious to assess its economic potential, and did some drilling and other investigations, under the direction of Aubrey Flegg.

Borings through the sand, which in places is 8m thick, came upon clays rich in organic debris, and these were looked at by Bill Watts and Pete Coxon. Pollen counts showed that there was coniferous woodland and heath interspersed with areas of open ground. In pre-glacial times the woods of Europe were much more diversified than they are today, as many trees failed to survive the violent climatic swings of the Ice Age. Several trees not growing in Europe today were recorded at Pollnahallia, and of these the most striking was the redwood (*Sequoia*), now only surviving in California, though formerly widely distributed in many parts of the world. It is thought to have become extinct in Europe about 2 million years ago, when the Ice Age was beginning, and the clays must be of about that age.

The geological investigations also showed that the sand had made its way into already existing karstic channels and tunnels, probably carried in by wind. We can now produce images of sand-grains with the scanning electron microscope, and see surface detail, just as we can with pollen. Ice-transported sand usually has a jagged outline, water-transported sand is roughly rounded, but wind-borne sand is very rounded and smooth; such were the grains at Pollnahallia. Where did the sand come from? Croagh Patrick is of quartzite, a solid mass of pure silica, widely distributed in Mayo and Galway. Under pre-Ice Age tropical weathering even quartzite will have broken down into small particles, and such weathered rock may well have been the source of the wind-blown Pollnahallia sand.

Now we come to our real problem, the rate at which limestone weathers away. If we analyse the water flowing out of a cave, it contains a considerable amount of dissolved limestone, indicating cave enlargement, which must ultimately lead to lowering of the ground surface. As we shall see when we get to the Burren, and even more so at Carrigacappeen in Kerry, there is considerable evidence that a limestone surface can be lowered relatively rapidly. But at Pollnahallia the blown sand cannot have gone down to great depths to reach the limestone cavities; the cavities must then have been near the surface as they are today. In other words, when we look around us at Pollnahallia we are looking at a landscape that has been fossilised for the past 2 million years.

We make our way along by-roads to Claregalway, and there see another Franciscan abbey, and also a dramatic castle. Both buildings are essentially fifteenth century, a time when sheep-raising was making the area prosperous. Some later tombstones show ploughs and other agricultural implements, but not as elegantly as the example we looked at at Skreen. From Claregalway we go directly to Oranmore, thus bypassing the traffic of Galway, and from there it is a short run to Kinvarra.

CHAPTER 14

# Clare

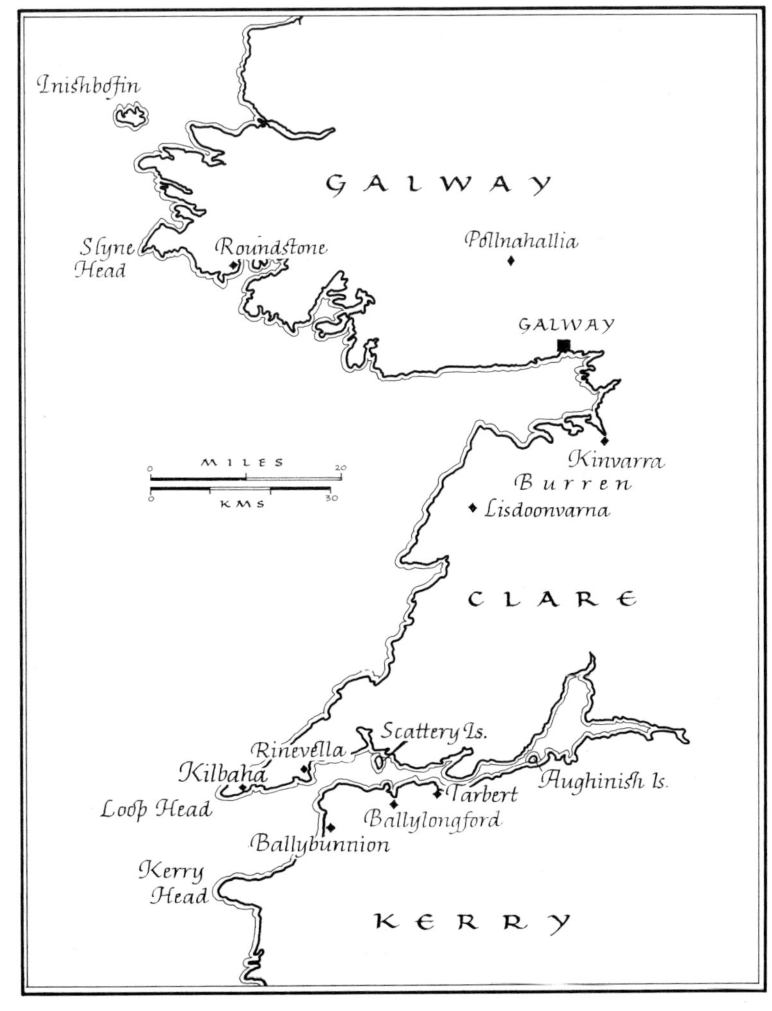


THE BURREN · SOUTH-WEST CLARE

SCATTERY ISLAND · LOOP HEAD

## THE BURREN

When we reach the pretty harbour at Kinvarra we see the bare grey hills of the Burren rising to over 300m ahead of us. I do not intend to linger in this fascinating area, about which so much has already been written. I shall look at three topics only.

I regard these bare hills as land to which soil came, and from which it later removed itself. An analogy can be found in central Sweden where the weight of heavy ice depressed the land to a great extent, from which it is still recovering, although the ice itself disappeared many thousands of years ago. Below the Baltic Sea off Stockholm the rock surface is irregular, and so islands are created in an archipelago as the land continues its recovery.

Uplift causes a bare rock to appear above sea-level. Birds rest on the rock and leave their droppings there. Soon the rock reaches such a height that waves can no longer wash away the droppings, and these become invaded by lichens and mosses. As these decay the formation of an organic soil begins, and grasses and other flowering plants emerge. The soil becomes thick enough to anchor larger roots, and bushes of birch and willow appear, and ultimately forest trees can flourish. We can follow this in a transect if we move inland from our outer rock, and reach the area where continued uplift has transformed what once were islands into continuous wooded land. The Burren hills were not submerged, but were stripped bare by passing ice, and I believe that the build-up there of organic soil, and its colonisation by woodland, followed this type of pattern. Bill Watts has traced the post-glacial vegetational succession from open tundra to closed woodland in several pollen diagrams from lakes in the area.

How was the process reversed, and where have the forest and the soil gone? Farming activity is the answer I prefer. There is pollen evidence of Neolithic presence in the region, and it was certainly heavily settled when the Neolithic was giving way to the Early Bronze Age about 4000 years ago, because there are numerous megalithic tombs scattered across the Burren uplands. In the Burren we see the tomb in its simplest form, built of a large slab at each side and two smaller slabs at each end, roofed by a large sloping slab. One well-known portal-dolmen at Poulnabrone, dug in 1985 by Ann Lynch of the Office of Public Works, yielded artefacts which suggested a Neolithic age. Small as the tomb was, the remains of about twenty people had been buried in it. In general such tombs, as in the Burren, are on high pasture lands, and their abundance in the Burren shows that there was very early extensive woodland clearance.

As long as the primeval vegetation was not disturbed, the organic soil on which it grew remained intact. But if its plant cover was disturbed, or burned—a very common practice with prehistoric peoples—and the decayed vegetable debris of which it was composed was exposed to the air, then the soil material began to oxidise and disappear. The classic example of this is of course the Fenlands in England, where ever since arterial drainage was first carried out in the seventeenth century, the peat has been thinning and shrinking, and has in some areas virtually disappeared. In the Burren it has been completely destroyed, and the rock surfaces are grey and barren.

At Pollnahallia we seemed to have good evidence that there the destruction of limestone by weathering proceeded only very slowly indeed. In the Burren we have what seems to be equally good evidence for very rapid solution. Ice from the last glaciation passed over the area about 18,000 years ago, and as it retreated it left rounded rock surfaces, patches of deposit here and there, and a wide scatter of erratic blocks, many of them of considerable size. Such a block gave some protection from rainwater to the rock on which it rested, and some now stand on slight pedestals, the block remaining at its original level, while the surface of the surrounding rock has been lowered by solution during the past 18,000 years.

In the Burren we can see many ancient walls. These have been recently studied by Emma Plunket Dillon, who sought to identify different wall types and different field patterns. She was puzzled by one type of wall which appeared to rest on a particularly hard foundation, and it was only after she had done a considerable amount of work that she realised that the 'foundation' was in fact solid rock. The overlying wall had given the same protection as the erratics gave elsewhere, and the rock below the wall now rose as a low plinth standing some centimetres above the rock in the adjoining fields, which had not been so protected. She thought the walls in question might go back to the Bronze Age.

The limestones of the two areas, Headford and the Burren, are similar in type and age, and the apparent difference in erosion-rates between the two areas is very puzzling. We will meet the problem again at Carrigacappeen in Kerry. Much work still remains to be done on the rate of limestone solution in Ireland.

For me the most attractive man-created features in the Burren are the droving-roads. Before railroad-waggons and cattle-lorries came into existence, cattle had to walk to market, often along these special tracks. Several droving-roads cross the Burren, bearing no relation to the

*Formoyle, Clare. This route-way, now abandoned, was a droving-road along which cattle made their way to a distant market.*

present road-system, and provide splendid walking. One very good example crosses the north tip of Slieve Elva, drops eastwards to cross the Caher River at Formoyle, and then climbs over the next ridge to Feenagh, where it joins the modern road to Ballyvaughan.

## SOUTH-WEST CLARE

So far all the rocks of Carboniferous age that we have seen in Clare have been limestone, calcareous and porous. After the primary calcareous debris had been accumulating on the sea-floor in relatively shallow water for some 40 million years, the sea-floor appears to have sagged, and currents were able to carry in muds, silts and sands from land-masses which were not too far away. These sediments were later uplifted to form dark-coloured, infertile, poorly drained shales; the sandstones, though also infertile, did allow for some soil drainage.

These types of rock appear at Lisdoonvarna, bringing about the well-documented dramatic change in landscape from bare dry limestone with sparse vegetation on the north, to wet dark-coloured shale crowded with rushes (*Juncus* spp) on the south. These rocks continue southwards for a distance of 120km to Killarney itself, where a small patch of the underlying limestone first emerges, and the ground then rises into the dramatic landscapes of the Kerry mountains. Though it does vary in altitude, rising to over 400m east of Castleisland, to the average onlooker the landscape between Lisdoonvarna and Killarney can only be regarded as dull, a dullness emphasised by great stretches of bog. Before it was heavily cut away, the whole area was covered by blanket-bog.

For the specialist, however, the area holds a great deal of interest, and I have lodged for a week or more at several places, Kilrush, Glin, Ballybunnion, trying to trace out the local glacial history or to understand the complications of the local river systems.

The Shannon estuary demonstrates very clearly the contrast between limestone and shale country. The estuary begins on limestone at Limerick and widens westwards as it expands north and south over great areas of low-lying limestone. Then between Killadysert and Foynes it narrows sharply as it meets the shale. The shale on the whole is gently tilted to the west, and so it rises into an irregular cliff or escarpment along its eastern limit. South of the estuary to the west of Newcastle West, the cliff is particularly well developed, and both the road and the railway are forced to crawl diagonally up it. There is a car-park half-way up the slope, and a stop here to look back at the fertile limestone plain will make the landscape contrast that is awaiting when the top of the cliff is reached all the more striking.

West of Foynes the estuary narrows to a channel cut through the shales. The ice of the last main ice advance pushed into the channel, but came to an arcuate halt along a line joining Kilrush, Scattery Island and Ballylongford. As long as it could keep moving it carried with it limestone from the inner estuary, and when this was deposited it was a parent material for good soils. West of the line there was no such additive, and the soil remained poor. At Ballylongford the sudden change from rich land to poor is particularly striking.

## SCATTERY ISLAND

Although Scattery Island lies in the middle of the estuary, it is infested by rats, in numbers I never saw anywhere else. It covers 85ha, and is entirely built up of glacial deposits. I went there in 1976, primarily because Francis Synge on a visit some years previously had reported that one cliff-face showed peat covered by a considerable thickness of glacial deposit; I did not see the peat, which might have been carried away by erosion in the intervening years, but I did see glacial deposits of great complexity, far beyond my powers of decipherment. When lecturing on ice and glacial deposits, I always said that ice was entirely capricious in its behaviour, and that it was virtually impossible to sort out what it might have done at any specific locality. Scattery Island is built up of end-moraine, and such moraines are notoriously difficult to interpret. An end-moraine forms along a line where for a time the margin of the ice stood still, while fresh ice brought more debris at the same rate as older ice was melting away. There was not an exact balance; a minor fall-back would dump new debris, and a new advance would create push-structures in the existing material. Scattery Island displays such features splendidly.

There are other things to see too. There are the ruins of an extensive early monastery, founded in the sixth century by St Senan. One of the six churches, which has projections on the wall-corners and a flat-lintelled door, may be of considerable antiquity. There are records of numerous Viking attacks, and the round tower, with a height of 35m, reputedly one of the tallest in Ireland, may have been attacked several times.

Occupation continued, and there are the remains of a fourteenth-century church, a sixteenth-century castle, and a nineteenth-century anti-Napoleonic fort. But the number of inhabitants has dwindled, and at the time of my visit was down to two, a brother and sister. There had been another brother who went to sea, and had bought a house in Kilrush to which he intended to retire. He died, leaving the house, which was furnished, to his kin. At times the brother and sister would occupy the house, trying to reconcile themselves to a land-bound life, but after a short stay they always returned to the island.

## Loop Head

From Kilrush we push west along the coast to Loop Head. There are many coastal sections showing glacial deposits resting on a striated surface of bedrock; the striae run essentially east–west, and so ice must have moved westwards out of the mouth of the estuary at an earlier stage of the Ice Age than the time when it halted at Scattery Island. Ice movements along the west coast have still to be clarified, because if we look closely at the glacial deposits there, or at the pebbles on the beach which have been derived from them, we can pick up pieces of the granite that outcrops west of Galway city, and also pieces of metamorphic rock from further north in Mayo. Did a sheet of ice once advance down the west coast from the north, or do the pebbles come from icebergs loaded with glacial deposit drifting in a southerly current?

Just west of Kilcredaun Point, where we have another nineteenth-century fort with cannon, we come to the small Rinevella Bay, which has another still smaller bay tucked in just to the east of it. This small bay contains the finest example of 'submerged forest' that I know of in Ireland. A layer of pine and other tree stumps embedded in peat stretch down below modern tide-level, just as we saw near Belmullet, and are probably of about the same age, 4000 years. Some of the pine stumps are more than 60cm in diameter, and are the remains of truly massive trees. But the stratigraphy of the peat is rather puzzling, and requires detailed examination.

An item of touchingly human interest can be seen in the church at Kilbaha. Although members of the Roman Catholic faith were entitled from early in the eighteenth century to erect and use churches, there were estates where the local Protestant landlord would not make land available as a site for a church. In such areas the faithful would assemble at a prominent land-mark, such as an upstanding rock, and many such mass-rocks are identified. At Kilbaha in 1850 another solution was reached. The landlord's territory ended at the high water mark, and the strand was beyond his jurisdiction. So an altar was mounted on a wheeled platform, and when tides allowed it was drawn down onto the foreshore, where Mass was celebrated. The altar, shaped rather like a Victorian bathing-box, is still preserved in the church.

CHAPTER 15

# North Kerry

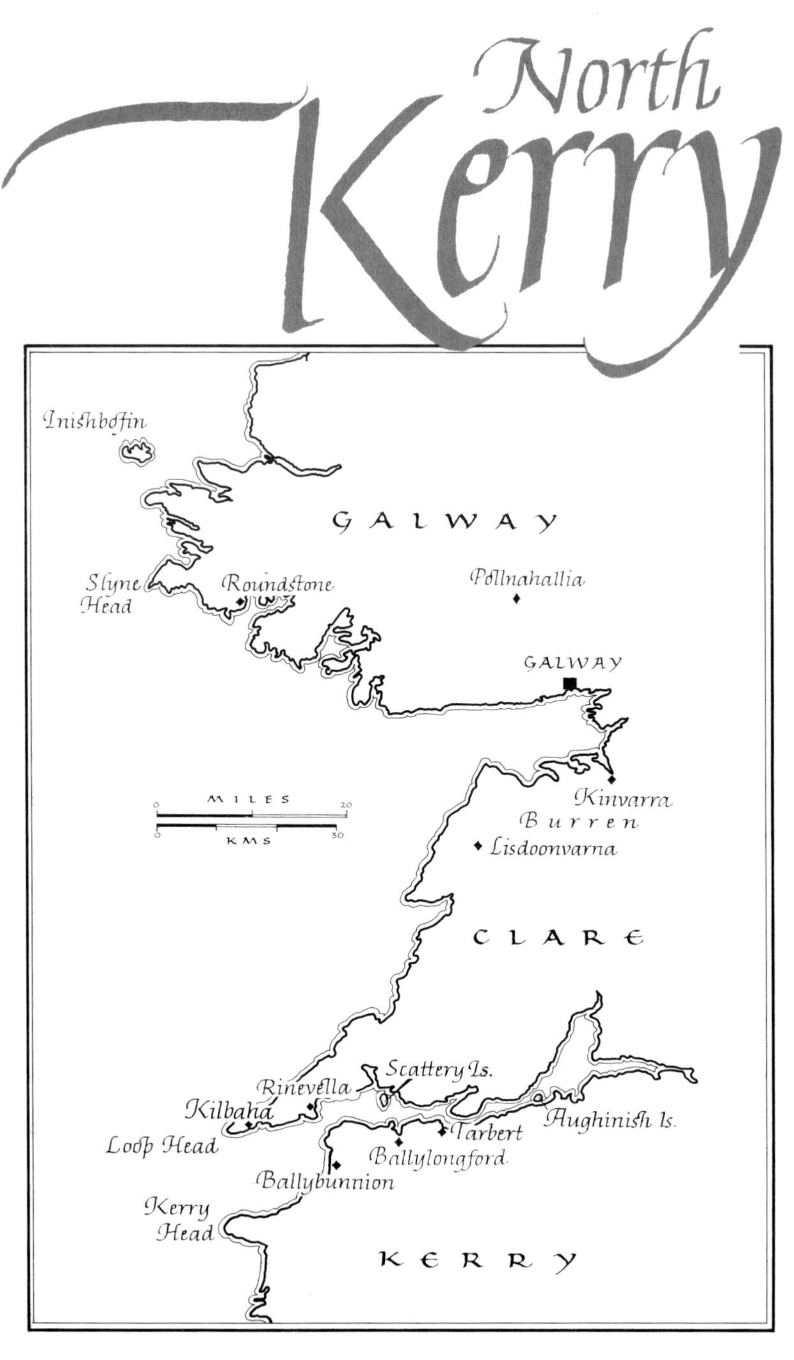


KERRY HEAD · BALLYLONGFORD

BALLYBUNNION · FENIT TO SPA

## Kerry Head

Although there are some isolated knolls, the countryside near Loop Head is on the whole gently undulating. But if we look south across the estuary, we see a different feature, a short rocky ridge, Kerry Head, which rises to over 200m. It gives us a mild foretaste of the great ridged mountain-ranges we shall come to further south in the county. Over much of Ireland the limy deposits of the early Carboniferous seas were laid down on top of material of very different character. The old mountains of Donegal and Connacht are the degraded remnants of a very much higher Caledonide landmass which has been greatly lowered by erosion. The erosional debris was shed into mountain torrents, into meandering streams, and into transient lakes. When the transporting water lost its strength, the debris was sorted into gravels, sands and silts, rich in silica, red because of the presence of iron, but devoid of nutrient materials. As we have seen, the rocks into which they were later transformed are collectively known as Old Red Sandstone.

Later Hercynide earth pressures from north and south crumpled both the ORS (as it is affectionately called) and the overlying Carboniferous rocks into something like a sheet of corrugated iron tilted slightly to the west. The tough, siliceous ORS was resistant to erosion and stands up in ridges, while the weaker Carboniferous rocks survive only in some trough floors. As Charles Holland, Professor of Geology in Trinity College, Dublin, has put it, 'The splendid Atlantic-type coast line of Kerry and West Cork is formed by rugged peninsulas of Old Red Sandstone rocks, separated by long bays and valleys floored by the less resistant Carboniferous.'

At Kerry Head the crest of an ORS ridge makes a brief appearance, and when it comes to the surface then the Lower Carboniferous limestones have to appear also, and they wrap around the sandstone ridge in a great arc from Ballybunnion, past Listowel to Fenit. To the east of the arc of limestone the overlying shales continue as far as Killarney.

Still in Co. Clare we retrace our steps to Kilrush, and continue on, passing the vast coal-fired power-station at Money Point. We gaze in despair at its smoke-stacks, pumping out—contrary to EC regulations—the ingredients of acid rain. The plea is the usual one, so fatal to environmental protection, that the amount which Moneypoint produces relative to other producers is so small that the atmosphere will not notice it. But as some of us remember from our Sunday School hymns 'Little drops of water, little grains of sand, make the mighty ocean and the giant land'. At Killimer we take the ferry to the Kerry side of the estuary. Landing at Tarbert, we pass another giant power-station, but this one is oil-fired, and perhaps not quite as damaging.

As we drive from the quay to the village, we pass a small isolated stone building, a lock-up of days gone by.

## BALLYLONGFORD

Ballylongford, a sleepy little village, lies at the head of what is, according to my taste, one of the most beautiful inlets in Ireland. How long the village will sleep is another question, for the Industrial Development Authority has for a long time been trying to entice some massive development to the estuary in its vicinity; an oil refinery, a smelter, a deep-water port, all have been on the cards. The deep, sheltered, isolated waters of the Shannon estuary are tempting to industrialists. The Electricity Supply Board already has its power-stations at Tarbert and Money Point. Further up the estuary where it widens out on the limestone the whole of Aughinish island is covered by an enormous plant processing imported aluminium ore.

As a digression we may note that the building of that plant provided further demonstration, if any be needed, that throughout Ireland the Carboniferous limestone is deeply penetrated by karstic cavities. This had not been fully realised when the construction of the Aughinish plant started, and substantial extra costs were incurred in coping with the geological difficulties when they revealed themselves. When I taught geology to engineering students, I always impressed on them the necessity for adequate site investigation before extensive works were embarked upon. Here one comes up against the financial planning of the enterprise. Most financiers want to take a chance on it. An adequate site investigation will be expensive, and no difficulties may be revealed. So the accountants say that the site investigation can be skimped, but a substantial sum can be set aside for contingencies. If there are no problems they still have their money; if there are problems then they will dip into the contingency fund. But there are far too many examples of cases where serious problems arose, and the contingency fund was very rapidly overdrawn. The same attitude is encountered when pre-development environmental assessments are being planned.

Selfishly I hope that large-scale industrial development will not come to the Ballylongford inlet, which as well as its beauty has many historical associations. Moving north from the village we quickly come to the interesting ruins of a Franciscan friary, founded about 1470, by John O'Connor. A very remarkable find made one hundred years ago in a nearby bog shows both the wealth of the O'Connor family and the skill of Irish craftsmen. The find was the broken-up remains of an elaborate gilt silver processional cross, which carried a long inscription telling that it had been made by William O'Connor in 1479 for Cornelius and Eileen O'Connor in memory of their father, the founder of the abbey, where it would have been carried on special occasions. Skilfully repaired, it is now in the National Museum. I had the privilege of handling it when I was preparing a catalogue of an exhibition of *Treasures of Irish Art; 1500 BC–1500 AD* in the United States in 1976. Only four other pieces of Irish church art from the period are known, a mitre and crozier of 1418, and a chalice and paten of 1494.

We continue on to the quay at Saleen (Pl. 3). In the late eighteenth and early nineteenth centuries very large sums of public money were spent improving the navigation on the Shannon, and these improvements even reached Ballylongford, where a substantial stone wharf and sheds were erected. From the wharf, now deserted, there is a splendid view with wide skies down the inlet, across salt-marshes to a castle, and it is one of my favourite picnic-points.

In spring and autumn there is a constant movement of wading-birds on the tidal muds, which extend right to the mouth of the inlet. Rising from the salt-marsh in the middle distance are the ruins of the very large tower of Carrigafoyle castle. Such towers usually had at their base a small walled area protected by minor corner towers, called a bawn, where livestock or goods could be protected. This castle stood a short distance out from the shore, and the walled area provided a dock for boats. Built in the sixteenth century, it had the usual bloody history until it was blown up by the Cromwellians. It fell apart very neatly, and in its present state provides an excellent cross-section of castle architecture. If we pass the castle we can move on to Carrig Island, which has some not very impressive church remains and another nineteenth-century fort.

The Ballylongford inlet is a place I return to; long may it remain unspoiled.

## Ballybunnion

I was very intrigued by a right-angle bend in a river about 4km south of Ballylongford, as geographers tend to view such bends as due to river capture. The Galey River drains the high shale ground west of Newcastle West, and flows in a west-northwesterly direction towards Ballylongford. Emerging from the high ground it crosses a wide valley running south–west towards Listowel, and beheads the stream which drains it. It then cuts through a low ridge, and into another valley also running south–west. It meets the stream in that valley, and joins it at right angles. The Feale, which drains the high ground further south, shows a similar anomaly by making a sharp bend east of Listowel where it cuts through a north–south ridge in a deep gorge. At Listowel it leaves the shales and flows out onto limestone, across which it wanders, collecting the Galey river as a tributary, and entering the sea south of Ballybunnion, where it is known as the Cashen River. I spent a lot of time wandering round the area, but in the end I decided there were too many imponderables, and I abandoned any attempt at analysing the drainage history.

Ballybunnion has the same uncertain air as many other small towns on the west coast, which owe their origin to the nineteenth-century rise of sea-bathing as a holiday occupation, and the family fortnight at the sea to indulge in the practice. The eccentric Lartigue monorail brought visitors from Listowel, just as Limerick citizens reached Kilkee by the West Clare Railway, immortalised by Percy French. Sun and Spain were unknown. Today the extended family holiday is extinct, the sun is king, and resorts like Ballybunnion struggle to survive. Takeaway foods, amusement halls, and discos sit uneasily in buildings of an earlier age.

Just south of the castle that stands on the cliff-edge, high cliffs of glacial deposit rise above a rough rocky platform that is covered by high tide. In the deposit, near its base, and not much above high water mark, there was a layer of well-rounded gravel. At first I thought it was just a layer of glacial gravel, but I suddenly realised that it was remarkably level, remarkably uniform in thickness, and that all the rounded pebbles were around the same size. The penny dropped—I was looking at a raised beach. I then looked at the material above and below in more detail. That below was certainly till, probably deposited directly from ice. In the upper material I could see a tendency for the stones to have their long axes more or less parallel, an arrangement that arises if the material subsequent to primary deposition has been sludged downslope under the influence of repeated freezing and thawing. Thus the rough history was that ice had deposited the lower till; the ice had then retreated, and waves at a higher level than those of today had come, cut a flat platform with a cliff behind it in the till, and thrown beach pebbles up upon it. The sea probably then retreated, and cold returned. Frost action sludged till from the cliff behind down out over the beach.

But there was no evidence for the most important question: What was the temperature of the waves that emplaced the beach? Beach deposits within quaternary sequences are well known in many parts of the world, and they often contain fossils on which estimates of contemporary temperature can be based. Such deposits occur at a number of localities in Ireland, but a miasma hangs over them all—none contain fossils. This is curious because fossiliferous beaches buried by till occur no further away than Wales. Was the formation of the Ballybunnion beach a transient feature of little climatic significance? Did the waves cut the platform as the ice was retreating and was it the same episode of cold that buried the beach? Or did the ice disappear, and did the warm water of an interglacial sea emplace the beach, and did its burial have to await the coming of a new cold period?

I left the question open, but Willie Warren, who succeeded Francis Synge as head of the Quaternary Unit in the Geological Survey, has plumped for the cold-warm-cold interpretation. He regards the till below the beach as the oldest glacial deposit yet recognised in Ireland.

If the beach does represent a high-level warm interglacial sea, then every effort should be made to find fossiliferous deposits laid down in its waters. The Cashen River, as the mouth of the Feale is called, lies in an area of extraordinarily low ground, on limestone, between its mouth and Listowel; around Lixnaw great areas of ground are less than 10m above mean sea-level. As the area doubtless contains karstic hollows which might have served, as at Pollnahallia, as sediment traps, a search should be made for such hollows which might contain deposits from an interglacial sea. I toyed with the idea of doing some work here with a mechanical digger, which will open up quite deep pits in a remarkably short time. My friend, Mireille Ters, who worked on such matters in western coastal France, had persuaded her chiefs to buy a digger for her, which she operated herself, but as I was already in my middle sixties, I decided against trying to emulate her. But it is an area that should be investigated.

Miss Stacpoole had made interesting finds in some kitchen-middens in the Ballybunnion sand-dunes, and I hunted them out. In one I found the usual scraps of shell, bone and iron slag. In addition there were rubbed pieces of crystalline calcite. Calcite is the pure form of calcium carbonate, and is common in veins in limestone; it has diagonal cleavages, and breaks into rhomboid pieces; it is relatively soft, much softer than iron. The pieces had clearly been used for rubbing, as their cleavage-edges were well-rounded; I wondered if they could have been used for burnishing bronze or polishing leather. The only other place I ever saw them was at Freestone Hill in Co. Kilkenny, when Gerhard Bersu was excavating a hillfort there. The site had Late Bronze Age and Late Roman material, and there were numerous pieces of rubbed calcite.

Gerhard was a very distinguished German archaeologist. Hitler's Germany threw him out because his wife was Jewish, and they moved to England. When war started, the Bersus were interned in the Isle of Man, where he conducted excavations from his prison camp. On their release they moved to Ireland, where de Valera financed a professorship for Gerhard, and he carried out quite a lot of excavations. Reinstated in post-war Germany, he disappeared.

## Fenit to Spa

We move on to Fenit, where we are on limestone; as we look across Tralee Bay we see the ORS ridge of the Slieve Mish Mountains rising to over 850m. These mountains form the eastern end of the Dingle Peninsula. Around Fenit we are near the limit of the shaly material that was carried in from the north, and beds of limestone alternate with beds of shale. This complex sandwich was structurally weak, and when the later Hercynide earth movements that thrust up the Kerry mountains came along, the sandwich crumpled and cracked, leaving a confused distribution of limestone and shale, which has been dissected out by later erosion. A short distance west of Spa the coast road, which is on shale, is forced to make a sudden bend to avoid an upstanding block of limestone. The block contains a quarry, and if we look at the quarry face we can see black blobs of a pitchy substance scattered through the rock. The substance is essentially a solid hydrocarbon, related to the hydrocarbons of oil and gas, and it is rumoured in geological circles that it was the recognition of this material that led to the concept that there might be lighter hydrocarbons nearby, and this in turn led to the search for gas and oil off our coasts.

Moving only a very short distance north from Fenit, we cross to Barrow Island on a narrow storm-beach ridge which blocks one exit from Barrow Harbour, leaving the harbour almost entirely land-locked. The quiet water here provides ideal conditions for grass-wrack (*Zostera marina*), a curious flowering plant with long green strap-like leaves which lives shallowly submerged in sea water. It provides a splendid food for geese, which feed greedily on it in winter. Limestone forms the north shore of Barrow Harbour, and from this pinnacles of rock arise. In some way these pinnacles escaped removal by ice, and they are the best surviving example of the deeply fretted surface that much of the karstic limestone landscape of Ireland must have had before the Ice Age. We look north over Banna Strand, where Sir Roger Casement was landed from a German submarine in 1916, only to be immediately arrested.

Between Spa and the limestone block already referred to, waves at some time cut a wide platform across the complicated sequence of limestones and shales; on the land side there is a low cliff in quaternary deposits. In the middle sixties R.G.S. Hudson, then Professor of Geology in Trinity, led an excursion to see the limestones and shales. In British geology there is a strong tradition that only things you can hit with a hammer, hard rocks such as limestone and shale, are worthy of geological study. In the United States a wider view is taken, and there geologists are divided into hard-rock men who carry a hammer and study rocks, and dirt-men who carry a spade and look at superficial unconsolidated materials. Hudson was a hard-rock man. John Jackson, who combines both interests, was in the party, and the deposits in the cliff immediately caught his eye, causing him to loiter behind. He was sharply told by Hudson not to waste time looking at that sort of thing; John conformed and joined up with the party, but he told me of what he had seen. I looked at the deposits on many occasions, and ultimately wrote a paper about them in 1970, but I am afraid I have to admit that my interpretation was flawed.

As the waves retreated from the platform they had cut, beach deposits at about 5m above mean sea-level were abandoned on the platform. They were covered by a thin layer of peat whose pollen content indicated open woodland growing under relatively cool conditions. Cold got more severe, and fine-grained silts with some content of organic material were washed down over the peat. The silts contained some battered pollen, probably derived from the local soils, and as the pollens included fir and rhododendron, there obviously had been interglacial forests in the area. Coarser shaly debris then began to sludge down, and in this, at one horizon, there were large ice-striated boulders. These were the beginning of my downfall, because some distance to the west there was intercalated in the shaly debris a layer of poorly sorted glacial material which I mistook for primary till; if it was primary till, then the shaly debris was not all of the same age, but was divided into two by an ice-advance, and I elaborated on this idea in my paper.

When I later took an excursion party of dirt-men to the site, the tide was fully out, and when we went to the water's edge and looked back to the cliff my 'till' showed up as an isolated oval lens. There must have been old till further up the slope, and repeated freezing and thawing had moved this down as a tongue of debris without changing its structure very greatly, and the cliff-face showed very clearly a neat section across the tongue. The large ice-striated boulders were another version of the same thing. I capitulated at once. So Willie Warren places all the material above the beach in the last cold stage, to which he has given the name Fenitian. Tony Farrington called the material of the last cold stage Midlandian, as such deposits cover most of the midlands of Ireland. Willie regards the till below the beach at Ballybunnion as belonging to an older cold stage which he has termed Ballybunnionnian. Pete Coxon is re-examining the Fenit deposits, and is trying to get a uranium-thorium date for the peat; I had sent a sample for radiocarbon dating, but the answer was greater than 42,500 years, which only showed that the carbon in the sample had lost all its radioactivity.

Spa, as its name implies, was a place where the folk of Tralee went in the late eighteenth century to take the waters, and part of the old pump-house still remains. In the nineteenth century Tralee was an important British army base, and many officers lived in the vicinity of Spa. There are several large Victorian houses, and their names 'Frogmore', 'Kent', clearly indicate their political affiliations.

CHAPTER 16

# Dingle Peninsula

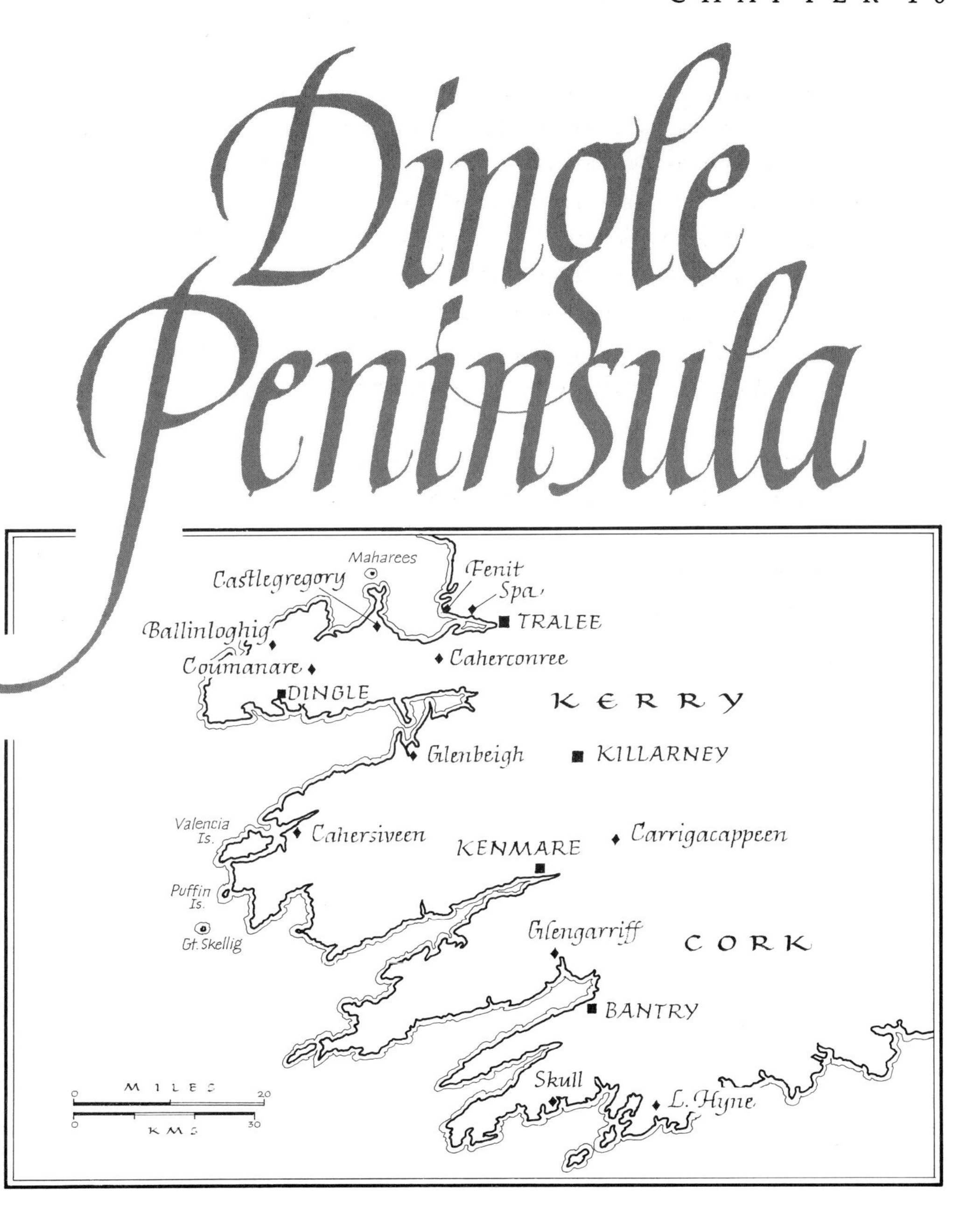


CAHERCONREE · MAHAREE ISLANDS

LOUGH ADOON · COUMANARE · BALLINLOGHIG

We pass through Tralee and turn west, and quickly come to Blennerville, a landlord's village with some pretty houses, at the east tip of Tralee Bay; a large windmill has been recently restored.

## Caherconree

We run west along the north foot of the Slieve Mish Mountains, and as we cross the mouth of a valley on our approach to Camp, we look south up the valley. Here on the left-hand slope, at a height of more than 600m, we see the wall of an inland promontory fort, perched on a projecting rock-nose. Small, but strongly defended, it raises the question of what was the function of Ireland's Iron Age promontory forts, best typified by Dun Aengus on Inishmore in the Aran Islands. Were they defensive or offensive? If defensive, as the details of their structure would seem to imply, who were the attackers? Caherconree is shrouded in mist for many days in the year, and the mist would provide a smoke-screen for advancing foes. I am ashamed to confess that for me the fort remains an elusive pot of gold, as three attempts to reach it were foiled by mist. I know it is stupid to think that in Kerry one can demand mist-free days, and that I should just have sat around until a clear day came, but I am afraid that a capacity to sit around is not part of my nature.

At Castlegregory we turn north out on a narrow promontory about 5km long. Its rock foundation is Carboniferous in age, a continuation of the rocks we last saw at Fenit, but this is largely buried by glacial deposits, in turn capped by a mass of enormous sand-dunes, which splits as it reaches two former islands, on which the small villages of Fahamore and Kilshannig sit. Until recently these villages were remote, and still carried on their farming in open undivided strip-fields, but now holiday-land has installed itself in the sand-dunes, and new houses and caravan-parks abound. Interesting juxtapositions in lifestyle are to be seen everywhere.

## Maharee Islands

Just to the north of the promontory there lies an archipelago, the Seven Hogs or Maharee Islands. These rock-rises are above sea-level, but between here and Fenit lie a host of similar rises, only shallowly submerged, and among them three which do break the surface. Were sea-level to drop by no more than 20m, we would see a spectacular limestone landscape, dissected by rock-pinnacles and turloughs. Near Fenit we have already looked at rock pinnacles which were too high to be submerged.

But southward moving ice did come here, as the beaches around Fahamore have many erratics from Mayo and Connemara. I made a collection, and Michael Max, then of the Irish Geological Survey, examined them microscopically, and was able to identify typical metamorphic rocks from Mayo among them. In addition, just north of Fahamore, one very large erratic sits on top of a knoll of glacial deposit. This is a block of granite, perhaps from Galway, almost three metres in diameter, sure evidence of long-distance ice-movement.

The island nearest to the shore, Illauntannig, has the well-preserved remains of a monastery. This is the first of a long chain of monasteries that extends south from here, at least 60km along the south-west corner of the Iveragh Peninsula, to Lamb's Head. There are coastal headlands with islands offshore, almost like an Aegean Sea turned inside out, and if we draw a line from Illauntannig to Lamb's Head we find west of that line an archipelago of monasteries which extend landwards on to the tips of the Dingle and Iveragh Peninsulas. One can picture busy ships criss-crossing this sea, a maritime ecclesiastical province. Here the sea was the means of communication, not a barrier. St Brendan was Ireland's first navigator, and he is well remembered in this area. His monastery is on the top of Mount Brandon, and on Valencia Island he is honoured by a well with crosses in its immediate vicinity. And so we can visualise a sort of consortium of monasteries, not a diocese, because the early Irish church had no bishops, but a group of various monastic units, varying in size from quite extensive monasteries, such as we see at Illauntannig, to one which consisted of no more than a surrounding wall, one oratory and one cell, as at Illaunloghan, beside Portmagee.

If we move further north, we see the same thing off the coasts of Connemara and Donegal. We can start with the Aran Islands, and continue in an almost unbroken chain to Tory Island, off the north-west corner of the country; inland monasteries are less frequent here, perhaps because most of the country was covered by inhospitable blanket-bog. The chains of monasteries are there, and if we like we can picture that the two chains, north and south, are linked at an anchor-point, St Senan's monastery on Scattery Island in the Shannon Estuary.

In the name, Illauntannig (Oileán tSeanaigh), and also in Kilshannig on the mainland nearby, we again meet St Senan. On Illauntannig there was plenty of space, and so the buildings are set in an area about 50m in diameter, protected by a massive drystone wall. It was an important monastery, and there are the remains of two small churches or oratories, three bee-hive huts, three small arrangements of vertical slabs, or *leachts*, perhaps marking the graves of important members of the community, a burial ground, and some cross slabs. At other places of similar importance a spacious level site was not available. At the Great Skellig the buildings are crowded together on the flank of a steep rock-ridge high above sea-level, and at Killabuonia, overlooking St Finan's Bay south of Portmagee, the buildings are scattered on a stepped hillslope.

*Illauntannig, Kerry. This important island monastery has several well-preserved features.*

As we approach Castlegregory on our return journey, Lough Gill lies on our right. This is a fairly large body of shallow water, dammed up by the coastal dunes. At certain times of the year it holds a good variety of birds, but more importantly it is the headquarters for Ireland's only toad, the natterjack toad (*Bufo calamita*), which is restricted to this part of Ireland. There is debate as to whether the toad was brought into the country relatively recently, or whether it has a long history here. Personally I believe that it came here in the general immigration of animals and plants that took place after the Ice Age ended. In 1979 it was proposed to lay out a golf course among the dunes, and environmental voices were raised in protest. But just how tangled such debates can be was well demonstrated, when it was recalled that sixty years ago there had been a golf course here, and that it was still possible to identify the sites of some of the greens.

## Lough Adoon

We continue on westwards, and at Kilcunmin bear left towards the Connor Pass. Four kilometres on we cross the small river that flows down from Lough Adoon to the east, and we leave the car here and walk upstream, across the bog-covered hillslope. After a short distance tributary streams come in from right and left, and we find ourselves in a magical area of former farmland, with huts and a network of field-walls, many still largely covered by bog. John Dodson, who has now moved to Australia, did a lot of work here, and he has shown that this settlement probably dates to about AD 1000, when there was farming, including cereal-growing, in the valley.

But people were here much earlier, as a rock-knoll between the main stream and a tributary carries an Early Bronze Age megalithic wedge-tomb. As the name implies, the structure is usually higher and wider at one end and was originally embedded in a stone cairn. At Dodson's sampling-site peat formation began about 3700 years ago, when the tomb was probably already in position, and the area was wooded. Some ground must already have been cleared for fields, as the lower layers of the peat contained pollen of cultivation. The area then became wetter and peat spread, but the return of drier conditions allowed Early Christian folk to colonise the valley. Later peat-growth has buried much of the settlement.

If we push on up to Lough Adoon, we can see the source of its name. A small island, close to the shore and only separated from it by shallow water, is protected on its landward side by a length of drystone walling, which creates a simple *dun* or fort.

Throughout our walk we can enjoy, if the day is clear, splendid views of the eastern ice-dissected slope of Mount Brandon. We return to the car and continue up the valley to the Connor Pass.

As we climb, evidence of former ice becomes more and more apparent all round us. Rock surfaces are rounded and deeply grooved by glacial striae, where stones at the base of the moving ice cut away the rock below. It was this overwhelming evidence of former glaciers that, almost one hundred and fifty years ago, convinced a visiting group of geologists that Ireland had once been covered by glacial ice. Water streams over the rocks around us and every crevice carries a plant of the fleshy-leaved St Patrick's cabbage (*Saxifraga spathularis*), a plant at home in the Pyrenees, which must have reached Ireland after the end of the Ice Age.

## COUMANARE

The top of the Pass is at 400m, and we leave the car in the car-park. Again, if the day is clear, we have a splendid view of Brandon Bay, hemmed in by mountains on either side. We walk to the east, out onto a flat tableland at Coumanare at about 550m. The area was formerly covered by blanket-bog, but this has largely been stripped away by erosion, leaving only some detached masses of peat. For almost a century it has been known that the bare area is strewn with short sticks of yew wood, about 15cm long and pointed at both ends. Where peat survives they are very occasionally found embedded near the base of the peat. I have never seen one *in situ*, but in 1945 Arthur Stelfox did find one, and he took a set of pollen-samples for me.

The basal layers of the peat had quite large quantities of pine pollen, but this fell away to insignificant values just at the level of the stick. Radiocarbon dating now tells us that pine fell to very low levels in Ireland about 4000 years ago, and it is probable that the points are of this age. If I could find a point *in situ*, I would send it off for radiocarbon dating. From Dodson's work down in the valley we also know that Early Bronze Age peoples were farming in the area at this time, and indeed the base of the peat at Coumanare contains pollen associated with cultivation. The points thus belong to the Early Bronze Age.

What were they used for? I can only think that the points were used in association with wooden deer-traps, of which several specimens are known from Irish bogs. The trap was a heavy plank of wood, pierced by a hole containing a spring device. If a deer put a hoof through the hole, the spring snapped and the leg was trapped. If a band of sharp wooden points was set up across the bog, it would serve as a cattle-grid. Deer would not cross it, but would wander along it till they reached a gap, across which a trap would be set. In those days herds of red deer probably travelled over the uplands, and occasional animals would be caught.

From the pass we run down into the town of Dingle, which sits on the side of an almost land-locked bay. This was the only safe harbour between Valencia and Galway, and the town has a long sea-faring tradition. From the hill-top, Brandon Peak, just south of Mount Brandon, a long rock-ridge runs south-west; it rises into Mount Eagle, and continues on into the Great Blasket Island. It makes road communication with the north-west tip of the peninsula very difficult. The picturesque route follows the coast, round Slea Head at the foot of Mount Eagle, but we turn almost due north from Dingle, up the valley of the Milltown river.

## Ballinloghig

We cross the ridge, and come immediately to a small lake below to the left, not far from Ballinloghig. I had long marked this out as a place likely to hold an extended vegetational record in its sediments, so I was delighted when Cathy Whitlock, now of the University of Oregon, went there with her drill in the early 1980s. She went through a deep deposit, which contained at its base a record of the final cold snap of the Ice Age, that we have already seen at Ballybetagh. So even the south-west corner of Ireland, which today is almost frost-free, knew arctic conditions as recently as 11,000 years ago. I feel that the natterjack toad and the spotted slug (*Geomalachus maculosus*)—another Kerry special, today otherwise only occurring in Portugal and the Pyrenees—must then have been far, far away.

Ballinloghig itself is a small house-cluster on the east of the road a little further on. A track leads through the houses towards the Feohanagh valley, which ends in a corrie below Brandon Peak. Surprisingly the road gets better. This is due to the fact that some of the shots for the film *Ryan's Daughter* were taken here, and the road had to be made up to give access to the equipment. I stumbled in here when there was a low cloud ceiling, so that nothing but the bare cliffed rock-walls of the valley were to be seen; no trees, no bushes; the quality of the light meant that everything, cloud-base and rock alike, was grey or black; it seemed as if the valley could only lead to some demons' dwelling round the corner (Pl. 4).

I looked towards the stream and saw large tree stumps, oak and pine almost 1m in diameter, which had been revealed by peat-cutting, and were themselves rooted in peat. I went over and inspected them, and as I looked a kaleidoscope of the vegetational changes which the now bare valley had seen passed in front of me. Barren tundra gradually being clothed in woodland, trees being slowly choked by developing bog, drier conditions enabling trees to colonise the bog surface, a second disappearance of trees perhaps assisted by human hands, and now bare rock walls rising from heath and bog, a picture that we could see in parts of Lapland today.

# CHAPTER 17

# South West Kerry

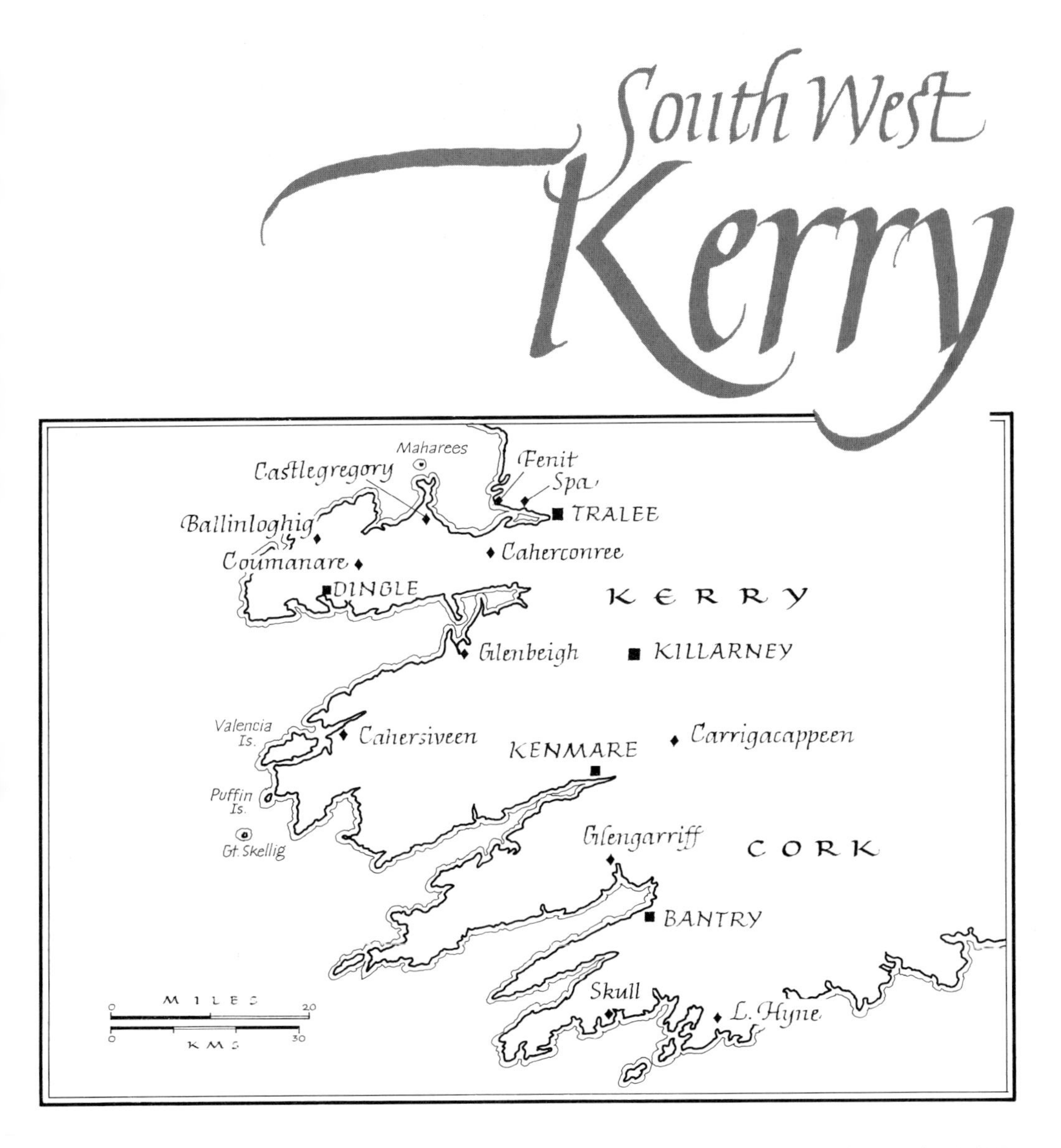


BEHY VALLEY · EN ROUTE TO VALENCIA ISLAND

GREAT SKELLIG · VALENCIA ISLAND

ISLAND MONASTERIES · PORTMAGEE TO BALLINSKELLIGS

PUFFIN ISLAND · BALLINSKELLIGS · CARRIGACAPPEEN

## Behy Valley

We return to Dingle, and then turn eastwards, keeping as close to the coast as we can. As we approach Inch the road rises a little, and we get a splendid view of the huge spit with dunes that runs south from Inch, and also of the two spits that stretch out from the south shore, and guard the entrance to the tidal Castlemaine harbour. We continue on to the village of the same name, and here we make a hairpin turn and set out along the south shore of Dingle Bay in the Iveragh Peninsula.

We pass through Killorglin, and on the next stretch of road from Killorglin to Glenbeigh we have splendid views across bog to the great mountain mass of Carrauntoohill, Ireland's highest summit at 1040m. We get a glimpse of Caragh Lake, and carry on to the village of Glenbeigh. Here we make a turn to the left, and drive up into the valley of the Behy River.

If we eat half an avocado pear with a spoon, we end up with the gutted empty skin; if we do the same with a pear, and tilt the gutted skin a little to the north-east, then we have an outline model of the Behy valley. It falls to the north-east, surrounded by a rim of higher ground, which rises into cliffs on the south-west side, and then constricts and narrows the valley, only allowing the river a narrow exit to Glenbeigh, just where the stalk of the pear would be attached to the fruit. In the Ice Age corries were cut into the high ground to the south-west, and from these glaciers, which gradually coalesced into a small ice-sheet, flowed down the valley. When the ice melted away, its snout shrank backwards in intermittent steps, leaving a rim of melted-out gravel, a moraine, at each stage of pause. Ultimately it shrank right back into the corries themselves, leaving the corrie mouths blocked by little crescentic moraines. Thus the valley, as well as being remote, beautiful and largely undisturbed, also provides a textbook illustration of the stages of retreat of a small ice-sheet.

In 1988 the valley was the scene of a curious planning battle. The European Community is very concerned, not unnaturally, about the ultimate exhaustion of the earth's supply of fossil fuels, and it is anxious to develop schemes to produce energy from renewable natural resources. Accordingly there are generous European grants available for the development of hydro-electric plants. This opportunity caught the eye of the Electricity Supply Board, who decided that the little lakes, perched high in the corries at the head of the Behy Valley, would be suitable water-storage sites. Admittedly the lakes are very small, and the amount of flow could not be expected to generate more than about 500kW of power, probably about enough to supply the demand of one large luxury hotel.

Another attraction was that the power produced would be three-phase, more powerful than that available in Glenbeigh at present. But as Killorglin, only 12km away to the east, has three-phase power, it would have seemed a simpler plan to run an extra wire out from Killorglin, without the elaboration of a hydro-electric scheme.

A scheme was presented to Kerry County Council, which granted planning permission, subject to certain conditions. Objections on environmental grounds were immediately lodged, both by Bord Fáilte, who did not wish to see the attractive remoteness of the valley disturbed, and by walking groups, one of whose favourite routes was around the high rim which formed the perimeter of the valley. I was asked by Bord Fáilte to support their protest, and a list of objections was drawn up.

A public hearing was arranged in Tralee in the spring of 1988, but then a very dramatic development took place. On his way to present Bord Fáilte's case, their representative was flagged down as he passed through Limerick, only to be told that the minister responsible for the Board had directed that the objection must be withdrawn. This deprived the opposition case of a powerful spokesman, and also left me rather high and dry. However, I was co-opted to be a member of the mountain group, and took my place at the hearing with the other protesters.

Apart from the general objection that one of Ireland's few remaining 'wilderness' areas was about to be invaded by development, particular points of objection were the construction of obtrusive dams across the mouths of the lakes, the disturbance of the natural vegetation during the construction period, and the erection of power-lines in the valley.

We questioned the economics of the scheme, as the ESB already has more generating power available than is necessary for the current level of consumption. But the arithmetic presented by the ESB appeared to run as follows: a substantial grant to cover part of the costs was available from the European Commission; the balance would have to be borrowed by the Board, and the interest incurred paid; but if all the electricity produced by the scheme was separately sold to consumers in Glenbeigh, the money thus raised would pay the charges on the loan, and therefore there would be no increased net cost to the Board. We suggested that this calculation was flawed as there was already current generally available at a price less than that to be charged by the scheme.

When we went into the hearing we thought that the material necessary for the dams would be obtained in the immediate vicinity of the corries themselves. Then it transpired that that was not to be the case, but that the construction material was to be carried up from the valley below. We asked where the material was to come from, and we were told it would be taken from the gravel ridges in the valley. We asked if planning permission for a quarry had been sought, and we were told no, it was not necessary, as they were not exactly going to quarry, they were just going to scrape what they wanted off the tops of the gravel ridges. We pointed out that this would destroy the form of the morainic ridges, and so this classic example of glacial geology would be seriously disturbed.

The gravel would have to be transported from the valley floor up across the bog-covered slopes to the lakes above, and Kerry County Council had inserted a curious, but laudable, planning condition. The condition was that vehicles carrying the gravel must have very broad tracks and very wide tyres, and must not cross the same area of bog more than once, in order to avoid serious damage to the vegetation of the bog. But the corrie approach was very narrow, and a certain quantity of material had to be transported, and it soon became apparent that if all the trips proposed were laid side by side, there would not be sufficient width in the valley to get the material up without crossing the same area of bog more than once.

I am glad to say that after patiently listening to the evidence all day, the inspector advised against the proposal, and the permission granted was rescinded by An Bord Pleanála.

We leave the Behy Valley by a crossroad leading north-west, and soon join the road that is climbing up the ridge on the north side of the valley, before crossing it to reach the coast, with splendid views of Dingle Bay and the mountains and islands beyond. We follow the coast for some distance, and then the road swings inland into very different country.

## En Route to Valencia Island

We soon enter a long straight valley, running north-east/south-west, and leading on to Cahersiveen and Valencia Harbour. On the north-east side of the valley the ground rises in a steep straight slope, which reaches its highest point in Knocknadobar (690m). To the south there is very different country indeed, and geologists consider that the contrast is due to a major fault which runs down the valley and separates the two types of terrain.

We look across into two great horse-shoe-shaped flats, each surrounded by a rim of higher ground, with a sharp break in slope where the flat meets the rim. Here again is the kind of feature that I feel cannot have been brought about by the types of erosion that are going on at present; what we see are two fossil etch-plains, shaped by different processes millions of years ago. And indeed it was this unusual topography here that first aroused my interest in the geomorphology of this part of Ireland. We pass through Cahersiveen, and 2km further on we make a sharp turn to the right, which quickly brings us down to the edge of Valencia Harbour at Reenard Point.

## Valencia Island

At Reenard we see Knightstown directly ahead of us, with the sweep of the Portmagee Channel that separates the island from the mainland on our left, and Valencia Harbour, one of the finest anchorages in the British Isles, on our right. Centre to it, and protecting it, is Beginish with its satellite, Church Island, to its east.

But what we do not see is the bridge that ought to link us to the island at Knightstown. There is a bridge, but to reach it we must drive 15km along one side of the channel to Portmagee, and then back along the island another 7km to reach Knightstown. If we take the cost of a bridge in isolation, then arithmetic would point to Portmagee as the site. But if we place the bridge in a wider socio-economic setting, then it should have been at Knightstown, and not Portmagee. Placing it at Portmagee ruined Knightstown and the island, without bringing much advantage to Portmagee, which is by-passed by the approach to the bridge.

Knightstown is a carefully planned nineteenth-century village, nestling at the foot of the high ground of the island, and looking out to splendid views of the Kerry hills. Given a bridge, it would lie only 3km from the Ring of Kerry circuit, which runs from Killarney round the Iveragh Peninsula. Hundreds of tourist cars and dozens of tourist buses trundle round the Ring every day in the summer, and many would break their trip in Knightstown, just as they do in Sneem later in the day. Knightstown and the whole island would be awakened from the torpor into which it has sunk.

I find it very hard to write about Valencia except in terms of 'the smile and the tear'. 'The smile' because of Des and Pat Lavelle, who in their houses in Cable Terrace—a relic from the days when the island was an important cable-station—give their guests the most sincere welcome in Ireland. Des is almost a merman; put him on board his boat, the *Béal Bocht*, and he becomes part of it. If he said 'I filled the boat up this morning, and we are not going to the Skelligs today, but to the Canaries', I would go without a qualm. He is equally at home under water, and runs a Diving Centre to which divers come from all over the world to be guided by him to the underwater wonders of the area. Pat provides the welcome in Cable Terrace, where everything is in apple-pie order, and good food is abundant. Their daughters chime in on the same wave-length. Nothing that can be done to help visitors is left undone.

Sometimes when I am eating my dinner in Cable Terrace, looking out at the channel, the Irish Lights vessel, *Granuaile*, anchors in front of the window. I should like to have been one of the Commissioners, and to have made an annual trip round the Irish lighthouses. I would have learned a lot about the islands they stand on, and my knowledge of geology might have been of some practical use. But on committees I tend to be a member of the awkward squad, and poke my nose into matters that the establishment would prefer to leave undisturbed.

It was quite some time after I had joined the Council of the Dublin Zoo in the early forties that I discovered that the Society had rules, a matter of which most members of the Council were unaware. I asked some questions arising out of the rules, and was promptly made secretary for my pains. I had the job for many years, and was quite happy in it, because in those days the zoo was a fun place, enjoyed by visitors, staff and, I believe, the animals themselves. Today, alas, the zoo is a beleaguered island, beset from many sides. But as I survey the *Granuaile*, I congratulate myself that I am probably enjoying a better dinner ashore than aboard.

I know Valencia well because I worked there for twelve years—often staying a month at a time—chiefly trying to trace the archaeological features that were swallowed up by the growth of peat, and later partly revealed by turf-cutting over a long period of time. The island is extraordinarily rich in antiquities, which stretch from the arrival of Mesolithic peoples about 6500 years ago to the industrial archaeology, quarries, cable-stations and lighthouses of the past century. I have written about this in my book *Man and Environment on Valencia Island*, published in 1989.

Valencia has splendid high cliffs both at Bray Head on the west and Fogher on the north coast. Slumps and rockfalls repeatedly occur. The cliffs are clearly unstable, and in them I see evidence for my theory that there has been recent tectonic movement in south-west Ireland.

I have walked the island's boggy slopes from end to end, enjoying the wonderful views it affords of the Dingle Peninsula, the mountains of Kerry, the line of hills south of Portmagee, and not least the Skelligs to the west. At a personal level I enjoy its loneliness and its emptiness; I know no greater pleasure than to lie at a chosen point on its northern slope, with not a building, not even a ruin, in sight, looking out to the Blaskets, watching the ravens and the choughs playing above me, and hoping for a glimpse of a peregrine (Pl. 5).

But 'the tear' has to come when I realise that the emptiness I love has brought disaster to the island, whose population has fallen without interruption since 1841, and still continues a slow decline. The building of the bridge at Portmagee has turned the island into a suburb of Cahersiveen, and its farming has been reduced to the filling of milk quotas. The demand for milk meant a demand for more grass, and the expansion of grassland up hitherto undisturbed slopes has destroyed many relics of the past. But there is a demand from a growing number of tourists for lonely landscapes and walks uninterrupted by traffic, and to these Valencia can offer many opportunities. Such demand should be judiciously encouraged, but the island cannot really live on tourism alone.

## GREAT SKELLIG

So much has been written about the Skelligs, the Little Skellig with its massive gannet colony, and the Great Skellig with its remarkable monastic ruins dedicated to St Michael, that it is difficult to know what I can add. I recommend Des Lavelle's splendid book, *Skellig; Island Outpost of Europe*, and will largely confine myself to geology.

We have seen that south-west Ireland was subject to tremendous Hercynide compressive forces, and that the folds into which the bedded layers of rock were crumpled have since been dissected into ridges and valleys by prolonged erosion. In the crumpling a *cleavage*, that is a tendency to split, not at random but more readily in one direction than in others, was impressed upon them, giving rise to *slate* in many places. The rocks were further disturbed either by breaking across the beds to give *joints*, or by being translocated along *faults*. Most visitors are struck by the fantastic rock-shapes into which the Skelligs have been cut by erosion, and this was directed by the intersections of bedding, cleavage, jointing and faulting that run through the rocks. As progressive erosion slowly removed thicknesses of rock, the pressure of weight on the underlying rocks was gradually eased. As a result these rocks expanded—

*Great Skellig, Kerry. Vertical aerial photograph of the Great Skellig; the monastic remains are seen towards the lower right side of the picture.*

taking as it were a deep breath—and the cracks which had been imposed on them during earth movements opened out as joints.

If we look at the overall shape of the Great Skellig, it looks like two cones joined by a common slope on the south–east side, but divided by a deep wedge-shaped gash, Blue Cove, on the north-west. A great fault runs north–south right through the island along the east face of Blue Cove, and a second, which forms the west face of the Cove, runs south-east to meet it.

I could see no evidence that an ice-sheet had ever stretched out from the mainland to the Great Skellig, but it has been subjected to severe frost attack. Freezing water will have expanded in the joints and faults, prising the rock apart. When the ice melted detached blocks of rock slipped away down slope, leaving jagged outlines and pinnacles above, and gradually forming the conical profile of the island. The detached blocks built up slopes of scree which lay against the flanks of the island. The rock material that lay between the two faults was especially susceptible to attack, and as it slumped down it was gradually removed by the waves to create the modern Blue Cove.

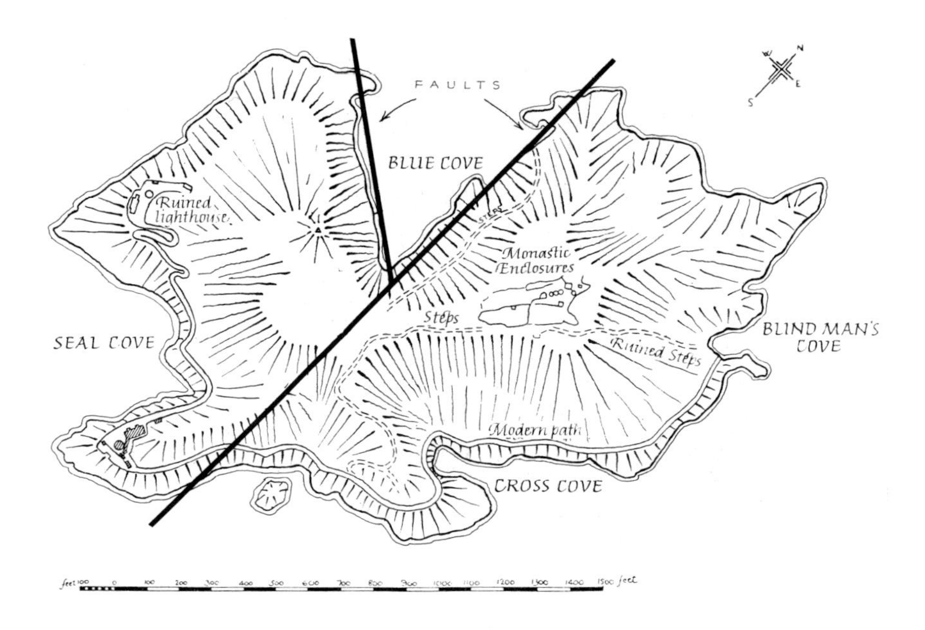


*Great Skellig, Kerry. Map of the Great Skellig, indicating the position of two major geological faults.*

Sea-level was lower than it is today, and the apron of scree ran right down to the sea-floor. Its rock fragments gradually became cemented together, and, when the waves of returning sea-level cut away most of the apron, some of that which lay above the modern waves survived, and we can still see patches of it today. At many points we can see perched blocks in 'impossible' situations; at one time they were surrounded by scree, but when this wasted away, they were left abandoned where we see them today. The whole island, and also the Little Skellig, are monuments to the efficacy of former frost action.

I was very fortunate to have a good opportunity to study the geology, because I was at the Great Skellig at a time when Walter Horn, Professor of Fine Art in Berkeley University, was making a detailed survey of the monastic remains on the island. Walter was lodging on the island, and he made room for me in the hut for a few nights. Unfortunately there were violent gusts of wind every night, and I was afraid to venture out, so I had lost a chance to see the storm petrels and the shearwaters returning to their burrows in the late evening. But it was splendid to have the daytime opportunity to see the other birds undisturbed by visitors; the birds appeared to know well the moment the first boat of the day disgorged its load.

*Great Skellig, Kerry. Bedding and cleavage can be seen in the rocks on either side of the picture; their jagged outlines are due to frost shattering. When alternate freezing and thawing was active, finer material sludged down the central gully between the rocks; today it lies in a stationary ribbon.*

I say nothing about the monastery perched against the sky, except that to visit it is an indefinable experience, which should be savoured in solitude, if possible. This leads immediately to the growing problem of tourism, as every year more and more people want to visit the island. In summer there can be as many as eight boats a day, each carrying about a dozen people, and all forced to arrive at about the same time because of the distance from land. Can the island, with little water and no sanitary facilities, carry one hundred visitors at one time? There must be guide control, but too much marshalling robs the visit of all sense of experience. Lavatories could be erected, but their final discharge must be into the sea, and the winter waves would make short work of the exit pipes. Control gates erected by the Office of Public Works to prevent unauthorised landings were swept away by the first gales. As at the great passage-grave at Newgrange, too much popularity brings special problems.

There is also another experience, but unfortunately it cannot be arranged to order. There are days in June when the return trip with Des is such an experience. The sun is shining, the wind has been blowing and the seas are still high, but now the wind has slackened and the waves are smoothing out. The foam that was whipped off the waves has settled into lazy ribbons. Gannets are diving all around, and there are lots of other birds to be seen. The *Béal Bocht* goes gently lolloping on, and I find it impossible not to feel, as I did at Goodland, that God *is* in his heaven, and that all *is* well with the world.

## Island Monasteries

The monastery at the Great Skellig lies in isolation about 12km offshore. I have already spoken of how monasteries are common on the islands and shores of south-west Kerry. They are particularly abundant in and around the water that separates Valencia from the mainland.

On our return trip we pass near the entrance to the Portmagee Channel, with Long Island on our right. For more than one hundred years the local 6-inch Ordnance Survey map has shown a tiny circle at its eastern end, labelled 'Burial Ground'. There the matter rested until late on an April afternoon in 1984 when Daphne Pochin Mould, who has discovered from the air and photographed so many interesting features, both archaeological and geological, looked down and saw a range of structures clearly visible in the short spring grass. She alerted me, and later in the same summer Des, with some difficulty, put me ashore on the island; tidal currents run very strongly in the channels around it, and opportunity does not knock very often. The site must be a monastery, as it has ruins of an oratory, huts and other features. It has since been examined by the South-West Kerry survey group.

As we run up to Portmagee we pass a tiny island, Illaunloghan, which can be reached by wading at low spring tides. Here we have a tiny monastic site, with one oratory, one hut, one souterrain and one tomb-shaped shrine. Was it the retreat of a hermit? If so, he must have had help during its construction.

We pass on up the channel, with Valencia Island on our left, which certainly had several monasteries, though these are difficult to plot in detail owing to the continued use of the sites as graveyards. They are now crowded with hundreds of small erect marker-slabs, which obscure older features. There is another slender chain of monastic sites along the mainland shore.

As we pass Knightstown, Beginish lies ahead of us. Again a ruined monastery, with huts and oratory, lies near the shore. Some little distance away, on a promontory at the east end of the island, Brian O'Kelly excavated a village of simple stone houses with an associated field-system. The lintel stone of one house was a re-used slab which carried a Viking inscription in runes of eleventh-century style. The settlement may perhaps be of this age. Though very different, the Runic letters were organised on the same principle as the letters of the Ogham alphabet.

From Beginish a sand-bar, passable at low spring tide, runs out to a tiny island, Church Island, about half a hectare in extent. Here stone buildings replaced earlier wooden ones, and there was an oratory, two houses, a tomb-shrine and a cross-slab to which an Ogham inscription had been later added.

To erect the stone buildings of these monastic sites required a certain amount of labour, a large amount of construction material, and a very considerable amount of skill in drystone construction methods. As the monasteries were so close together, it would be very interesting to have some idea of how large the local Christian community was, and how the building teams were organised, as it is hard not to think that the area was rather over-supplied with monastic establishments. If the monasteries were only open to men, what did all the local women do?

## Portmagee to Ballinskelligs

At Portmagee we turn south and enter the floor of another etch-plain, rather smaller than the ones we saw as we were coming down into Cahersiveen. This one is again horse-shoe-shaped, and surrounded by a rim of high ground which rises abruptly from it. The rim on the west side is now at the edge of the sea, and has been very deeply cut into by wave action, which has produced a line of unstable cliffs that gradually rise to a height of 300m. This is the etch-plain I know best, as I have walked backwards and forwards across it many times. It is floored by rock, which slopes northwards at an angle of only two degrees; it is a feature which cannot have been produced by today's processes of erosion.

Our road soon leaves the flat ground and starts to climb up the surrounding ridge, and although it mounts the slope diagonally, the gradient is nonetheless very steep. From the car-park at the top we have a splendid view, with Valencia Island and the Dingle Peninsula to the north, and to the south across St Finan's Bay to the Kenmare Estuary and the mountainous peninsulas which guard it.

## PUFFIN ISLAND

Our road descends the far side of the ridge by a series of hairpin bends; we do not take the third bend, but continue on down a lane, and sweep round a bend to the right, where we get a splendid view of the Skelligs. Immediately below us we have Puffin Island. In principle, the island is a larger version of the Great Skellig, being about three times its size. As in Skellig it has two summits, separated by a great east–west fault system, and a wedge-shaped mass of rock has been cut out of its western side, just as we have Blue Cove on Skellig. Puffin Island is also cut by a line of north–south faults, and wedge-shaped bites have been taken out at each end. The cliffs in the north bite are unstable, and there had been a big fall shortly before I first visited the island. Soon, in geological terms, the island will be cut into three separate units.

Jagged, frost-shattered features are not as pronounced on Puffin Island as on the Skelligs, and this may be because ice must once have reached the island. I saw ice-transported erratics to a height of 100m, and the ice may well have reached still higher levels.

There is abundant evidence of the power of the waves around these islands during winter storms. In December 1955 on the Great Skellig a wave broke the glass of the lighthouse which stood 55m above the sea. On the north-west side of Puffin Island, where the cliffs face the open sea, there are on the cliff-edge, at a height of about 30m, low ridges built up of wave-thrown stones, some of which are more than 30cm in length.

The Irish name of the island is Oileán na gCanóg, that is Shearwater Island, whereas the English name is Puffin Island. However, both birds are very common, and the givers of the names may have had different preferences. Storm petrels are also abundant, and there are many other birds on the cliffs. Happily the island now belongs to the Irish Wildbird Conservancy, and is a protected nature reserve.

In contrast to the Great Skellig, and, as we have seen, many of the other local islands, there is no evidence of substantial monastic activity. I could only find one small enclosure, about 50m square, with a circular hut, a pile of heat-shattered stones and a simple standing-stone inside it. Nearby there were some field-banks.

We return to the hairpin bend and drop down into St Finan's Bay. We can if we like make a short detour to Killabuonia at the head of the valley. Here is an extensive monastic site which is almost as little-known as the Great Skellig is famous. Scattered across some rock-ledges at the foot of the hillslope is a loose group of buildings, which, if crowded together as on Skellig, would be just as numerous. The site calls out for detailed planning and general investigation.

## BALLINSKELLIGS

Across another ridge, and we arrive in Ballinskelligs. Here on the shore are the rather featureless remains of a large church or 'abbey', where the monks from the Great Skellig are said to have settled after the island was abandoned. From the church a high spit of small boulders, out of reach of modern waves, runs north for a short distance; there is a small castle at its tip. The stones of the spit, like those of the beaches at Castlegregory, include far-travelled stones among which Galway granite can be identified. Some years ago at a short distance to the south of the church, Francis Synge found a boulder of Galway granite 1m in diameter sitting on the beach at about high-tide level; it was still there on my last visit.

In the late nineteenth century, when it was first recognised that great ice-sheets had travelled for considerable distances, carrying with them pieces of the different bedrocks over which they had passed, great attention was paid to erratics. The British Association had a special committee to record them. At that time it was thought that tracing erratics back to their source would give a clear indication of the route taken by the ice.

But more work has shown that successive ice-sheets moved in different directions, and an erratic may have had a spasmodic zig-zag course before reaching the spot where we find it today. Also floating ice-rafts, with boulders incorporated in them, may have carried erratics to points far beyond the ice-limits. Thus the evidence erratics offer has to be assessed with caution.

Nonetheless I continued my hunt at Ballinskelligs, and found a piece of black volcanic rock, which looked rather like the basalt that occurs in County Antrim at the Giant's Causeway and elsewhere. In the Atlantic Ocean west of the Galway coasts, a great deal of oil exploration is going on, and basalt is known from the Porcupine Bank, a relatively raised area of the sea-floor. If the piece of rock I found was from this phase of volcanic activity, then it ought to have an age of about 70 million years. I got thin slices of the rock cut for petrological examination, and showed these to Professor Mohr in Galway and Professor Stillman in Trinity College. They said that while the rock was a basalt, its mineralogical make-up showed that it could not come from north-west Europe, which lay at the margin of the volcanic activity, but must have a more continental origin.

This intrigued me, and I decided to get a radioactive date for it. Potassium breaks down into argon over a period of millions of years, not like radioactive carbon which largely disappears in about 40,000 years. Thus the potassium/argon method deals in millions of years, and measures its ages not in single years but in units of about 100,000 years. I sent the specimen off, expecting an answer of about 70 million years, and got back a reply to say it was so young it could not give a detailed date, but was unlikely to be more than 200,000 years old.

Then the penny dropped; some ship, quite possibly from Italy, carrying among its ballast boulders of Vesuvian lava, must have thrown some ballast overboard at Ballinskelligs. Over the past thousands of years there has been almost continuous volcanic activity around Naples, and the rock I found in Kerry is very similar to the type of continental basalt that Vesuvius produces today. The ballast possibility is really a very plausible one, because during the excavations on the foreshore of the Liffey at Wood Quay several boulders of Scandinavian rocks were found, presumably ballast from Viking ships. The result of my Ballinskelligs adventure is that I now look at erratics with even added caution.

We run round the shore of the bay to Waterville, where we make a short visit to the entrance lobby of the Butler Arms Hotel to see its myriads of photographs of Charlie Chaplin, who with some typical quirk chose to spend several holidays there. Here we re-join the Ring of Kerry and drive along the north shore of Kenmare Bay to the town of that name.

## Carrigacappeen

In my later schooldays and in college I had a friend, Jimmy Wells, a medical student, who—alas—was killed at Caen with the Royal Army Medical Corps. His father was a scholarly type of man, who curiously enough had spent his life as a bank inspector, and I am sure did his work more thoroughly than those whose accounts he examined would have wished. He collected early books on Irish natural history, and had a copy of Threlkeld's botany, published in 1727.

I attempted to follow him, and took to visiting the book barrows which were then in the lanes off Aston's Quay. I can remember getting a copy of White's *Natural History of Selbourne* for 3d. I soon started to come across odd bound volumes of the *Irish Naturalist*, which carried nature papers and notes of general Irish interest, but had ceased publication in the early 1920s. I gradually got most of the volumes, and Tony Farrington told me where back numbers could be obtained, so I was able to build up a complete set. There were valuable bird records scattered through it, and I ultimately gave the set to the Irish Wildbird Conservancy. Leafing through a volume one day in search of a reference I suddenly saw an illustration of a boulder perched on a pedestal, and as the text said the site gave 'a striking example of denudation by solution since the Glacial Epoch', I had to go to see it.

The site at Carrigacappeen lies just north of the Kenmare/Athgarvan road, about 5km north-east of Kenmare. It is some little distance north of the road, just beside the abandoned railway track. Local people know it, and it is best to ask for the easiest route, because the whole area is covered by dense scrub. My hopes were high as I made my way towards it, as I crossed an area of bare limestone, much fretted by solution. But when I found it, I felt it was just too good to be true.

The perched sandstone boulder is over 2m long and 1m deep, and does I am sure weigh about thirty tonnes. The pedestal of solid limestone on which it is poised is 1.5m high, squarish in cross-section, with sides of about 1m wide. As far as I could see the top on which the boulder rests is striated. The limestone in the immediate vicinity is generally at the same level as that from which the pedestal rises, and has a lightly fluted surface. On the west side the flutes run below the boulder, up to the very base of the pedestal.

*Carrigacappeen, nr. Kenmare, Kerry. As ice melted away 18,000 years ago, this erratic boulder of sandstone came to rest on a relatively even limestone surface. Since then, solution by rainfall has removed 1.5m of limestone, except where it was protected by the erratic, which now stands perilously perched.*

Ice probably disappeared from the area about 16,000 years ago, when the boulder appears to have been deposited on a striated surface. Can 1.5m of limestone have been dissolved away in that short time? Joe Jennings, an authority on karstic features, writing about perched blocks in his textbook *Karst Geomorphology*, says: 'A method that commands much confidence, if not a great degree of precision, is the use of pedestals that have formed beneath glacial erratics on limestone pavements scoured by ice in the last glacial maximum and lowered by solution since, except under their protection.' He quotes values for surface lowering of 15cm in the Burren, and of 50cm in Yorkshire, but these values fall far short of the 150cm at Carrigacappeen. Perhaps the very great degree of solution at Carrigacappeen reflects the high rainfall and the high mean annual temperature of south-west Ireland. If, as seems must be the case, the surface of the limestone here has been lowered by 150cm in the past 18,000 years, it makes the apparent lack of surface solution at Pollnahallia all the more difficult to understand.

The site is one of the seven wonders of Ireland; I urge my readers to go and see it for themselves.

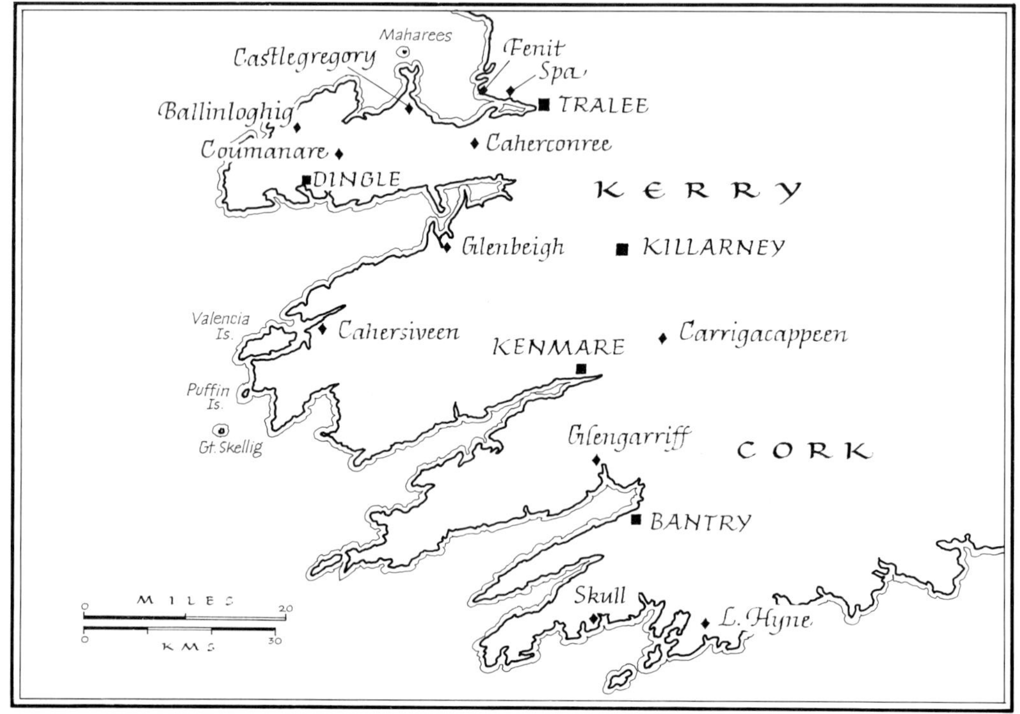


# CHAPTER 18

GLENGARRIFF · SKULL

LOUGH HYNE · SOUTH CORK UPLANDS

## GLENGARRIFF

We return to Kenmare and take the winding road up the valley of the Sheen River and over the Caha Mountains to Glengarriff. As we curve over the hills we are everywhere surrounded by bare rock, much cut away and deeply moulded by the passage of recent ice, as the stone here is fine-grained and relatively soft. Not sufficient time has passed for soil to form, and only scattered rugs of blanket-bog partly cover the rock. My purpose in Glengarriff is a nostalgic one, to visit not a ghost town, but a ghost hotel, Roche's.

In college in the thirties I made another friend, Cecil Allberry, who was reading physics, and went on to a successful career with ICI. Cecil's mother had been born Bessy Roche, and was a daughter of the hotel which was then managed by her sister May, who had married a Cork solicitor named Flynn. May ran the hotel in a very open-handed style, and developed into a character, known far and wide in the British Navy as 'Auntie May'. In previous years British warships had lain at anchor in the bays of south-west Ireland, and the dispense bar in Roche's, where Auntie May presided, was a favourite haunt, decorated with caps, bells and other souvenirs from visiting ships.

Members of the Allberry family stayed in the hotel at token rates, and this privilege was quickly extended to me. In fact Auntie May's chief failing as a hotelier was that it was more important to her to give her guests good food and drink than to see that an adequate charge was made for her bounty. The fuller the hotel was, the less profit was made, and this led ultimately to financial collapse.

As soon as lectures ended in early March and the hotel re-opened for St Patrick's Day, Cecil and I would drive down in my elderly car and we would stay for a week or more. For us the chief attraction was Jimmy Flynn, the eldest son of the house. Jimmy was a born naturalist, with a special interest in birds, and the three of us, with a generous lunch in the car, would head out down the Beara Peninsula to tramp its mountains or wander round its lakes. It was my first introduction to untrammelled wandering, and in addition to revelling in the countryside, I learned a great deal of natural history from Jimmy.

My friendship with him and my visits to Glengarriff continued after Cecil had gone to England. One of our outings in 1943 made Irish ornithological history. On a bright frosty December morning we set out for the grounds of Glengarriff Lodge to shoot woodcock, as Jimmy thought the severe weather would have brought the birds in to the holly woods. I should add that Jimmy, who was a crack shot, would bring the birds down, while I would discharge harmless salvoes in their general direction.

Just inside the entrance gates a telephone wire crossed the avenue to a gate lodge, and there was a small bird which had struck the wires lying dead below them. I picked it up as a goldcrest, but then I saw the white eyestripe and passed it to Jimmy who also saw the stripe and said firecrest. And so it was, Ireland's first and only specimen of the bird, now in the Natural History Museum in Dublin. With more and better bird-watchers about, occasional firecrests were seen in south-west Ireland in the twenty years that followed. Since 1961 there has been a general expansion of the firecrest in Europe, and it has now been spotted in almost every Irish county. When I made my pilgrimage in 1989, the telephone post was still there, but the wire had gone.

The hotel did not survive the war, and the family was dispersed. Jimmy and his brother Teddy went to work at Ford's in Dagenham, and their sister Mary went to the catering section of the Coal Board in Horsham. I lost touch with them, but I cannot help feeling that Jimmy must have felt the exchange of Dagenham for Glengarriff a severe cultural shock. The hotel was sold to CIE, who demolished it, and asked Michael Scott, the distinguished architect, to design a successor. But the project never got beyond Michael's drawing-board, and Michael had considerable difficulty in collecting his fees. Since the demolition, sand and gravel have been quarried from the site, which is now a deplorable wasteland. After ferreting around for some time I did find the steps from the driveway down into the garden, and with my bearings established I soon found the foundations of the porch. It is a shame that the site was never re-developed, because the windows of the porch, where we often sat, looked out on one of the finest views in Ireland, with the Sugarloaf Mountain as the centre-piece and the water of Bantry Bay to the left. The view was at its best in early April, on occasions when the conical top of the mountain was carrying a light dusting of snow, and sunlight was dancing on it.

## SKULL

The slopes of Mount Gabriel, which lies 3km north of Skull, are well known to have been the site of early copper mining. I first visited the area in 1947 with Seán Ó Ríordáin, and we were very excited as we climbed up the hill to find a thin scatter of big rounded beach cobbles, carried up by the early miners for the purpose of pounding the rock.

The rock on the upper slopes is irregularly impregnated with copper ores. Many short tunnels (about thirty have been recognised to date) have been quarried into the hillside, and lying across the mouths of the holes are heaps of broken stone and charcoal. John Jackson started to examine the mines in the sixties, and he obtained a radiocarbon date of about 3500 years ago for the charcoal, showing that the mines were almost certainly operated by Bronze Age people. Since then he and, more recently, Billy O'Brien of University College, Cork, who has excavated in the mines, have secured many more dates which confirm the first one.

The rounded beach cobbles which Seán and I saw on the slopes were found, both broken and intact, in the holes and on the tip-heaps. That the cobbles had been used as mauls was clear, as many had abraded ends from use in pounding; a few had grooves cut around them to give better purchase for a wicker handle. We can thus picture the early miners, after they had located a suitable outcrop of ore, first lighting a fire against it to expand the rock, and then throwing on water to shrink and shatter it. With the aid of the mauls, and also with wedges of pine wood, which have recently been found in the mines by Billy O'Brien and dated by radiocarbon to about the same age as John's charcoal, the shattered rock was removed. It was then further pounded, to make it easier to pick out ore-rich pieces for smelting; the smelting seems to have been carried on elsewhere.

Subsequent growth of peat, both on the hillslopes and on the tip-heaps, concealed the mouths of several of the tunnels. In 1947 I had made some pollen-counts, which showed that pine was still present in the area when the peat covering the pit-heaps started to form. Later work has shown that pine disappeared from the region about 3000 years ago, and this further confirms of the antiquity of these small mines. Mining activity was resumed in the area in the nineteenth century, and quite recently ill-founded claims were made that all the mines fell into this period.

There is another area of mining at Derrycarhoon, about 8km to the north-east, and here I was able to show that there were two layers of mine detritus separated by a layer of peat. My pollen-diagram showed that pine pollen was present in the peat, though in reduced quantities. Therefore the peat must have been forming about 3000 years ago. The lower detritus was thus Bronze Age, and this dating was strengthened by the fact that I found a broken stone maul embedded in it; the upper detritus may well have been nineteenth century AD.

*nr. Dunmanus, Cork. This megalithic grave, a large boulder resting on smaller stones, is perhaps Bronze Age in date. Today the area round it is a salt-marsh, flooded at spring tides, which suggests, as at Killadangan in Mayo, a relatively recent change in sea-level. John Jackson stands beside the tomb.*

There are in the vicinity several megalithic wedge-tombs, also called gallery-graves, and this type of monument is generally associated with the first metal-users in Ireland. There is also another type of megalithic monument, the boulder dolmen, apparently associated with areas where copper ores occur in south-west Ireland. This consists of a large boulder capstone resting on several low boulders. John Jackson, who has gone to live in Skull, brought me to see a fine example in a salt-marsh between tide-marks just north of Dunmanus. It was in a situation immediately comparable with that which we have already seen at Killadangan outside Westport.

We have thus, at Westport and Dunmanus, two sites with megalithic affinities at a considerable distance from one another, and both sites are now flooded by high tides. Presumably when built they were above the reach of the tides, and it is possible that detailed investigation of the sites might suggest a regional rise in sea-level rather than movement of local sand-bars. In Brittany megalithic sites flooded by the tides are well known.

When in 1989 I visited John and Sally in Skull, one of the bees in my bonnet got a fine opportunity to take some exercise. As I drove along the road from Skull to Ballydehob, I could not fail to notice that the ridge of which Mount Gabriel forms the summit rises abruptly at about 100m from a markedly level surface below, which strongly suggests an etch-plain. In fact the Mount Gabriel ridge is part of a huge semi-circle of higher ground above 100m that starts immediately west of Skull Harbour, and swings around encircling the Ballydehob lowland as far as Knockonna (150m), 4km west of Skibbereen. The etch-plain below 100m has been slightly dissected by the numerous centripetal streams which drain the curved ridge and converge in the northern end of Roaringwater Bay.

## Lough Hyne

We make our way into Skibbereen, where we cross the River Ilen, and then turn back south-westwards for a distance of 6km along minor roads to reach Lough Hyne. Here another of my bees came under heavy anti-aircraft fire but managed, though not unscathed, to get back to base.

Lough Hyne is another of Ireland's seven wonders. It is a small lake, square in outline with sides about 1km long, and more than 40m deep in places; it is very close to the sea. At the end of the Ice Age its water was fresh, but the later rise in sea-level enabled salt-water to flow in along a very narrow channel, 'the Rapids', where at low water the depth may be less than a metre. The channel has enabled a rich marine flora and fauna to invade the lake, and so make it a most attractive place for study by marine biologists.

I saw it first in the thirties with David Webb. David was a fellow student with me in Trinity, and he then went on to Cambridge to do post-graduate work in zoology. As a zoologist he was attracted to the lough, which was then being closely studied by a Cambridge group in association with Professor Renouf of University College, Cork. Similar studies have continued intermittently ever since, and the lake is now Ireland's first marine reserve. David later decided to make botany his priority, and he returned to Trinity to become Professor of Botany. He produced a much-used *An Irish Flora*, and later played a leading part in the production of *Flora Europea*, which ran to five volumes. He used to take groups of his students on week-long excursions to different parts of Ireland, and it was by attending these for some years that I gained my knowledge of Irish plants. I shall always be grateful to him.

*Lough Hyne, Cork. The origin of this small deep hollow, first a lake, but now connected with the sea, remains an enigma.*

So much for the lake today; but what is the origin of the remarkable rock-basin that holds it? In 1986 I wrote that its formation could not be due to marine erosion, river erosion or rock solution. A glacial origin had been suggested, that a deep corrie had been excavated by ice when sea-level was lower, and that the hollow had later been flooded. I could not go along with this, and so fell back on late tectonic movement, the steep face of the west side of the lough suggesting a fault. John Whittow of the University of Reading thought that erosion along a fault might account for the genesis of the basin.

My colleague in Trinity College, the Professor of Geology, Charles Holland, will have none of this. He and other hard-rock geologists have studied the local rocks, and can see no sign of fault movement. The lake lies where a band of sandstone runs east–west between slates and finer sandstones on either side. The sandstone is cut into blocks by a series of regular joints, and Charles considers that ice plucked away these blocks, and created the depression. He thus rejects the corrie theory, and substitutes scouring by passing ice which carried the blocks away.

Charles draws an analogy with Windermere in the English Lake District, but such analogy I cannot accept. Windermere is a long narrow lake, 16km long, and up to 1.5km wide, whose floor has been deeply scoured out. Lough Hyne is a very small square lake, which reaches a depth of over 40m. The glacier that scoured the Windermere valley was a very powerful one, formed by the confluence of two strong glaciers fed from the massive ice-cap on top of the Lake District mountains. The ice at Lough Hyne cannot have been more than a relatively thin sheet, which was spreading out as it reached its outer limit. Charles would see two converging glaciers coming generally from the north-east; most glacial geologists, including myself, would see the ice coming from the north-west, as striae which are to be seen in the Lough Hyne area indicate such movement. Charles would see the confluent ice-streams creating a swirling movement which presumably drilled downwards for a depth of more than 40m, and then by some eddying lifted the detached blocks up to the surface and carried them off downstream. I am afraid that I just cannot see this happening.

But if I reject Charles's glacial hypothesis, I accept that no convincing evidence for tectonic movement can be demonstrated in the field. However, I still look at the topography, and my slightly winged bee manages to remain airborne. It is perhaps appropriate that our next stop will be at Cork Airport.

## South Cork Uplands

As we make our way to the airport we are in the middle of topography with a marked east–west trend, and the features which accompany this trend, as we have already seen in Kerry. We have low-lying narrow valleys, floored by the region's last remnants of the former cover by rocks of Carboniferous age, separated by relatively flat-topped uplands composed of the Old Red Sandstone, which stratigraphically lies below the Carboniferous rocks; the sandstone slopes which margin the uplands are surprisingly steep.

Cork City lies on low-lying Carboniferous limestone where the River Lee runs into a tidal estuary, and the first settlement was on islands in a tidal lagoon. This promoted a street pattern which bedevils traffic movement in the city even to this day. Steep sandstone slopes rise to north and south of the town, and the airport had to be sited on the upland south of the city. The airport road from Cork climbs up a steep slope to reach the flat on which the airport is placed, and we have to make a similar climb as we approach the airport from the south.

We go up onto the viewing platform in the airport, and we find we are standing on a high point on a gently undulating facet of very considerable extent cut into the upland at about 125m. Were we to commandeer a light aircraft and fly westwards, we could follow the facet for about 50km before it breaks up against the slopes of the Shehy Mountains, which rise from it to a height of almost 600m. This facet, which varies in height from 60m to 125m, is regarded by geomorphologists as a planation-surface cut by erosion of some type. And this surface is only one of many at different levels which can be recognised on the higher ground of sandstone rocks that are found in east Cork and west Waterford, to a degree unparalleled elsewhere in Ireland. The surface on which the airport is sited is one of the more prominent ones.

To have produced such a surface erosion must have removed a considerable quantity of rock, and it is hard to conceive just how vast this quantity must have been. Earth movement had bent the beds of sandstone upwards, and we can picture them as originally sloping downwards and outwards, like the sides of the letter A. Erosion has decapitated the A, and cut it down to the level of the cross-bar of the letter, which forms the surface we are looking at. Sandstone at least several kilometres thick must have been removed.

Although geomorphologists are unanimous in recognising the existence of these surfaces, their views on their origins are highly divergent. Discussion of the problem started in the 1860s, and still continues. It was ably stimulated by a paper written by Gordon Davies in 1970 on 'The Enigma of the Irish Tertiary'. At the start of his career in the geography department in Trinity College Gordon worked on geomorphology, but later he has turned more to the history of earth sciences.

# CHAPTER 19

# Waterford

SURFACES IN WEST WATERFORD

LISMORE CASTLE

## SURFACES IN WEST WATERFORD

I ran into the problem of erosion of surfaces again in west Waterford. We make our way to Lismore, traversing valleys with limestone and ridges with sandstone, with steep slopes separating valley and ridge. From Lismore we turn north towards the Knockmealdown Mountains, an impressive sandstone ridge which rises to 800m, on our way to Caher. Once across the Blackwater River we take a side road to the east towards the Cistercian monastery at Mount Melleray.

We climb steeply at first, but as we approach the monastery we realise we are on a remarkably flat surface at about 210m. We look north and see an isolated hill, Dyrick (365m), rise with cliff-like abruptness from the surface. Are we looking at a flat bench cut by the waves of a long-vanished sea, which ended in cliffs cut into the slopes of Dyrick? This was the view put forward by Austin Miller, Professor of Geography in Reading, in the fifties; he pictured that during the Tertiary sea-level had started very much above today's level, and had fallen intermittently, each pause in the fall making possible the cutting of a platform by wave abrasion, hence the sequence of planation-surfaces to be seen so well in southern Ireland today. Most of Miller's surfaces fell into two groups, his South Ireland group between 180m and 240m, such as we have here, and his Coastal group between 60m and 125m, which we saw at Cork Airport.

The publication of his paper in 1955 revived the controversy. Tony Farrington would have none of the marine idea; he saw the platforms as remnants of *peneplains* cut by slow sub-aerial river erosion.

Another school of thought about platform production sprang up. Its exponents took the view that valleys formed as much by the lateral retreat of their walls as by the cutting down of their floors. 'Erosion moves sideways and not down' was their motto, and they called the resultant broad surface a *pediment*. They pictured that typical erosion processes were most active where the gradient steepened as the floor curled up into the boundary slope, and that debris released from the slope was quickly swept away across the floor. This picture is very attractive in continental regions, in places round the borders of mountain masses, such as the Rockies in North America.

And there is still another concept, that of deep chemical weathering. Again attack will be most severe where the slope changes, and the floor will slowly expand at the expense of the slope. I have tried to show such a picture near Cahersiveen and Portmagee in Kerry. On the floor there will be a limiting depth to which chemical attack can proceed, and the surface of the unaffected rock below will be relatively level; sweep the weathered debris away, and an etch-plain will appear. On the whole, I now give my support to this last view.

In 1980, however, when I wrote a paper on possible Tertiary events in Ireland, I supported the Miller view and described the platform at Dyrick as wave-cut, but now I have abandoned that position and invoke chemical weathering instead. Of course I cannot quantify my view in any way, and quantification is now the rule in modern geomorphological studies. But I do try to avoid the trap of pushing pre-conceived notions too far. I do try to follow the caution—'Remember that if you didn't *think* that it was there, you wouldn't *see* it'.

## Lismore Castle

My conversion arose from a more detailed visit I paid to the Knockmealdowns in 1982. The trustees of the Lismore Estates, controlled by the Duke of Devonshire, were anxious to investigate the possibility of mineral deposits on some of their mountain lands, and I was asked to look at a particular area, including that around Dyrick. I think they expected the result would be negative, and so my report was, but it gave me several days of pleasant walking in the area.

The agent for the estate, Paul Burton, lived in part of Lismore Castle, and he and his wife asked me to stay with them during my visit, and there I was most hospitably received. The present castle dates largely from the 1850s, and was built by Joseph Paxton, of Crystal Palace fame. The stone was imported from Derbyshire, and a special canal was constructed so that barges which had come up the Blackwater carrying stone could deliver it right to the building-site. The position overlooking the river is of course superb, but to my taste the building is rather over-heavy.

*Richard Boyle's 17th-century manor stands on a cliff-edge overlooking the Blackwater. It was replaced in the 19th century by a new 'castle'. Below the cliff at the river edge there is a small stone-roofed church with a stumpy round tower, very like St Kevin's church in Glendalough.*

Occupation of the strategic site overlooking the river crossing goes back at least to Early Christian times, and later rebuilding of a doorway disgorged a very handsome crozier, fabricated about AD 1100. There was next a Norman castle occupied by the bishops of Lismore, and then there was a major reconstruction by Richard Boyle in the early part of the seventeenth century. Boyle, an Elizabethan adventurer who aggrandised himself by many shady deals, assembled an immense fortune and became First Earl of Cork.

A gatehouse tower led into the old courtyard, which was surrounded by ranges of gabled houses, some of which held very elegant apartments. A number of old illustrations of the mass of buildings still exist, and it must have been a picturesque and imposing sight. It is a great pity it has not survived because Ireland has almost nothing left of buildings of that period. Had it been there today, it would have suggested a mini-Carcassonne. It largely fell into ruin in the eighteenth century, and was almost completely obliterated in the later reconstructions.

Only the gatehouse tower survives. It still forms the main entrance to the castle, and thus no articulated lorry will ever make its way into the courtyard. Alas it is also too small for furniture-vans, and serious thought has to be given to any changing of pieces of furniture in the castle, where the immense size of the rooms means that furniture must be on a corresponding scale.

In addition to hospitality, I also secured a valuable piece of apparatus at Lismore. Paul Burton had a hollow steel walking-stick of a type I had never seen before, designed for the taking of soil samples. It was essentially a steel rod hollowed out by a very deep groove, with a length of 70cm, and graduated in centimetres. Needless to say the steel rod had to be of very high quality in order to remain strong after being gutted for most of its length, and I was delighted to see the name Beuss & Mattson engraved on it. The firm is a specialist Swedish one, and it made the hand-operated Hiller-type borers which Knud Jessen brought with him to Ireland in 1934. I did all my work with such a borer, though my colleagues have moved on to much more sophisticated pieces of apparatus.

In this borer, a number of steel rods, each 1.5m long, can be coupled together by a simple locking device. A sampling chamber goes on at the bottom, and a handle at the top, and increasing depths are reached by adding more rods to those already extended. In this way it is possible to sample to a depth of 12m, beyond which the device becomes too cumbersome and heavy to handle in the field, particularly on a quaking bog-surface. Fortunately few Irish bogs are as much as 12m deep. Most peats and muds are easily penetrated, although layers with heavy timber may be encountered. The bottom is usually of stone or stony clay. There is always the temptation to try to get up some of this bottom material, and this involves forceful twisting. This is where the temper of the steel is important, and here Beuss and Mattson succeed. It is also trying on the limbs of the investigator. Harry Godwin damaged his right shoulder through over-screwing, and suffered arthritis in the joint for the rest of his life; mercifully I escaped serious injury.

I have since used my steel walking-stick with great success on many occasions. It was particularly useful when I was tracing bog-buried walls on Valencia, as it was possible with one movement both to probe down through, and bring up a sample of, the peat overlying the wall. When I finished my field-work on the island, I lent the borer to John Sheehan who was surveying on the mainland, and he also made good use of it.

We re-join the road through the Knockmealdowns, which climbs to 350m at the Gap, and here we cross out of Waterford into Tipperary. We look out over the limestone plain below, and quickly drop down the north face of the sandstone ridge by a series of hairpin bends. As we start the descent we have a splendid view on the west of a small corrie, cut into a north-east facing slope. I know that during the course of my wanderings I have nodded many times, but, like Homer, Praeger only rarely nodded. He dismissed the Knockmealdowns as monotonous, and failed to notice the corrie.

We reach the limestone at Clogheen, and can, if we wish, make a short detour to the west to see the Mitchelstown Caves. Despite the name, the caves are not in the town, but lie about 12km east of it. If we continue north we quickly reach Caher, strategically placed at the eastern tip of the great sandstone ridge of the Galty Mountains. We turn north-west to Tipperary town, and from there continue on by minor roads till we reach Lough Gur.

CHAPTER 20

# Limerick

LOUGH GUR · PARTEEN

## Lough Gur

In the early 1940s I decided that I would have to take archaeology more seriously, and I enrolled as an occasional student in University College, Dublin, where I attended Seán Ó Ríordáin's lectures. There was another mature student in the class, Eric Dorman-O Gowan. As Brigadier Dorman-Smith, he had had a brilliant career in the British Army, and served in North Africa in the Second World War as Chief of Staff to Auchinleck. After the battle of Alamein, Auchinleck was sacked by Churchill—a step which many thought was not one of the best-judged of his career—and Eric went with him. Eric left the army in 1944, and came to Ireland, where he changed his name from Smith to O Gowan. He had an interest in antiquities, and seeking to fill his time he had enrolled in Ó Riordáin's classes. We became lecture friends, and I found him an intelligent and amusing man. Liddell Hart, the distinguised military strategist, was a close friend of his; I met him at dinner with Eric, and listened with fascination as they discussed military topics I never knew existed.

During the later part of the war my wife was away in England teaching in a boys' prep school, and I was relatively foot-loose. Seán and I had also become friends, and I asked if I could join his excavation programme at Lough Gur, where over a period of many years he carried out a series of very important digs. Unfortunately he died prematurely before all the work was published, but this has now appeared after Eoin Grogan and George Eogan did an enormous amount of work piecing together Seán's detailed drawings and notes.

We dossed down in an old school-house, where Seán's only contribution to the house-keeping was to wake us up as he went out to the pump in the yard where he filled the porridge-saucepan. He put it on the stove and went back to his ablutions. After some time I noticed that a man of about my years, or a little older, was also taking part in the excavations; he was John Hunt, and we became friendly. I of course didn't know that he was a very distinguished medievalist, but I enjoyed his company.

John and his wife, Putzel, had recently come to Ireland, and had chosen the Limerick area, as John had family connections with the county. Being of German origin, Putzel found life in wartime England at times trying, and they had set up in a small farmhouse on the edge of the lake, which they gradually enlarged and transformed. Putzel had a flair for interior decoration, and John could direct tradesmen without the intermediary of an architect, and the house quickly changed out of all recognition.

Our friendship developed, and after a time Putzel suggested that I would be more comfortable lodging with them, with twenty-four-hour hot water assured, rather than continuing to survive in the school-house. This I was very glad to do, and on subsequent visits I always lodged with them. It took some time for it to dawn on me that they were both medievalists of world-wide reputation, who had spent many years dealing in medieval antiquities, as well as objects from other periods. Like Somerset Maugham, John had started life as a medical student in London, but drifted into constant attendance in salerooms. Putzel was the daughter of a museum director, and had been brought up surrounded by art. John was one of Sotheby's chief cataloguers, and together they had bought many things for Sir John Burrell; these are now to be seen in his museum outside Glasgow.

Thus it was in the Hunt home in Lough Gur that my interest in, and knowledge of, medieval and other antiquities was born, and I shall always be grateful to them for that awakening. Not only was I surrounded by beautiful objects, but I was encouraged to handle them, and also to browse through their wonderful library of art books. The knowledge I gained there was to be turned to special advantage many years later, when I became involved in the organisation of an exhibition of Irish art treasures, including the Book of Kells, in the United States. I would never have undertaken the preparation of the catalogue without this grounding in medieval material from John and Putzel.

After some years at Lough Gur the Hunts moved to Dublin, but John's attachment to the Limerick area continued. They secured the establishment of the Craggaunowen Centre, 5km south-east of Quin, where John supervised the construction of a crannog and a rath; there was a small castle on the site, and this the Hunts furnished with some of their medieval collection. John's collection of prehistoric Irish material was lodged in Limerick University. Towards the end of his life, with the assistance of Peter Harbison, John published a comprehensive two-volume survey of Irish medieval carving. In Trinity College his name was on the list of those proposed to receive honorary degrees, but he unfortunately died before the formalities were completed.

At Lough Gur (Pl. 6) I was once more in familiar karstic limestone country, as the lake was surrounded by limestone slopes with a thin soil cover. A limestone knoll, Knockadoon, stood on one side of the lake, which formed a horse-shoe around it. Thus the area, with the knoll surrounded by fertile slopes, and the lake with abundant fish and wildfowl, was obviously most attractive to early inhabitants, particularly in the Neolithic period.

There was a tremendous scatter of prehistoric debris; at one site which we excavated, a house of seventeeth-century age, with a floor of beaten earth, yielded an Elizabethan brooch, and when the mud walls were demolished, pieces of Neolithic pottery which had been embedded in the mud fell out of them. As in the typical Irish farm until very recently, the Neolithic farmhouse had a manure-heap near by, and as earthenware vessels got broken, the pieces were thrown into the manure, to be later spread on the fields. When earth was later gathered to build the house-wall, pieces of pottery were also collected.

John fitted me out with a crude raft made by lashing oil drums together, and from this I made a boring in one of the arms of the lake. There was a considerable depth of deposit, which reached right down into the late-glacial period, and also recorded a splendid development of Neolithic agriculture. Unfortunately the lake had been partly drained in the nineteenth century, and when the water-level fell, and exposed the marginal muds, these were rapidly re-washed by rain out into the basin to accumulate once more. Thus the upper layers of the muds I brought up were contaminated by pollen in secondary position, and I could not carry the record up to the present day, as I had hoped to do.

Another boring was made in the lake in 1986 by a Swedish worker, Liz Ahlmgren. She was armed with a new line of approach, unheard of when I made my boring. Iron, an element with high magnetic response, is very common in the earth's crust. Nearly all soils have some content of iron, and this content can be detected by magnetometers. Whenever the plant cover on the soils on the slopes round Lough Gur was broken by tillage, some of the soil, carrying magnetic iron particles with it, was washed into the lake, to be incorporated in the mud.

When the columns of undisturbed mud taken up by the borer are laid out along a laboratory bench, a sensitive magnetometer can be passed along the line of mud. The instrument will pick out the layers of mud that have a content of inwashed soil. This record can then be compared with the pollen counts, where it will be found that richness in pollen of weeds associated with cultivation will coincide with layers of higher magnetism. Under ideal conditions the layers of mud doubly associated with agriculture can then be dated by radiocarbon determination. All this detail is reported by this new investigation.

The prehistoric peoples who had lived round the lake had lost many objects in the shallow lake margins, and as the muds were washed away a large collection of material, including some very fine Bronze Age objects, came to light. Some of this material reached the National Museum, including a splendid shield of beaten bronze, fabricated, perhaps, about 700 BC.

In late-glacial times, 10,000 years ago, long before the arrival of humans, the area was also attractive to animal life. Remains of the giant deer are commonly found in the vicinity, and one small cave near the lake, the Red Cellar Cave, produced the bones of arctic lemming and arctic fox. The cave had later been used by a bear as a hibernating den, but after the bear had dug itself into the underlying deposit, it expired during the course of its winter sleep. When the cave was excavated the bear skeleton was found, surrounded by and embedded in bones from a much earlier period. I looked without success for scratch-marks on the cave walls where the bear might have sharpened his claws; John Jackson did find scratch-marks in a Sligo cave where there was a bear skeleton, again probably from an animal that died during hibernation. It is not known when the bear became extinct in Ireland; at Dalkey Island David Liversage discovered bear canine teeth in association with Neolithic material, but the Irish language has no native word for bear, using instead a loan-word from Latin; it may have disappeared from Ireland before the beginning of the Christian era. We proceed on from Lough Gur and cross the Shannon at Limerick.

## Parteen

Just before it passes through Limerick, the Shannon makes an enormous loop to the north, and at the tip of the horseshoe, about 5km north of the city, is the village of Parteen. Here in pre-Shannon Scheme days one of the sons of William Smith O'Brien, Donough O'Brien, built himself a house overlooking the river and a picturesque ruined weir, popularly known as King John's Weir, as it is thought to go back to the thirteenth century.

The house was of a very individual style; the main part, which faced the river, could be likened to a hay-barn because it was a long rectangular structure with a curved roof; the drawing-room was here, with a splendid bow-window looking straight down the river. At either end there were wings, that at the east housing the bedrooms, and that at the west the kitchen and other smaller rooms. When the Shannon Scheme was being developed in the twenties, the house narrowly escaped demolition, because the tailrace from the power-house upstream at Ardnacrusha passed within a few yards of it. Thus the house which until then stood on the banks of the Shannon now found itself at the tip of a peninsula between the river and the tailrace.

Donough O'Brien left the house to his niece, Lucy Gwynn. Lucy Gwynn was a sister of Edward Gwynn, a don in, and later Provost of Trinity College, and Edward's children, who included my wife, also a Lucy, enjoyed many happy childhood holidays at Parteen. After our marriage, my wife brought me to the house, and I made good friends with her aunt, Lucy Gwynn. When returning from Lough Gur, I would stop off for a few days with her. The house had been built by an educated man, who had in some way imparted a very special atmosphere or flavour to it.

Donough O'Brien had been very interested in natural history and antiquities, and many distinguished workers in those fields had frequented the house. W.J. Knowles, a distinguished antiquary, was frequently there, and also his sister, Matilda Knowles, who was a distinguished botanist with a special interest in lichens. Matilda, or Matty as she was generally known, worked in the herbarium in the National Museum for many years, and when I first began to visit the herbarium in the early thirties, Miss Knowles, an elderly lady with an ear-trumpet, was occasionally to be seen, sitting at a microscope, examining some lichens in detail.

I cannot be certain that Praeger ever visited the house, but I think it more than likely that he must have done so. At one stage he was very keen on promoting joint meetings of the various field clubs dotted round Ireland; Donough O'Brien was a leading member of the Limerick club which certainly acted as host on more than one occasion, and it would have been at such a meeting that Praeger would have had an opportunity to visit.

The tradition of education was strong in the Gwynn family, and the aura of the house continued uninterrupted during Lucy Gwynn's occupation of it. The library, in addition to books and journals on natural history and antiquities, also contained the full range of nineteenth-century novels that sat naturally in such surroundings. During my stays at Parteen I took to reading these to my great profit. Up to that point my acquaintance with English literature had been based on a somewhat pot-boiling book, *Masters of English Literature,* compiled by Lucy's elder brother, Stephen, author and Nationalist member of parliament. This had been the material on which I was prepared for my school examinations.

I read the novels avidly. I read all the Brontës, all the Trollopes, and much of George Eliot, though I got stuck in *Daniel Deronda,* and I did not get any great distance with Meredith. Thus my visits to Limerick in the early forties proved very fruitful for my further development; with the Hunts I widened my horizons; with Lucy Gwynn they deepened rather than widened.

CHAPTER 21

# The Shannon

SHANNON SOURCE AND LOUGH ALLEN · LOUGH ALLEN TO LOUGH REE · LOUGH GARA · GLACIAL DIVERSION · TERMONBARRY · LOUGH REE · LOUGH REE TO LOUGH DERG · ATHLONE · CLONMACNOISE BOORA · MEELICK · LOUGH DERG · GLACIAL DIVERSION · KILLALOE TO LIMERICK CASTLECONNELL

## Shannon Source and Lough Allen

When I was laying out my 'circuit of Ireland', I pictured that we would follow the Shannon upstream from Parteen to its source in Co. Leitrim. But when I set to the task, I found I could only think in terms of moving downstream rather than up. So I am afraid that at this point I must ask you rather lamely to get into the waiting helicopter to be whisked 150km north to Lough Allen, the most northerly of the three large lakes of the Shannon. We shall work our way back to Parteen.

I have to confess that as we follow the course of the river, one of my bees will be hovering overhead. When I look at a map of the basin of the river, I see a gutter-like depression running

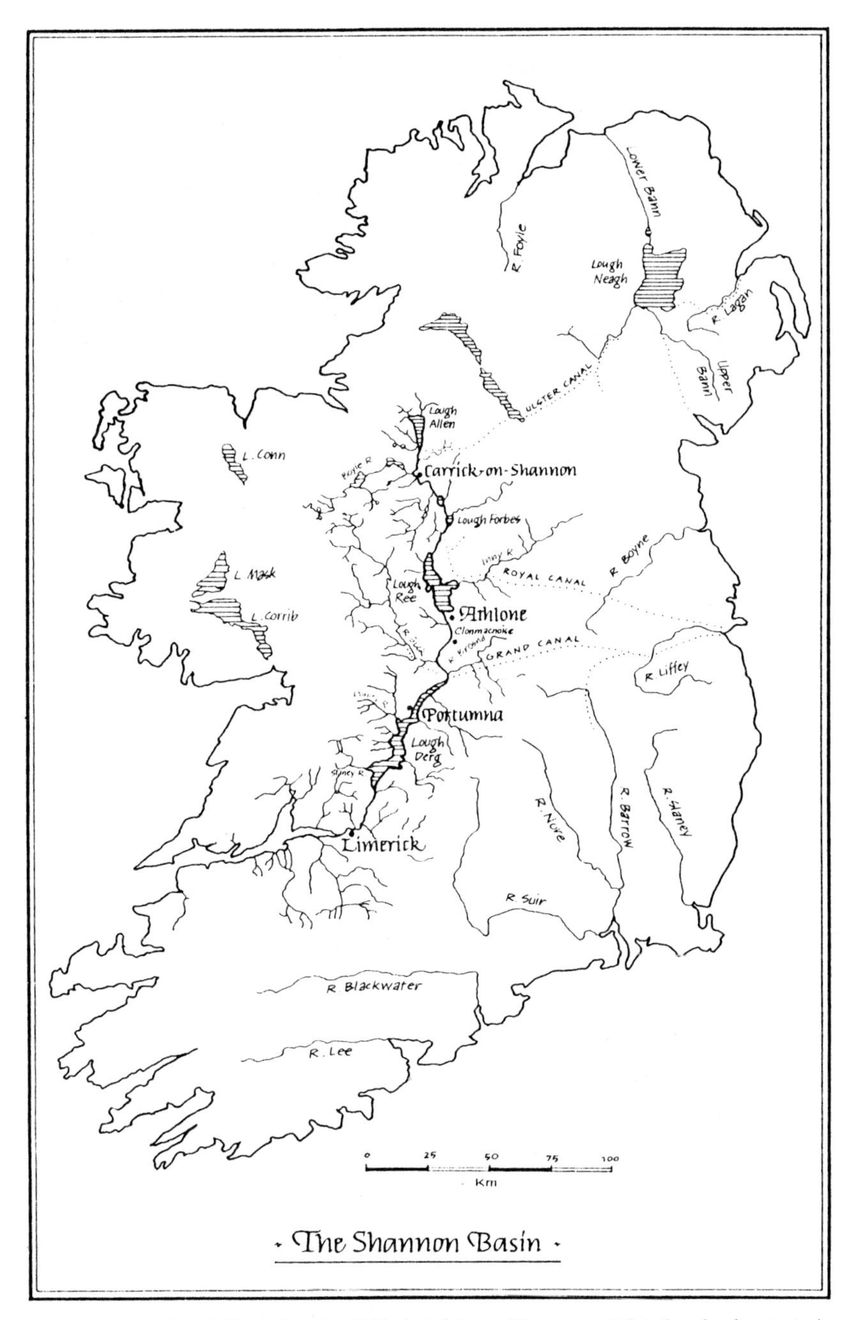


*The Shannon and its winding tributaries which drain lakes and bogs suggest that there has been tectonic subsidence which created a kidney-shaped basin in central Ireland. It is only with difficulty that the drainage water escapes to the sea.*

north–south from Lough Allen to Lough Derg, and I have to think that this has been created by a fairly recent down-sagging of the earth's crust. I am further persuaded that this is so, because in early post-glacial times, before much open water had been overgrown by fens and raised-bogs, great areas of the basin would have been a vast lake. We know this because

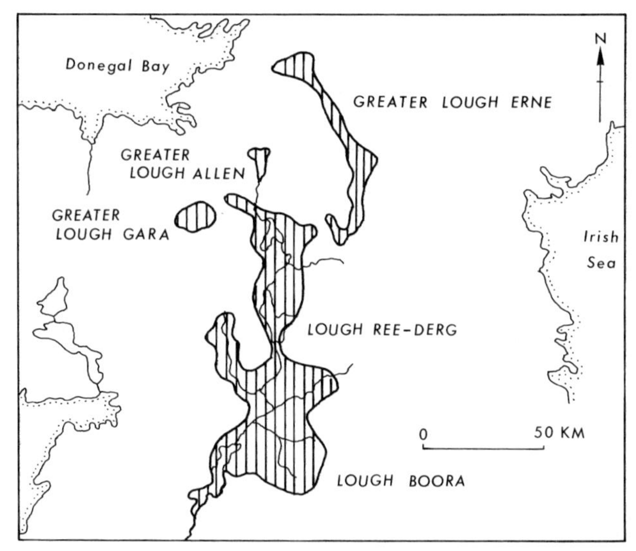


*If we turn the clock back by 10,000 years, the lake-muds and peats which now largely fill the Shannon basin will not yet have formed, and there will have been vast expanses of open water.*

we can trace the clays which were deposited on its floor below the fens and bogs. Other lakes in central Ireland would also have been much larger than they are now. We can regard today's Shannon as a residual thread of open water. If we accept this concept of sagging, we can understand that any major effort 'to drain the Shannon'—a political catch-cry that arises at every election—would be superhuman.

If we imagine a clock with only one hand, a heavy hour-hand shaped like a wedge, then Lough Allen is such a hand, pointing to six o'clock. The hand is sunk into the clockface, which forms a tableland, about 25km in diameter and standing at about 400m. It is composed of sandstones and shales of upper Carboniferous age, higher than the limestone; these are the same rocks which erosion has largely removed from the Cork area, though we have seen them before where the Shannon finally meets the Atlantic Ocean. The tableland is deeply dissected by valleys, and the sandstone is confined to the remaining high flat areas, while the shales form the valley slopes. Thin layers of poor coal occur in the sandstones, and coal

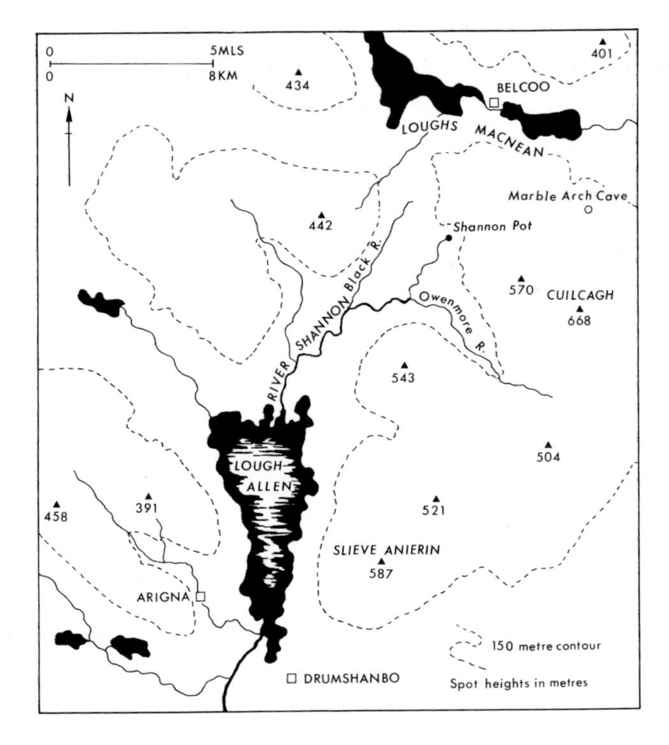


*From the Shannon Pot the river follows a zig-zag course till it reaches Lough Allen, a triangular lake sunk into a plateau of sandstones and shales.*

has long been mined near Arigna, on the western side of the tableland. The mined coal is burned in a power-station on the west side of the lough, but its operation has ceased to be economic.

A valley which cuts through the tableland runs north—north-east down into the north-east corner of the lough. Ice moved south down the valley, and on its retreat left behind long oval mounds of glacial debris, like attenuated drumlins, aligned along the valley floor. Six kilometres south of Belcoo, they reach a height of 100m, and separate the modern catchment area of the Shannon from that of the Erne to the north.

The southward draining water is first called the Black River. As it moves on towards Lough Allen, it is joined from the east by a tributary in one of the dissecting valleys which, in its upper reaches, is called the Owenmore River. But just before the Owenmore reaches the Black River, it loses its name because it receives from the north a modest quantity of water which has sprung from the legendary source of the Shannon, the Shannon Pot. Thus the infant Shannon has a zig-zag course before it reaches Lough Allen, and changes the names of two rivers, the Owenmore and the Black, *en route*.

Though not the real source of the river, *Log na Síonna*—the hole or pool of the Shannon, anglicised Shannon Pot, is a romantic place. Some would see in the name Shannon a relation with St Senan, whose headquarters we visited on Scattery Island in the Shannon estuary. At the pot a circle of willow bushes surrounds a small round pond from which, except in the driest of seasons, water gushes endlessly. Throughout the area the limestone which underlies the shales is full of solution channels, through which water under artesian pressure circulates. Remove the shale cap, and water bubbles up. At the Shannon Pot the shale covering is either very thin or absent, and water rises in a massive spring. The released water then flows away through water-meadows to join the Owenmore River.

Wells and springs have been much venerated down through the ages, and many in Ireland still are. This sentiment was particularly strong in Late Bronze and Iron Age times, when votive offerings, often numerous, costly, and diverse in nature, were thrown into selected wells or bogs. It is very probable that the famous hoard found in a bog at Dowris, near Birr, which contained more than two hundred Late Bronze Age objects, originated in this way. I am sure that the Shannon Pool cannot have failed to receive many such offerings, and I have often speculated as to how the particular difficulties that the site offers to excavation might be overcome. It may well be that the scouring effects of flood waters at times when the outflow was very rapid will have swept away any deposited objects. Still I should like to try.

During the Ice Age the tableland area was the site of active glacial movement, and two streams of ice, one from Fermanagh moving down the valley in which the infant Shannon lies, and the second from Sligo down another similar valley running north-west from the head of Lough Allen, converged at the head of the lough. The joint stream then moved south, excavating the basin of the lough.

The lake level now stands at about 50m, though this is artificially controlled by a weir at the point where the Shannon emerges from the lake. The lake is used as a holding pond by the ESB, who control the volume of water in the river so as to have a constant supply available to the power-house at Ardnacrusha. In a spell of dry weather the lake level can fall quite low, and considerable expanses of mud are laid bare along some of its shores. Wandering around, a local archaeologist picked up chert flakes in Larnian style from the mud surface, and as he knew I was interested in the Larnian to be found around the lakes of the Irish midlands, he contacted me and we went there together. We found quite a number of very large flakes roughly struck in Late Mesolithic style. This was not surprising, as, had we crossed the watershed at the head of the Black River and moved a short distance down the far slope to Upper and Lower Lough Macnean, which drain to the Erne, we would find, again at times of low water, large quantities of similar material around Cushrush Island in the lower lake. There is no doubt that about 5500 years ago there must have been quite large numbers of Mesolithic fishermen wandering up and down the rivers and lakes of central Ireland, as well as along the coasts.

## Lough Allen to Lough Ree

At a late stage of the last advance of ice in Ireland, enormous numbers of drumlins were shaped below the ice along a broad arc of country that stretches from the north coast of Down, where we have already seen them, to Sligo Bay. Thus streamlined ovoid masses of glacial material scattered at random over the countryside, and interspersed with small lakes, presented the Shannon, as it emerged from the lake, with a broad watery *chevaux de frise*, through which it was quite impossible to establish any logical course of flow. Today it threads its way through the drumlins past Carrick-on-Shannon as far as Roosky, about 20km further on, where the drumlins gradually fade away. The drumlins not only block the general drainage, but are themselves composed of poorly-draining materials, and much of this part of Leitrim has some of the poorest soils in Ireland. Tests suggest that the soils are capable of producing good timber, and strenuous efforts are being made to afforest much of the county.

Five kilometres downstream from the exit of the lake the Shannon reaches the village of Leitrim, and this today is the upper limit of navigation. A canal did run from Leitrim up into the lake, but this was blocked when the ESB harnessed the river. This is also the point at which the Ballinamore and Ballyconnell Canal, constructed to link up with the Erne navigation system, enters the Shannon. While the canal threaded its way from lake to lake in a most ingenious manner, it was very expensive to construct, and never had any viable life. Long fallen into disuse, it has been gravely damaged by minor agricultural drainage schemes. Now it is being suggested that it should be reopened, as a symbolical link between North and South, but such a development, while praiseworthy, would give, just like the first construction, a very poor return for a great deal of money.

At Leitrim we step into our cabin cruiser, and from here to Killaloe, 135km further on, we shall be largely afloat. At Leitrim we are at 45m, at Killaloe we shall be at 33m, so a fall of no more than 12m has to carry us all that way. Only five shallow locks are required to enable our descent.

I first went on the Shannon in 1956, when our children were teenagers; my most recent trip was in 1988, when my eldest grandchild was approaching teenage status, and I have been there many times in between. The river has changed greatly during that period as tourist traffic has developed, but it retains its charm for me. It gives me the very greatest pleasure to loll—often very well wrapped up—in the front of the boat as it chugs slowly along, both when it is crossing some small lake with great crested grebes and tufted ducks, and when it is winding between water-meadows, on whose flats corncrakes can be heard making one of their last stands in Ireland. The cooling-towers of the peat-fired power-station in Lanesborough, the ruins of Clonmacnoise, slowly rise in front of the boat, and equally slowly disappear behind. It does not matter whether I am on a small four-berth boat, or a floating mobile home with central heating, the charm remains the same. One very cheering feature is that despite the great increase in the numbers using the river, it remains virtually litter-free.

Approaching Carrick-on-Shannon we skirt the eastern shore of the first largeish lake we have encountered, Lough Drumharlow. We turn up the lake to the north-west, and having passed through a very picturesque lock at Knockvicar, enter the beautiful Lough Key, cross the lake and go up the Boyle River towards the town of that name. We leave the boat and walk some 7km upstream to Lough Gara.

**Lough Gara**

As we walk along, the Curlew Mountains rise above us to the north. Here, as in Munster, the Old Red Sandstone has been brought upwards by folding, and stands up as a ridge above the surrounding limestone. If we were to climb to the top of the ridge, we would see the terraced Carrowkeel Hills and their passage-graves, which we have already visited, laid out before us.

In the early 1950s an extensive drainage programme was carried out in Lough Gara, which lowered the water-level by about 1m. Many crannogs came to light, and also, just as at Lough Gur, many archaeological objects were revealed as the marginal muds were washed back into the water.

Among these were chert flakes struck in Larnian style, and I felt that somewhere around the lake and its many islands there must be a relatively intact occupation-site of the period, where, because of the wet conditions and the alkaline nature of the water, objects of wood and bone might have survived. I dreamed of finding another Star Carr, an amazingly rich Mesolithic site on the shore of a drained lake in Yorkshire, discovered by John Moore and later excavated by Grahame Clark. In addition to many flint implements, the site, dated to 9500 years ago, also produced harpoons fabricated from antlers, and vessels made of birch bark. I enlisted Hilda Parkes and Bill Watts in the search, and although we walked many kilometres of shore-line, we failed to find anything *in situ*. We were rewarded, however, by stray finds which included countless chert flakes, Bronze Age pottery, a bronze 'door knob' butt from an Iron Age spear, and coming to more modern times radio valves and wellington boots. The Trinity College radiocarbon laboratory was then functioning, and we were able to provide some dates for Joe Raftery of the National Museum for the crannogs he was excavating. We move on to Carrick-on-Shannon.

Leaving the town the Shannon makes a shimmy to the east in a big S-shaped loop. After the first bend, below Jamestown, a historic but failed plantation settlement, where the arch of an entrance gate survived until recently, rock appears in the bed of the river. There is then a series of rapids before the river completes its second bend and turns south again at Drumsna, another sleepy village. To avoid these rapids the Shannon Commissioners in the 1840s cut a channel across the neck of the second bend, with a lock at its eastern end, to compensate for the change in level due to the rapids.

A recent discovery has shown that this was not the first cut across the neck. The canal-cut was to facilitate movement; the earlier cut was to impede it. Archaeologists from the Office of Public Works have discovered a big ditch-and-bank, almost 2km long, constructed across the neck about 500m north of the canal. A well-defended entrance pierced the bank. The finders believe that the fortress was built to protect the area of Iron Age settlement centred on Rathcroghan in Roscommon, about 10km to the south, from attacks by Ulster tribesmen. There was much fighting in this area in Iron Age times, and the Ulstermen had built their defensive line, a bank and ditch, with a fortress, the Dorsey, near Armagh; the Dorsey has recently been dated to about 100 BC. An intermittent bank and ditch runs west from Armagh towards the Sligo coast; we could have seen a part of it by a short diversion at the point where the Shannon enters Lough Allen, about 30km north of the Drumsna fortress. The bank and ditch are traditionally known either as the Black Pig's Dyke, supposedly cut by the snout of a giant boar, or the Worm Ditch, being supposed to be the upcast of a giant worm.

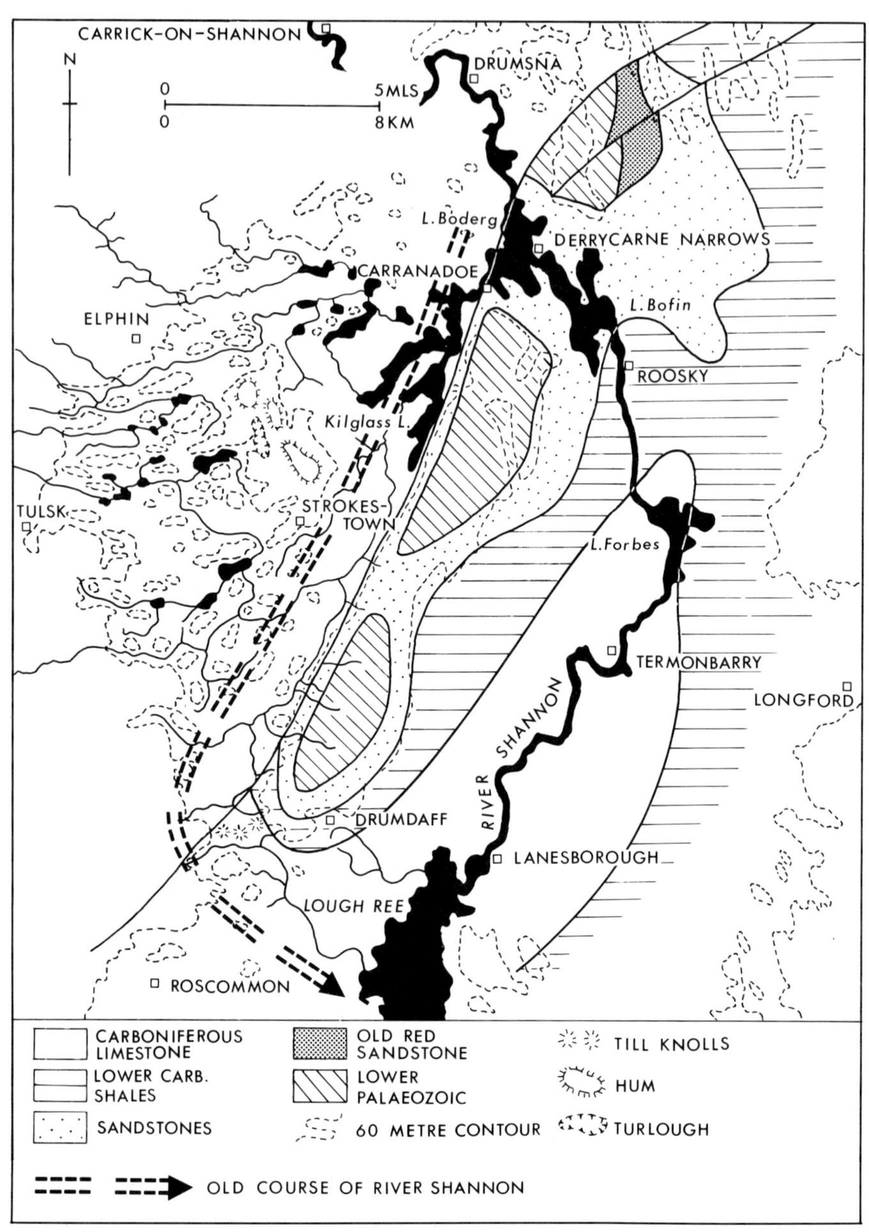


*Between Carrick-on-Shannon and Lanesborough a ridge of older rocks rises across the course of the Shannon. Until late in the Ice Age the river flowed down the western side of the ridge. The retreating ice blocked that channel, and a new one was cut across the ridge at the Derrycarne Narrows.*

A short distance to the south of Drumsna, the river enters Lough Boderg, and at the point of its exit an impediment arises. A narrow whale-back ridge of rock, 30km long and rising to 250m in height, lies diagonally across the course of the river. Here there was a Hercynide upfold in the rocks, and erosion has removed the overlying limestone to expose basal Carboniferous sandstones and shales; at some points even these rocks have been removed to expose Old Red Sandstone and still older rocks. The main road from Longford to Strokestown crosses the ridge, from whose highest point there is a superb view over the surrounding lowlands, across which the Shannon is trying to thread its way.

**Glacial diversion**

Today the river leaves the lake by a cut across a low point on the ridge at Derrycarne Narrows, but it is my opinion that before the last advance of ice in the area the river failed to cross the ridge, and instead flowed down the west side of it to enter Lough Ree (if it then existed) on its north-west side, somewhere south of Lanesborough. The ice in its southward advance cut across, and lowered the low point in, the ridge at Derrycarne Narrows. On its retreat it left, on the western side of the south end of the ridge, a bar of moraine which rises to 65m across the former channel of the Shannon at Drumdaff.

In consequence all the drainage on the west side of the ridge runs back northwards from the moraine, passes through and widens into Kilglass and other lakes before it passes through a channel at Carranadoe to join the waters of today's Shannon in Lough Boderg. Thus I believe that glacial action brought about a significant change in the course of the river in this area.

The quay below the bridge at Carranadoe was for long one of my favourite stopping-points. An ESB line crosses the river here, and it was a preferred perching point for a snipe. I did not realise that snipe could perch on slender wires, but this one habitually did so, flying off occasionally to do some drumming and then return to his perch. The waters of Kilglass and the other lakes gave a good opportunity for lazy cruising. There is now a large marina above the bridge, and I have not stopped there in recent years.

The route by which the Shannon today crosses the ridge from Lough Boderg into Lough Bofin closes in at the Derrycarne Narrows, where rock nears the surface. There was once a ford here, but a narrow channel, with a marker on each side, has been cut through the rock to allow canal-barges to pass. On about my third trip to the Shannon I had become very blasé about navigation, and used to amuse myself by steering as close as possible to buoys and other channel-markers. I did this in the narrows, and there was a loud crash, crash, crash, as the boat struck rock, fortunately without major damage. I then, with a red face, consulted my navigation guide, and read 'Keep at least four feet away from all markers, as some are built on a shelf of rock'.

Below the narrows the river widens out into Lough Bofin. The rock here is Carboniferous sandstone which gave way by the solution of its calcareous cement, and allowed the river to expand into a lake, but just above Roosky the sandstone gives way to more resistant shale, and the river follows a very narrow channel until it expands again when it comes back to the limestone at Lough Forbes. It constricts again as it approaches Termonbarry.

**Termonbarry**

At Termonbarry we get an opportunity for industrial archaeology. We descend from the level of Lough Forbes to that of Lough Ree through a massive lock of splendid masonry built by the Shannon Commissioners in the 1840s; the river water gushes down a broad weir beside the lock—I always remember a splendid sight of a kingfisher here. One kilometre to the south-east the old Royal Canal finally reached the banks of the Shannon in Richmond Harbour in 1817. Its terminal level was some height above the river, and the canal dropped down to join it by a short stretch of canal with a small lock. The Camlin River flowing down from Longford also enters the Shannon here, but its course has been much altered; it is possible to go up the river for a short distance and then enter Richmond Harbour, again by a small lock. When I first went on the river the harbour was abandoned, but it has since been restored and it, and its dry dock for barge repairs, now form a very attractive old-world picture.

From Termonbarry it is a short run, with raised-bogs on either side of the broad winding river, to Lanesborough at the head of Lough Ree. The main features of Lanesborough are the splendid nine-arched stone bridge and the power-station, whose chimney forms a landmark visible for many miles around. The power-station has had a curious side-effect on the local fishing. Very large quantities of water are drawn from the river to feed the cooling-towers, and the re-condensed water is returned to the river several degrees higher in temperature than when it left it. Fish delight in the warmer water, in which they not only congregate, but also grow to larger sizes than usual, and the nearby banks are always lined with fishermen.

## Lough Ree

We now enter Lough Ree, the second largest lake on the river system; its surface lies at about 40m. It has a highly indented shore, and an irregular floor, studded with numerous islands; joints in the limestone, which underlies the whole lake, clearly have an influence in the general alignment of peninsulas, islands, shoals and deeps. Much of the lake is relatively shallow, with a depth of less than 10m, but there are numerous deeps, and the floor of the deepest of these is only 2m above sea-level. Because the Shannon was obviously going to be a major line of defence if Napoleonic forces invaded the west of Ireland, the Admiralty charted the lake, and also Lough Derg to the south.

Studying the charts, Professor Charlesworth of Queen's University, Belfast, whom we have met before, thought that the deeps were excavated by moving ice plucking away blocks of limestone. But in pre-glacial times weathering of limestone went to very great depths, often in the form of vertical pipes which were filled with highly weathered clays. At Aughinish Island in the Shannon Estuary such pipes went to 60m below modern sea-level without bottom being reached, so when we think about chemical weathering we have to ignore modern sea-level; when such weathering was taking place sea-level must have been much lower than it is today. So it is quite possible that solution of limestone to considerable depths may account for some of the deeps in Lough Ree. Some readers may say that this is just one of Mitchell's bees out for another airing, but in this area I am supported by the fact that highly weathered clay still exists in a pipe at Knockcroghery, a little inland from the west shore of the lake, where it was exploited on a small scale for making clay-pipes until relatively recently.

Not far away Blackbrink Bay indents the shore-line. From the bay a short length of canal runs up to Lecarrow where there is a small harbour, recently renovated. This is a convenient if sometimes crowded place to lie, but if the wind is light I prefer to anchor in the bay. A point, covered with woodland, protects the east side of the bay, and this is one of Ireland's most favoured haunts for the garden warbler. Pulling ashore in the early morning, and walking in the wood, one is drowned by the elegant song on all sides.

Lough Ree has also many sites of historical interest. Many of the islands have remains of early churches; of these the most important are Inchbofin and Inchcleraun. Bofin has two churches with Romanesque features and some early gravestones; Cleraun has several early churches and again gravestones, though there are reports that some of these have been stolen in recent years. How to prevent such thefts is an ever-present problem.

Warren Point, near the centre of the west shore of the lake, has considerable remains of an early medieval town. A large castle with a strong keep and a curtain wall was built here in the early thirteenth century. The town grew up in the protection of the castle, and this was itself fortified by building a wall 175m long, with towers and a central gateway, across the neck of the peninsula. From here we run down to Athlone.

## Lough Ree to Lough Derg

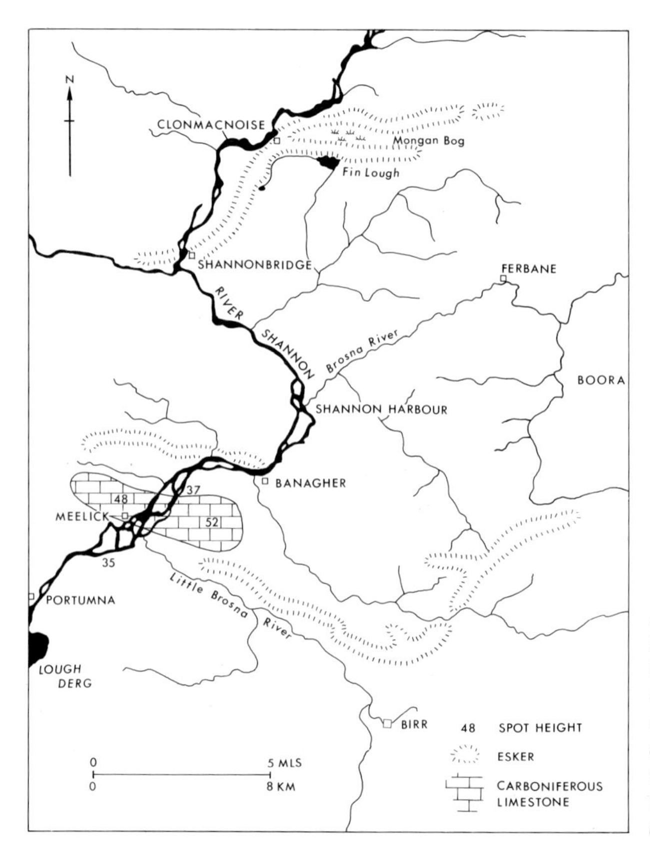


*At Clonmacnoise, Shannonbridge and Banagher, eskers lie close to, or across, the course of the river. At Meelick the river cuts across an upstanding ridge of limestone, breaking up into lesser channels as it does so.*

At Athlone we have left the drumlins far behind, and are now in esker country. When an ice-sheet is melting away, great quantities of water are set free at the base of the ice. Discharge tunnels gradually develop to carry away water, sand and gravel, and if the main flow of water changes direction, a tunnel may be abandoned, and gradually silt up with sand and gravel. When the ice finally disappears a cross-country ridge of sand and gravel, an *esker*, is revealed. From Athlone south to Meelick, a distance of 30km, the river approaches, or cuts through, several eskers. Such places obviously offered crossing-points, and they have been used by people, certainly since Bronze Age times.

**Athlone**

At Athlone an esker is cut through by the river, and the crossing here has been of high strategic importance down the ages. The main point of defence has always been on the west bank, to guard the bridge leading to the east. The Normans built a strong castle in the early thirteenth century, and this has been the nucleus of fortification ever since. There was fierce fighting here in the Williamite war, and the nineteenth-century threat of French invasion led to a further strengthening of the approach to the river by building forts and redoubts a little further to the west. We shall find splendid examples of nineteenth-century fortification all the way to Meelick.

The Shannon shallowed as it crossed the gravel ridge, and a ford long preceded the bridge. Later excavations to improve navigation produced many Bronze Age finds, and such finds have been supplemented by the activity, both legal and illegal, of sub-aqua divers. A splendid Bronze Age shield, rivalling that from Lough Gur, was recently found by divers. In the eighteenth century a canal with small locks was cut to the west of the town, but this had become virtually impassable by the early nineteenth century. The Shannon Commission then stepped in, and in the early 1840s rebuilt the road bridge and constructed a large lock, 38m × 12m, as part of their programme to open up the river for steamboat services.

**Clonmacnoise**

We drop down from Athlone to Clonmacnoise on a broad river flanked by hay-meadows which are often flooded in winter. If the season is right we will be serenaded by corncrakes as we go, as these late-cut meadows are one of their last refuges in Ireland. Behind the meadows we see raised-bogs, with low farmland rising beyond them. Clonmacnoise is of course a very historic site, with one of Ireland's most important early Christian monasteries, with high crosses and round towers. It was plundered by the Vikings around AD 800, and again by the

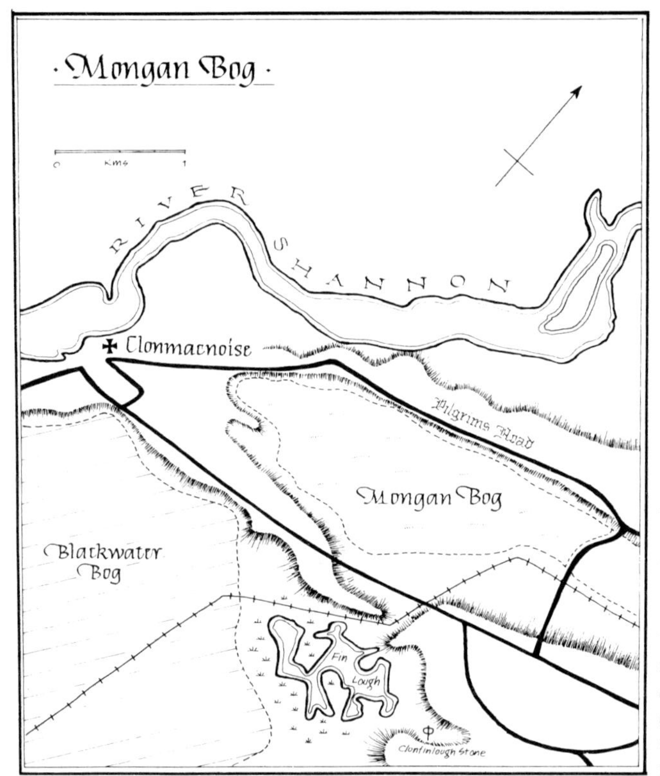


*Mongan Bog, still relatively intact, and now protected, lies between eskers. Fin Lough, a still uncovered remnant of former widespread lakes, survives beside Blackwater Bog, almost destroyed by development. The Clonfinlough Stone is nearby.*

Normans, though the latter did add Romanesque churches as well as a castle. The monastery was destroyed in Elizabethan times, and the castle was slighted by the Cromwellians.

My interest here is chiefly environmental, an interest greatly augmented by the work of a study group drawn from the Environmental Services Unit of Trinity College, and the County Offaly Vocational Educational Committee, who carried out a detailed study and proposed that the area should become a Heritage Zone. Such a zone is 'a defined area with a sufficiently rich inventory of heritage items to warrant a concerted and coordinated approach to conservation'. The Clonmacnoise area certainly comes within such a definition.

We had here at the end of the Ice Age a series of eskers, and the monastery was sited at the point where two eskers converged and then turned south along the east bank of the river. Roadways ran along the crests of the eskers, and this meant that the monastery had good communications. The northern esker carried 'the Pilgrims' Road', an important route through the midlands.

Immediately after the eskers had formed, the huge lake, to which I have already referred, flooded the area, covering great tracts of land, and on the floor of the lake, whose waters were still icy cold, deposits of sterile gray clay were laid down. As the temperature rose, plants and animals invaded the lake waters. The water was rich in dissolved calcite, and algae such as *Chara* deposited a limy ooze on the lake-floor in which the shells of freshwater molluscs were incorporated to form shell-marl. As the water shallowed, fen-plants invaded the margins of the open water, and the lake began to be transformed into the river-channel we see today. Fen-peat began to accumulate, and as this thickened nutrient supplies for plant-life fell away, and gradually the plants of the fen gave way to those which needed very little inorganic nutrient for their growth, and raised-bogs began to build themselves up on top of the fen.

At Clonmacnoise an arm of the lake was trapped between two eskers, and here today we have an almost intact raised-bog, Mongan Bog, whose conservation for the benefit of posterity is of the greatest importance. If we make a boring in the bog, we can go backwards in time through the events outlined in the preceding paragraph, and trace the history of forest development and subsequent disappearance in the Shannon basin. We also get an insight into the activities of early peoples.

Across the esker on the south side of Mongan Bog, we come to a small patch of open water, Fin Lough, a tiny successor of the former great lake, trapped between the esker to the north and another raised-bog, Blackwater Bog, now largely destroyed by commercial peat-winning, to the south. Here alkaline water flowing out of the esker has enabled fen-vegetation to survive, and so this patch avoided being swallowed up by bog. The complex habitat, an intimate mixture of open water and fen, enables a wide range of plants to flourish, and these in turn provide breeding ground for residential birds, while the open water gives refuge to migrating swans, geese, ducks and waders. As an ecological unit, Fin Lough very prettily complements Mongan Bog, bringing together two types of rich habitat now becoming all too rare, not only in Ireland but throughout western Europe. It was therefore most appropriate that the recent study should have been funded in part by the European Economic Commission.

A short distance to the east of the lough we find the Clonfinlough Stone, a large erratic boulder of sandstone, which carries enigmatic designs, part natural, part improved on by man, probably

*Shannonbridge, Galway. The Napoleonic fortifications were built to guard the river crossing here against an unexpected French invasion force, but the French took a different route and the guns that were here never fired a shot.*

in Bronze Age times. I have been present on many interesting occasions, such as the discussion on the bog at Roundstone, but one I missed was the examination of the stone by R.A.S. Macalister and the Abbé Breuil. We have already met Macalister. He had a fertile imagination, but he met his match in the Abbé Breuil, one of the landmark figures in European archaeology. As Praeger recounts, Breuil had been examining Spanish cave-paintings just before his Irish visit, and claimed that the Clonfinlough scribings were an exact analogue of these. I only spoke to the Abbé once, when he was over ninety years of age, but I should have loved to have been at Clonfinlough with a tape-recorder, and preserved for posterity the far-fetched and excited dialogue that must have taken place.

From Clonmacnoise we drop down to Shannonbridge, where the esker that has lain on the east bank of the river turns west and crosses it, and so provides a route to Ballinasloe. There is a fine early eighteenth-century bridge here, and on the west bank yet another very strong anti-Napoleonic block-house with supporting buildings. The buildings are still virtually intact today, and could well be restored as a tourist attraction.

Here we are surrounded by raised-bogs on all sides, and these are being vigorously exploited to feed a power-station at Shannonbridge. Work preliminary to development showed that the bog areas are underlain by sterile grey clay, further evidence of the former enormous lake in the basin of the Shannon.

From Shannonbridge we drift down to the point where the River Brosna joins the river from the east. If we were to exchange our cruiser for a canoe, we could follow the Brosna north-east upstream to Ferbane, and then turn south down its tributary, the Silver River, to Boora, where we would meet another peat-fired power-station. A short distance across the bog, we would come to Lough Boora which, like Fin Lough, is a surviving fragment of the former lake.

**Boora**

When a bog is exploited, a small thickness of peat is usually left undisturbed at the bottom of the bog. Unfortunately bog-exploitation results in large quantities of finely divided peat being carried away in the drainage water, and when the water reaches rivers with fish in them, the peat clogs the gills of the fish with disastrous results. At Boora the Bord decided to construct settling ponds to retain the peat fragments. This involved the stripping away of all peat in order to excavate the ponds in the basal glacial material. Such stripping revealed a gravel ridge on which early hunters had camped about 8500 years ago, about the same time as the occupation of the site at Mount Sandel near Coleraine, which we have already visited. Parallel to the ridge, but a little distance from it, was a line of storm beach gravels, built up by the waves of the former lake. This is the best proof I know of the former existence of the big lake. Its waters must have been wide enough for strong winds to whip up considerable waves; when the waves reached the shore, they built up a substantial storm beach. There would have been a lagoon between the beach and the ridge, and obviously the top of the ridge, overlooking the lagoon with its ducks and its fish, would have provided a very attractive site for early hunters.

We return to our cruiser, and after a few metres turn sharp left into the mouth of the Grand Canal, which finally reaches the Shannon at this point. When I was there in 1988 the canal-banks had been scraped down not long before, and showed a fine section of the basal grey clay of the former lake passing up into shell-marl. If we continue a short distance up the canal, passing through two locks as we do so, we come to Shannon Harbour, rather sad with derelict docks and hotel, the former terminus of the Grand Canal. We turn downstream, and quickly come to Banagher, an attractive village with some fine Georgian houses and a splendid bridge, built by the Shannon Commissioners; it also has associations with Charlotte Brontë and Anthony Trollope. The river skirts the east end of an esker, and there was a crossing-point here, which was fought over many times, just as at Athlone. Some little distance back from the river on its western side there is a splendid round nineteenth-century fort, rather like a giant Martello tower.

**Meelick**

Six kilometres downstream, we come to Meelick, one of my chief problem points on the Shannon. Here a more resistant block of limestone confronts the river, yet the river is not diverted, but cuts across it, breaking down into smaller channels as it does so. The river is at 37m above the cut, and the rock rises to 50m on either side of the cut. The site has been a strategic one for a long time, the earliest fortification being a Norman castle built in 1203, and the latest, anti-Napoleonic block-houses dotted here and there.

The Grand Canal Company carried their route with several locks on the east side of the river, but the Shannon Commissioners went straight through with a rock-cut channel leading to the largest lock on the river, 43m long. It is built of splendidly fitted stone, with its name 'Victoria' cut in large letters on one side. The lock projects like the high bow of a large boat into the lower ground downstream, and the view south is one of the most dramatic on the river. Below to the west are the partly restored remains of a Franciscan abbey, founded in 1445. Although it is almost inaccessible by road, the site is well worth a visit, as the graveyard round the church has the finest collection of beautifully lettered seventeenth-century gravestones that I know.

Whereas in other parts of its course the Shannon is obviously in a 'young' channel, controlled by the local glacial deposits, I feel that at Meelick the channel across rock must be 'old', and that the river maintained its course across the limestone block, while the surrounding country was being lowered in level by erosion. We shall meet the same problem at Castleconnell, below Killaloe.

As we emerge from the lock we have the exit of the old canal and the mouth of the Little Brosna River on our left. Here in winter there is often extensive flooding of the riverside meadows, or callows, as they are called, and the flooding extends far up the Little Brosna. The flooded callows provide wonderful winter feeding for geese, ducks and waders, and an observation hut provided by the Irish Wildbird Conservancy half-way between Birr and the Shannon gives splendid viewing of these birds. In addition many waders breed here during the summer, including black-tailed godwit, which have their only Irish breeding-station here.

The corncrake also flourishes. But such wetland sites are under continual threat from drainage and other 'improvement' schemes, and it seems that the only solution will be to designate the area as 'environmentally sensitive', and to pay the local farmers for maintaining the hay-meadows in their present state. EC funds are available for this purpose. From Meelick we drop down to the bridge at Portumna.

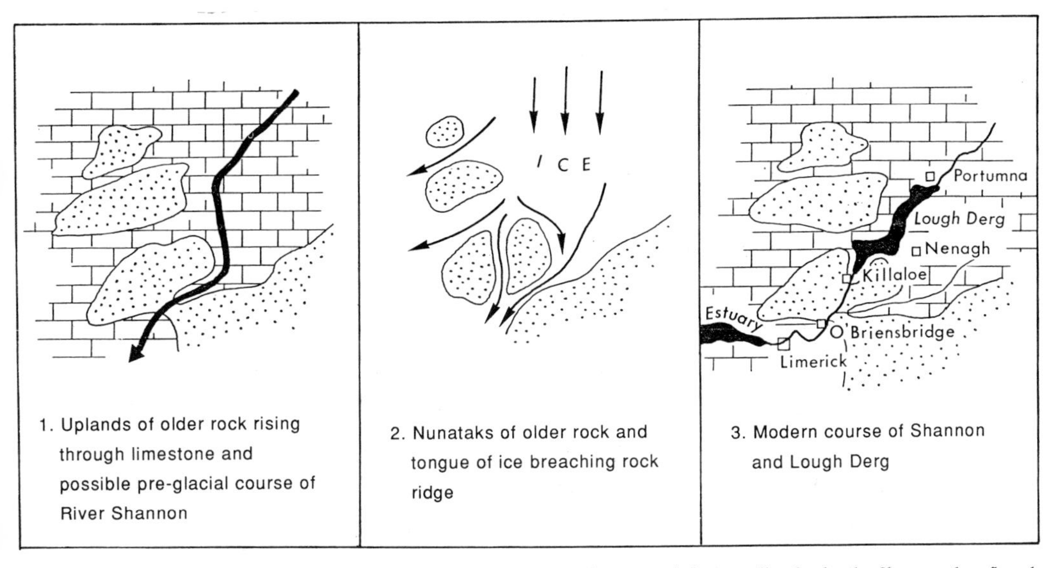


*Pre-glacial erosion of the underlying rock structures here created three small uplands; the Shannon then flowed around the southern one. Ice erosion modified the shape of the uplands, and the river now cuts through the southern upland, instead of flowing around it.*

## Lough Derg

Lough Derg is the biggest lake on the Shannon. Most of the lake lies on limestone, where it is shallow and island-studded, just like Lough Ree. But at its south end it is held up by a ridge of older rocks. In Lough Derg also many of the islands have remains of early churches, principally Inishcealtra, which has Romanesque structures as well as much earlier features.

I have never been fortunate enough to see the yellow-flowered composite, *Inula salicina,* which has on these limestone shores its only station in the British Isles. The shores make attractive walking over short grassland, with grass of Parnassus and the bee orchid, interspersed with juniper and yew. Today the water-level is subject to abrupt changes in accordance with demands for electricity, and this has provided problems for shore-line plants and birds. Island-breeding common terns are especially at risk, but recently local ornithologists have raised the height of Goat Island, an important nesting-place, to keep the nests out of reach of being flooded.

**Glacial diversion**

We now must give some attention to the exit of the Shannon from the lough, which provides one of the many puzzles of its course. To the south the river is confronted by four parallel Hercynide ridges of older rocks, aligned north-east–south-west, which rise through the limestone, strips of which survive in the low ground between the ridges. It would seem that the simplest course for the river would have been to follow one of these low-lying limestone corridors, and emerge on the far side of the ridges somewhere between Ennis and Limerick.

I believe that in pre-glacial times the river did take such a course, following the low-lying corridor that now carries both the main road and the railway line south-west from Nenagh; the southern part of the corridor is now drained by the Kilmastulla river, which joins today's Shannon just north of O'Briensbridge. But the modern river cuts directly through one of the ridges, with ground rising to over 150m on either side. My current opinion is that we have here what we already saw on a much smaller scale at Derrycarne above Lough Ree, a glacial diversion caused by a combination of erosion at one point and deposition at another.

The south shore of the lake runs along the north face of the ridge in an almost straight line from Scariff in the west to Youghal Bay in the east. This line marks the boundary between low-lying limestone to the north, and a steeply rising ridge of harder rocks to the south. But this regular line is now interrupted by a deep indentation, a gorge running down to Killaloe, where the river exits today.

I consider that the ridge lay athwart ice advancing from the north, and the ice was forced to divide to east and to west, further steepening the scarp by erosion as it did so. The ridge was interrupted by a short valley sloping to the north, and a lobe of ice pressed up the valley, deeply scouring it to a depth that in places lies below modern sea-level. Continuing south the ice breached the watershed at the head of the valley, and entered the head of another valley, which ran south to Killaloe. Ice erosion lowered the ridge to a level across which the modern Shannon flows today at a level of 30m.

The ice that had followed the low-lying Kilmastulla corridor, the pre-glacial course of the Shannon, left as it retreated great quantities of sand and gravel, including a bar at 60m across the corridor at Five Alley, about 4km south-west of Nenagh. South of the morainic bar, surface water today drains south as the Kilmastulla River; north of the bar the water flows north to enter Lough Derg in Youghal Bay at its south-eastern corner.

## Killaloe to Limerick

At O'Briensbridge, 7km south of Killaloe, a rib of sandstone crosses the bed of the river. Taking advantage of the sound foundation provided by the sandstone, the ESB erected their main barrage, a head-weir, across the river a little north of the village. In order to contain as much water as possible, the water-level above the weir was raised, so that the valley to Killaloe was flooded, and the level of Lough Derg was also affected. The weir was the take-off point for the head-race which carried the water to the power-house at Ardnacrusha, 12km further south.

Flooding of the river drowned a small island, on which there were the ruins of a small early stone-built church, dedicated to St Molua. Harold Leask, then Inspector of National Monuments, wanted to build a small platform on stilts, and re-erect the church above its original site, but this plan was thought too costly, and the church was re-built in the grounds of the Roman Catholic church in Killaloe.

As the name O'Briensbridge indicates, this is O'Brien country, and the great tenth-century king of the area, and later of all Ireland, Brian Boru, took his title from a large circular earthen fort, Balboru, about 2km north of Killaloe on the west shore of Lough Derg. Brian O'Kelly excavated here, but with, on the whole, disappointing results; no direct connection with Brian was established.

### Castleconnell

At Castleconnell, 6km south of O'Briensbridge, a spur of limestone which rises to a height of 60m projects westwards. The head-race skirts around this obstacle, hugging the slopes of the Clare hills to the west, and the old canal, which leaves the Shannon between O'Briensbridge and Castleconnell, does the same; it intakes from the river at a height of 28m, and drops sedately down through a series of locks to Plassy, where the river meanders on its final approach to Limerick.

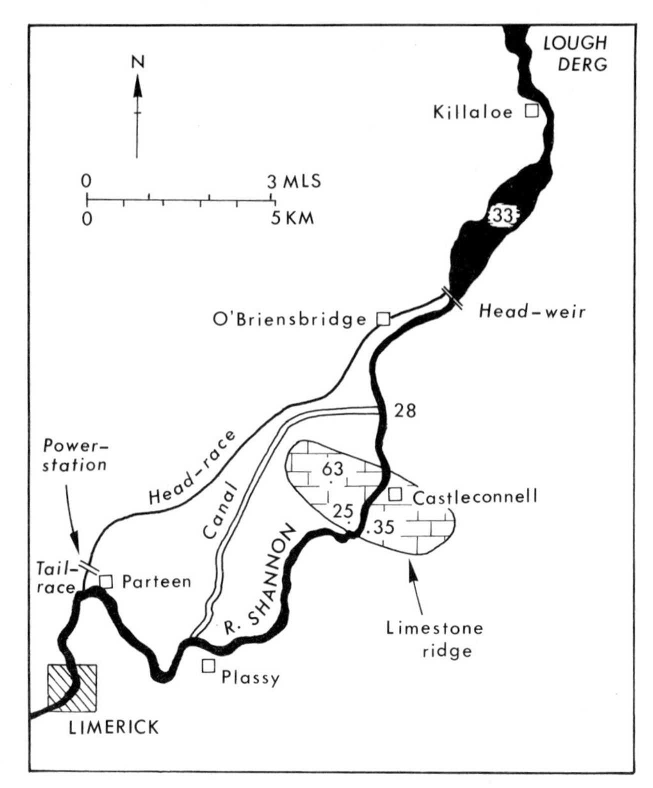


*As at Meelick further north, the Shannon at Castleconnell cuts across an upstanding ridge of limestone, although lower ground (now followed by the Grand Canal and the head-race for the Ardnacrusha power-station) lies to the west.*

But at Castleconnell the Shannon cuts directly through the spur in a rock-gorge whose walls rise almost 10m above the river; the Leap of Doonass, where the water tumbled down in a cataract, used to be one of the most scenic points on the whole course of the river. Today, with the bulk of the water siphoned off by the head-race, the falls are only a shadow of their former selves.

This is the second point on the Shannon—the first is at Meelick—where, on meeting a limestone obstacle, the river chooses to cut through the obstacle rather than follow what is today available lower ground. It would seem that at these points the river must be in an 'old' channel, rather than a 'young' one, such as we have seen at Derrycarne Narrows. We shall see the Boyne do the same when we get to the end of our journey. When I say 'old' I mean some millions of years, when I say 'young' I mean some thousands.

At Ardnacrusha, just above Parteen, which we have already visited, the water from the head-race drops 30m down the penstocks into the turbines, generating a substantial amount of electricity as it does so. In a token effort to preserve navigation on the river two locks with giant rises are incorporated in the barrage, but I can imagine nothing more likely to give me claustrophobia than to be sitting at the bottom of a black hole waiting for an inrush of water to lift me and my boat up 20m. Below Parteen, as we have seen, the tail-race returns the spent water to the river, which becomes tidal a little lower down before it reaches Limerick.

*nr. Rahan, Offaly. The tributaries of the Shannon flood as easily as the main river. Here the waters of the Brosna have burst their banks. The Grand Canal is seen on the upper left, circling round a large raised-bog.*

I am sorry if my chapter on the Shannon has offered some difficult reading, but the course of the Shannon has intrigued me for many years. About twenty years ago I drafted a paper on the topic, and had some of the maps which now appear here drawn by Mary Davies, who has helped me in many projects, but I never got down to finishing it, probably because the problem still remains unsolved. As I have already suggested, the low-lying Shannon basin may have resulted from a local down-warping of the earth's crust. The river has no valley, in the strict sense of the word, but consists of a system of incongruous units, linked in a shotgun marriage by the consequences of relatively recent glaciation. Today winter flooding in its middle reaches creates continual calls for elaborate drainage schemes. Such schemes, even if efficacious, would be costly to an extent that would far exceed the value of the land improvement that would be brought about. What is needed is maintenance of the wetlands in their present state, and compensation payments to the riverside farmers. We re-join our helicopter, and move north to Fermanagh.

CHAPTER 22

POT-HOLING · ERNE BASIN

LOWER LOUGH ERNE · UPPER LOUGH ERNE

## POT-HOLING

Having an interest in karstic landscapes, and having seen the water emerging at the Shannon Pot, I wanted to see an underground river in action in limestone country. An opportunity came when I learned, while staying with a friend outside Enniskillen, Co. Fermanagh, that there was an outdoor training school, which included caving in its activities, at Gortatole on the shores of Lough Macnean Lower, not far from Belcoo. We have already been to Lough Macnean, looking for Mesolithic flakes. I telephoned the School and they quickly agreed to show me some local features; when I arrived I was put under the charge of Sheila, a tall lithe girl about twenty years of age. I was over seventy.

By a scenic route, the Marlbank Loop, we drove up to a broad limestone shelf, at about 180m, about 3km south of the School. South of the shelf slopes of higher shales and sandstones rose above the limestone, culminating in the narrow ridge of Cuilcagh, which reaches 650m. Surface water runs down the slopes in a series of rills, but many of these vanish down channels in the limestone as soon as they reach it. South of the road a small stream, the Sruh Croppa River, continued southwards on the surface in a gutter-like depression, perhaps due to the collapse of the roof of a cave, like a small-scale version of the famous Cheddar Gorge in the Mendips in England. The valley ended in a cliff across whose top the road ran, and the stream vanished into a tunnel at the base of the cliff. The layout reminded me of the railway-line from Mallow to Cork, where as the train approaches Cork it enters first a cutting and then a tunnel, before it arrives abruptly at the station platforms.

So far so good, but immediately north of the road there is a deep narrow doline, the Cats' Hole, and Sheila invited me to descend into this, to see what I had come to see, an underground river in action. The hole was 30m deep, and its sides were steep and slippy. We then reached running water, hurling itself along with a loud rushing noise in a narrow and tortuous tunnel. There was no light, except for the directional beams from the torches on our hard hats. The river was only in moderate flow, but had recently been higher, and had deposited a thin skin of greasy mud on the bosses of rock along which we had to make our way. I found the going very treacherous, but Sheila leapt from rock to rock like a chamois, while I dropped further and further behind her. I was terrified that I would slip, and be next seen floating in the cave waters at the Marble Arch. At last, after what seemed to me an endless period of time, Sheila kindly asked if I had seen enough, and I replied 'Yes' in heartfelt tones.

The deeper pools in the channel floor had, lying at their bottoms, where the current was less swift, cobbles of local sandstone and probably glacial erratics as well. As these were swept along they would have had an erosional effect on the walls of the tunnel, which was therefore not entirely of solutional origin. In fact the erosional history of such streams must have been very different before and after the Ice Age. In pre-glacial times, before Ireland was littered with glacial deposits from which cobbles could be derived, the creation of the stream-tunnels must have been entirely due to solution. After the Ice Age the limestone disappeared both by chemical solution and by mechanical abrasion.

Somewhat shaken, and determined that once was enough, I drove Sheila back to the school, thanked her, and moved on to the Marble Arch Visitor Centre, which is very intelligently organised. Below the Centre the waters of the Sruh Croppa River and other underground streams move through a vast cave system, which includes a large lake. Praeger gives a vivid account of exploring the lake, swimming with a candle in his cap, but today the lake has flood-lighting and a boat. At one point there is a walkway through the lake, and the visitor can feel like Moses crossing the Red Sea. The overflow from the system emerges below the Marble Arch, an arch of limestone about 10m high. The water, now called the Cladagh River, emerges first into a narrow wooded limestone gorge—which is a National Nature Reserve—and then makes its way into Lough Macnean, about 2km east of Gortatole.

## Erne Basin

I cannot claim to know the Erne as well as I know the Shannon, but I find it equally puzzling. I once spent a week on a cruiser, going from Belturbet to Belleek, and I have spent many happy days with a friend near Kesh, on the south shore of Lower Lough Erne. In the Erne basin we are again in drumlin country, and the house is perched on the side of a drumlin, with the trees of the Castle Archdale Forest across a small bay. South it looks across the lake to high ground, and west it has the most beautiful sunsets.

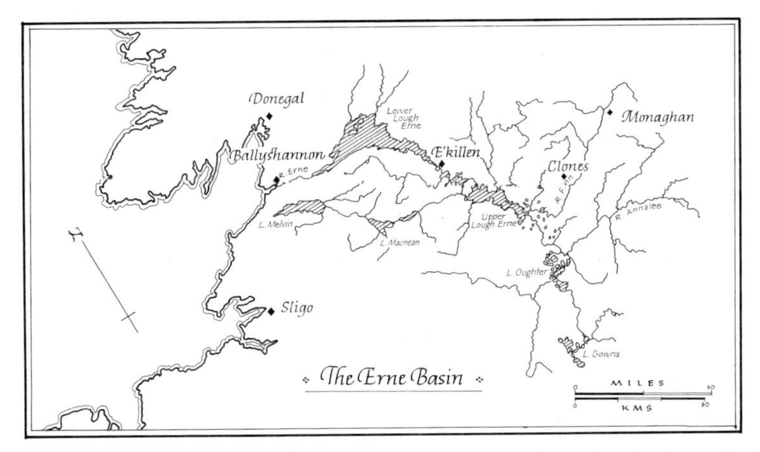


*Like that of the Shannon, the basin of the Erne tempts one to think that there has been regional subsidence in this area also.*

The Erne basin is quite extraordinary, and may, like the Shannon basin, be the result of local subsidence. It is like a roughly outlined rectangle, stretching north-west for 85km from Lough

Gowna in Cavan to Ballyshannon on the Atlantic coast; it is about 45km across. Lough Gowna lies at 65m, and Lower Lough Erne which reaches almost to Ballyshannon lies at 45m, so, like the Shannon, the gradient is very low. Again, just as the Shannon used to do at Castleconnell, the Erne at Ballyshannon plunged down a waterfall to make a quick descent to the sea. Today the fall has been harnessed to generate electricity.

## Lower Lough Erne

Lower Lough Erne is rather a conventional lake, lying between high Carboniferous rocks on the south and high ground of older rocks to the north. Much of the lake is floored by non-calcareous Carboniferous rocks, and in places its floor reaches a depth of 60m, 15m below sea-level. The lake-floor is very irregular, and has probably been scoured by ice.

The lake abounds in attractive islands, many with early Christian, and even earlier, remains. Boa Island has a very remarkable anthropomorphic pillar-stone, with two squat human figures back to back; there is a second single figure nearby; these are probably Iron Age. The monastery on Devenish, founded in the sixth century in honour of St Mo-laisse has, as well as other buildings, a Romanesque oratory and round tower; here the round tower must be a *cloich teach*, or belfry, because its door is at ground level, thus offering very little resistance to attack. White Island has a group of small enigmatic figure carvings; some are of ecclesiastical figures, others have a strongly pagan flavour.

As we move from island to island we should keep a sharp eye on the birds. The common scoter has one of its rare Irish breeding-sites here, and arctic, common and sandwich terns are also on the lake.

## Upper Lough Erne

The Upper Lough Erne area extends from Lisbellaw south to Cavan, a distance of 35km, and from Ballyconnell east to Clones, some 23km. The landscape is an intimate mixture of low-quality grazing lands resting on peat, drumlins, and open water, and if I try to work out the development of this countryside, I feel I must have some point outside time on which to stand.

If I turn back the clock by 10,000 years, the peat will not yet have formed, and the area of open water will be greater. If I go back another 10,000 years, there will be no drumlins, and the area of water will have increased again. I find it very hard not to feel that in pre-glacial times we may have had an enormous lake here, a lake even bigger than Lough Neagh. Lough Neagh lies in a basin, created by a down-sagging of the earth's crust; was there similar crustal movement here? The Lough Neagh basin contains, as we have already seen, enormous quantities of lignite, or brown coal, only recently discovered; could there be similar deposits here?

Most of the lake is very shallow, though it reaches a depth of 20m in one restricted part. There has been shallow drilling for wells in the lake area, and some have shown glacial deposits with a thickness of 20m—I am ignoring the height to which the drumlins rise—but as far as I am aware there has been no deep drilling here. In recent years much of Ireland has been criss-crossed by deep borings in search of commercial deposits; why not put down a wild-cat boring here?

I end with an aside. *Sheela-na-gigs*, stone carvings of female torsos with the pudenda heavily emphasised, are scattered through Ireland, often on church sites. Ballyconnell offers a variant. Propped against the wall of the Church of Ireland church, there is a stone carving, which I can only interpret as a representation of a man defecating.

CHAPTER 23

# The Midlands

DRUMURCHER · CROGHAN · CLONSAST BOG

LITTLETON BOG · DERRYNAFLAN BOG

## DRUMURCHER

I use the word *midlands* in a very loose sense, merely to indicate that I now propose to visit a few sites between the Shannon and Erne and the Irish Sea before we reach the Boyne. I use the word *Drumurcher* to name the site, because that is the name of the townland in which the site lies. In most European countries the countryside is divided into named units, which can vary very much in size, and may have been established at different times. In Ireland the townland is the unit; some townlands are of high antiquity, others were defined in the eighteenth century; but the units were 'frozen' in the mid-nineteenth century, when their boundaries and their names were engraved on the maps of the Ordnance Survey on the scale of six inches to the mile.

Everyone in rural Ireland knows the names and boundaries of the local townlands; the townland is shown on the local six-inch map; the National Museum records the townland location of all its antiquities and other specimens, and so I always used the name of the townland to label my sites. Sometimes this has led to cumbersome nomenclature; Drumurcher is not too awkward, but Ballymakegogue was a bit of a mouthful, particularly when the adjoining townland is called Spa. When I started work the National Grid did not exist; today it gives a simpler and more precise location of a site; Drumurcher becomes 252 317, lying 9km south of Clones; I use it in the Locality Index.

Jessen's work at Ballybetagh stimulated my interest in the late-glacial fauna of Ireland, and when in 1937 some reindeer remains were found near Ratoath in Co. Meath, I investigated the site and drew up a map of all localities in Ireland at which reindeer remains had been found.

I then moved on to the woolly mammoth, and of this animal the most intriguing record was that of many bones discovered near Clones in 1715, and described in the *Proceedings of the Royal Society*. The find had been made when a water-mill was being constructed. Thomas Nevill visited the site and described what he saw in a very vivid letter to the local bishop, who was a fellow of the society. The letter, together with an illustrated account of the molar teeth by Sir Thomas Molyneux, a keen student of Irish natural history, was published by the society.

Nevill regretted that he had not reached the site soon enough, as when he got there the water-wall of the mill had already been built, largely concealing the exact site of the find. But he noted that there was a compact layer of leaves which contained many hazelnuts, and he pictured an elephant lying on a bed of autumn leaves and munching away at the nuts. We now know that the remains were not those of a tropical elephant, but of the extinct arctic form, the woolly mammoth, whose frozen bodies are sometimes found in Siberia today. The Drumurcher elephant had no opportunity to feed on hazelnuts.

In 1939 I hunted the area for ruined water-mills, and of all those I saw, the surroundings of the mill at Drumurcher seemed most closely to tally with the 1715 description. A flat gravel spread floored the valley; I dug a small pit, and soon came to leaves and nuts; I decided that this was it.

I went back again in autumn of 1940 with Tony Farrington, and we lodged with old Mrs Guthrie at Annaghmakerrig, not far away. Mrs Guthrie was the mother of Sir Tony Guthrie, the famous Shakespearian producer, and Peggy Butler, wife of Hubert Butler, distinguished man of letters. Tony bequeathed the property to be a residential centre for artistic studies, and as such it flourishes today. The conditions now are less Spartan than those that Tony Farrington and I met, in the first autumn of the war. Mrs Guthrie's sight had failed badly, but if the hall-door was open she could see a patch of light. So the hall-door stood remorselessly open, even though it was letting chill September air through the whole house.

At Drumurcher the mill, which had been a flax-scutching mill, was abandoned, though all the fittings stood there idle. The small farmhouse nearby was occupied by the Andrews family, a happy group of Mr and Mrs Andrews and their two children, Sonny, about six, and Dotie, about five. They lived a simple frugal life. Mrs Andrews had hens, which were fed on 'yellow meal', a porridge made of crushed maize; the children loved it, and as soon as the porridge was cooked, they got the first spoonfuls. Barn-yard fowl in those days were often infested with gape-worms which lived in the windpipes of young birds, causing them to cough and gasp. A standard remedy was to fish them out, and I can still see Mrs Andrews holding a gasping chicken between her knees, skilfully inserting a twisted horsehair down its gullet, and fishing till she pulled out the wriggling worm.

Digging down in a series of pits, Tony Farrington and I went through first some silt, then fine gravel rich in wood and hazelnuts, and at a depth of 150cm thin peat and mud, resting on river-gravel; the mud was rich in fruits of arctic plants such as Jessen had found at Ballybetagh. We discovered no traces of bone of any kind, so we may not have been digging at the site of the original find. But there was no doubt that the flora we found and the woolly mammoth could have been contemporaneous.

I gave the arctic material a preliminary washing, and it was so rich in seeds and fruits of arctic plants I did not know, that I wrote to Knud Jessen, and asked him if he would look it over for me. In a way typical of his generosity, he immediately agreed, and not only identified as much of the material as he could, but also wrote detailed notes about each plant recognised; this material I later incorporated in a publication of my own.

When Knud tackled the identification of the heap of fine debris that was left after he had carefully washed the mud through a series of sieves, he always placed three extra tubes in front of him, one labelled Mosses, one labelled Insecta, and the third labelled Ignota. The tubes labelled mosses and insects would later go to specialist colleagues for detailed study, while the third was retained in the hope that increased experience would lead to further identifications. I followed his example with very great profit, because in due course I met Jim Dickson, now in the University of Glasgow, who looked at my mosses, and Russell Coope of Birmingham, who looked at my beetles.

I was delighted when, early in the seventies, Russell wrote to say that he was looking again at late-glacial beetles in the British Isles, and wanted to see all my insect tubes. I sent them off, and not long after, Russell wrote to ask what was this Drumurcher place, as its beetle remains were quite exciting in their richness. We decided to re-open the site to get more samples, and in 1975 a party of three returned, Russell to collect beetles, myself to get a radiocarbon sample, and Jacqueline McCutcheon to collect mud to wash for seeds and fruits. We also collected material for Jim Dickson.

I found the setting very different from what it had been before. The house and farm were abandoned, and most of the fittings had disappeared from the scutch-mill. Mr and Mrs Andrews were dead, Dotie had died when nursing in England, and Sonny had vanished. It rained throughout our short visit. A mechanical digger quickly brought up all the material we needed, and I was glad to hurry away from the site.

In his material Russell identified 100 species of beetle, including many no longer living in Ireland, and the assemblage gave a climatic picture like that on the slopes of the Scandinavian mountains or the tundras of the far north. But there were no dung beetles, which are often found on sites frequented by large herbivores such as the mammoth and the hippopotamus, and so the beetles gave no hint of mammoth presence. My radiocarbon date was 10,500 years ago, and as known radiocarbon dates for mammoth in the British Isles were then around the 18,000 mark, it seemed that the Drumurcher mud went rather with the giant deer and the reindeer, than with the mammoth. Jacqueline produced sixty vascular plants from her samples, and this richness was probably due in part to the topography of the site, where the gravel-flat with its ponds had a drumlin slope to the west and a rock-slope to the east, thus providing a variety of local habitats. The ponds on the flat were waiting to trap the debris. Her chief treasure was the only Irish find of a seed of the yellow-flowered arctic poppy (*Papaver radicatum*), which today is confined to gravel-flats in the high arctic; there are two fossil localities for this plant in Britain. Jim netted twenty-eight mosses, many of which today are at home in the tundras of arctic and alpine regions.

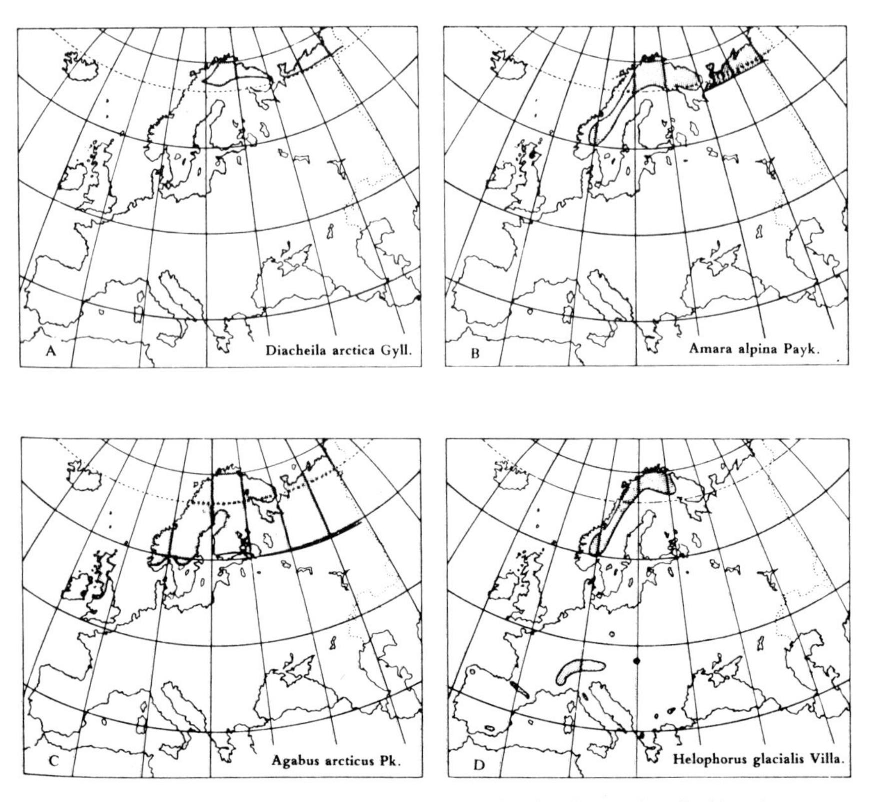


*Modern distribution of some beetles whose fossil remains were found at Drumurcher, Co. Monaghan.*

In all a most successful raid, but perhaps not yet the end of the story. In 1986 Russell investigated, in a sand-pit in Shropshire, the discovery of an adult, and also, almost incredibly, three infant woolly mammoths. Here the radiocarbon age was 12,700 years, showing that mammoths were still around 5000 years after they were supposed to have become extinct. The age of 12,700 is not too wildly far from the Drumurcher date of 10,500. I feel we should go back again, and work up along the base of the water-wall of the mill, seeing if we could recover even one scrap of identifiable bone. With modern advances in radiocarbon dating, one quite small piece would be sufficient.

## CROGHAN

Twenty-six kilometres east-north-east of Athlone, the Hill of Uisneach, an isolated relict knob or hum of limestone, rises to a height of 180m. It is reputed that on a clear day twenty of the thirty-two counties of Ireland can be seen from its top, and throughout prehistory and history it has been a very important site, with many remains of antiquities. Praeger and Macalister excavated here in the twenties, though not with any distinction. A large erratic boulder, now surrounded by a circular earthen bank, was described by Giraldus Cambrensis as the navel of Ireland.

I prefer to give this title of distinction to another upstanding isolated hill, Croghan, which lies near Daingean, 25km south-east of Uisneach. Croghan, which rises to a height of 230m, is a mass of volcanic rock. The rock was formerly embedded in the local limestones, but as erosion lowered the surface of the limestone, the more resistant volcanic rock held its level. Its antiquities show that it too has been frequented by people for a very long time, but they are less impressive than those at Uisneach.

I choose Croghan, because although it may not be at the geographical centre of Ireland, it lies in the heartland of the great raised-bogs of the midlands; bogs which reach an elevation of 100m lap up against it on all sides. I do not know how many counties are visible from its top, but the cooling-towers of at least four peat-fired generating-stations can be seen. In addition, it emphasises for me once again the fantastic drainage pattern of Ireland. I am sure that before man started his attack on the bogs, a continuous ring of living bog surrounded the hill. From the bog on the west water drains away to the Shannon and to the Atlantic; the bog on the north-east sends its surplus water to the Boyne and the Irish Sea, while water on the south-east goes to the Barrow and the Celtic Sea. Each of these rivers has to abandon open country, and negotiate a rocky gorge before it reaches the sea; the Shannon at Killaloe, the Boyne below Navan, and the Barrow below Graiguenamanagh.

## Clonsast Bog

I feel I should have written an account of *The Rape and Cremation of an Irish Raised-bog*. Clonsast bog was one of the largest and finest of Irish raised-bogs, and so it was early marked out for development by Bord na Móna.

The bog lies about 7km north of Portarlington, and while in places it merged into other nearby bogs, it was essentially an independent unit, about 6.5km long and 4km across. The peat was 6m deep, and its domed top rose to about 10m above the surrounding countryside. I saw it first in 1938 when I walked it with Tony Farrington, Felix Hackett, a professor in University College, Dublin, and a man of very wide scientific interests, and some members of the staff of Bord na Móna.

The top of the bog was very wet and quaky, and here I was glad I had mastered the art, necessary for bog survival, of walking with one's weight on the foot in the air. There was an extensive system of very large pools, known locally as the Duck Loughs, because they were used as a refuge by wildfowl in the winter. Discussing the ponds someone suggested that they were fed by deep springs at the bottom of the bog, but this seemed unlikely. The origin of these pools is not clearly understood. In some bogs they are aligned with one another, and suggest expansion-tears in the living membrane of vegetation that clothes the bog surface.

At times raised-bogs appear to be overcharged with moisture, and some of this escapes by sub-surface channels, which may have a tunnel-like exit towards the bog margin. Such exits are called soaks, and Clonsast had one splendid example near its south-west margin, from which water emerged so steadily that it was marked as a river on the OS map. Today, alas, opportunities for further study of this feature in Ireland have vanished, as most of the big bogs with good pool systems and soaks have been developed.

To initiate development at Clonsast an extensive series of drains and development trenches were cut into the bog surface, which gradually sagged towards the cuts as water drained away. After some time the surface became firm enough to carry complicated peat-harvesting machinery. The mechanical engineers of Bord na Móna showed considerable ingenuity in design, as the machines had to be as big as possible, so as to handle large quantities of material, without at the same time becoming so heavy that they would sink into the bog. These machines aroused wide international interest.

An electricity transformer station was erected flush with the bog surface, supported on columns which went down to the soil below the bog; as the years went by it was amusing to watch the station appear to climb higher and higher into the air, as the peat around it continued to sink. Much of the peat-winning machinery was powered by electricity, and it always seemed to me to smack something of the pelican engrailing in that some of the electricity produced by the bog had to be fed back to it to further its own destruction.

Sad as the destruction of the bog was, the sections cut into it afforded a wonderful opportunity to study the phases of its development. But the times could have been a little more favourable; it was in the war years, and cars had disappeared, and with them one might think the possibility of transporting my relatively heavy drilling-rods. Unfortunately I came across a photograph in a paper on bog survey in Sweden, which showed a keen worker with the rods strapped to the bar of his bicycle, and I realised I was still mobile. I found cycling with the loaded machine rather hazardous, as the centre of gravity was high, and one had to bend one's knee first outwards to get round the rods, and then in again to reach the pedal. So I continued to work at Clonsast, cycling out from the hotel in Portarlington. Once at the bog matters were easier, as the bog was now covered with a light railway, and the workers at the depot were very accommodating about running me out to the various parts I wished to visit. Levelling presented no problem as the bog had been very accurately surveyed.

About 7500 years ago woods in which pine and yew were common covered the area. Progressive formation of peat near by was steadily blocking the local drainage system, and waterlogging killed off the trees which gave way to fen plants. After these had formed about 2m of fen-peat, they could no longer get sufficient nutrient from the soil below, and they gave way to plants of the Sphagnum-moss community, which could gain all its needs from rainwater. At first peat-growth was slow, and decayed moss-peat built up to a thickness of about 1m. Bog-growth then accelerated, and about 3.5m of fresh moss-peat built up the upper layers of the bog-dome.

Unfortunately for the Bord, this simple pattern of growth had been interrupted by climatic periods when the bog-surface became drier, and the trees which had been driven out re-invaded the surface. Renewed bog-growth killed off the trees, but they left behind a horizon of tough, often interlaced, tree stumps, which caused great problems for machines designed to slice up soft wet peat. This was a problem the Bord were to meet over and over again throughout the country.

The last major invasion by trees was about 4000 years ago, and in that invasion pine was prominent. After that pine dropped back in importance in Ireland, though it did survive at least into the early centuries AD in some localities. It was then that it made a last feeble invasion of the bog surface at Clonsast. In one restricted area I saw a lot of uprooted small pine trees. At first sight they looked like weeping willows that some vandals had torn up in a nursery-garden. But closer examination showed that the projections that curved away from the stems were roots, not branches. The pines were trying to grow on a wet bog-surface; as tree-weight increased, the stem sank into the bog bringing the roots down into an over-wet layer. The roots responded by trying to climb back to the surface, with the result that when pulled from the bog the young tree looked like an umbrella inside out.

By 1988 the development of Clonsast bog had run its full cycle, and the power-station near Portarlington was dismantled. That operation brought its own problems. In the forties asbestos was a perfectly respectable building-material, and it was used in parts of the station. But by 1988 asbestos was a dirty word, and its removal and disposal caused difficulties.

But the greatest problem was the 'cutover', the derelict area from which the peat had been removed. Strenuous experiments were carried out to see how best to reclaim the area. A dairy farm was set up, vegetables were grown, trees were planted. The possibility of 'biomass' production, that is, the growing of woody bushes which would be harvested mechanically at a young stage and burned to produce electricity, was considered. But one is forced back again to the observation Charles Smith made in Cork over two hundred years ago: 'It may be a question, whether the labour and expense will not be more than the value of the land, after it has thus been reclaimed?' The European Community does not want more land, certainly not poor-grade land, and the wisest course is probably to let the cutover revert to the wetland from which it started. Possibly the slow cycle of raised bog development might begin all over again.

## Littleton Bog

A surviving patch of higher Carboniferous shales and sandstones with some coals lies on top of the limestone in Kilkenny, and a spur from this runs south-west into Tipperary, where it ends at Cashel. The shales and sandstones end in a long curved escarpment which overlooks the limestone to the west; the escarpment is very like the one we saw near Newcastle West in Limerick. The low-lying limestone is patchily covered by glacial deposits which blocked the drainage, and a band of raised-bogs about 30km long lies at the foot of the escarpment. But generally soils are good and the area was thickly populated in prehistoric and historic times.

Bord na Móna was active here in the fifties, and at Littleton there was an interested relationship between the bog-workers, the manager and the National Museum, with the result that a considerable number of archaeological finds were retrieved as the bog was cut away.

The most dramatic find was a well-preserved human body, dressed in fifteenth/sixteenth-century costume. As at Clonsast, in this bog there was always the possibility that the cutting-machine would strike heavy wood and be damaged. So in a rather Heath Robinsonian way a boom with a seat at the end of it was fitted to the machine over the excavating buckets; a man with a bell at his elbow travelled along with the machine, and it was his duty to keep a close eye on the buckets, and if he saw wood, to ring the bell. Work ran on a twenty-four-hour shift, and at night a spotlight illuminated the bucket. All of a sudden, in the middle of the night, the duty man saw a human form rising from the bog below, and he gave a violent ring to the bell. The body and its clothing emerged in quite good condition, so much so that rumour spread that the body must be that of a saint, and relic-seekers soon stripped the clothing of its buttons and the head of its teeth.

It was a different find that brought me to the site in 1954. A sword-like object of wood, probably a weaver's batten, dated to about AD 1000, had been found near the surface of the bog. I went down with Bill Watts, and we took detailed samples nearby. Our drill went down for 7.5m through much the same sequence of peats as at Clonsast, and below that there was a further metre of mud which contained the same late-glacial sequence that Jessen had first revealed at Ballybetagh. So the record here started at the end of the Ice Age. When Hilda Parkes looked at the pollen-samples she found that the top 10cm of the bog contained pollen of beech and pine. Planting of these trees on a wide scale in Ireland did not begin before AD 1700, and so at this bog peat must have continued to form until recent drainage attacked it. If we were working there today, we would be looking for evidence of nuclear fall-out in the top two centimetres.

Hilda worked her way right down though the samples and produced a fascinating story. In the wartime samples from Clonsast she was tracing out forest history only. But, as we have seen, during the war pollen-workers in Denmark revolutionised the whole pattern of studies. They showed, not only that forest disturbance by early farmers could be brought to light by comparing the quantity of tree pollen produced relative to that of grasses and other herbs, but also that the pollen of the weeds that grew in early fields could be identified and counted. Hilda was now looking for evidence of early agriculture as well as forest development, and this could clearly be seen as far back as 5000 years ago when the first Neolithic farmers arrived in Ireland. From this point on, an ebbing and flowing between land utilisation and land abandonment, as farming flourished and waned, could be demonstrated, and it was possible sometimes to tie these changes to specific archaeological periods. The final sweeping away of woodland in Tudor times was especially clear.

Twenty years later there was another twist to the Littleton story. Glacial deposits are notoriously difficult to link up with one another, and quaternary geologists are always trying to play the correlation game. Once it did become a card-game when Sue Deigan, one of Harry Godwin's research students in Cambridge, introduced into a pack a series of hand-drawn court-cards, each of which depicted a specialist worker in the field. Whether one was represented on a card or not was a true index of one's fame. Fredric Zeuner of the London Institute of Archaeology was notorious for his wild-cat correlations, and he appeared as the joker.

A new effort at correlation was set up by the Geological Society of London in the forties, and each region in the British Isles was asked to describe its local sequences carefully, and give titles and divisions where appropriate. *Post-glacial* was no longer an acceptable name for the time that has elapsed since cold conditions last disappeared from the British Isles, as most workers now consider we are heading for another cold period, unless the 'greenhouse effect' aborts it. In forest history in the British Isles the definitive return of post-Ice Age warmth is marked at the point in time when juniper bushes, the precursors of later forests, began to flourish. This marked rise in juniper, dated to about 10,300 years ago, was clearly seen in the Littleton diagram, and after that time the growth of peat in the bog appeared to continue uninterruptedly almost to the present day. So Littleton Bog was chosen as the type-site for this period in Ireland, which was duly named the *Littletonian*.

But during the last twenty years it has been recognised that the clearest record of Ice Age events lies in the muds and oozes on the ocean floors, and detailed studies show a rhythmical alternation between warmth and cold. It is to this pattern that we now have to try to pin the vagaries of the glacial deposits visible on the earth's surface, and the correlation-table, which was published by the Geological Society in 1973, with some panache, is rapidly finding its way into the wastepaper basket.

## Derrynaflan Bog

This big raised-bog lies 5km south of Littleton, and when I first saw it in 1980 it was relatively intact, except for Bord na Móna's preliminary drainage-cuts. When I saw it again some years later it was a sheet of brown peat dust, awaiting transport to a nearby briquette factory.

My purpose here was very different to most of my other bog-visits. A small island of glacial deposit rises through the bog, and this had been the site of early settlement. There was a very important Christian monastery here in the eighth and ninth centuries, but all that could still be seen were the walls of a ruined church—which is a National Monument—surrounded by some rather nondescript field-banks. In the autumn of 1980 two practising metal-detector users, Michael Webb and his son from Clonmel, swept the island with their instruments. They got a very strong signal from the base of one of the banks near the church, and digging quickly unearthed a remarkable hoard of early ecclesiastical silver altar plate, all lavishly decorated with filigree and enamel. There was a large paten, of a quality equal to that of the Ardagh Chalice. There was a large chalice not quite of the same quality, and perhaps a little later in date. There was also a spoon adapted to be used as a strainer. These precious items were partly protected by a simple bronze bowl. All these the treasure-hunters carried across the bog to their car, and they returned well-satisfied to Clonmel.

It must be recognised that the Webbs immediately appreciated the enormous importance of their find, and got in contact with Dr Elizabeth Shee of the archaeology department in University College, Cork, who happened to live in Clonmel. She said that to avoid deterioration the objects must go at once to the National Museum, and the Webbs delivered them there, thus initiating a tangled and prolonged story. Michael Ryan, the Keeper of Antiquities in the National Museum, decided that the site of the find had to be explored immediately to glean what further knowledge might still exist. So he went down with Mary Cahill and Ned

Kelly from the Museum, and he asked me to go along to make a preliminary assessment of the environmental setting of the site. Most of what I did was of a rather general nature, but I noticed that there was some debris exposed in the drainage-trench nearest to the eastern slope of the island. Apparently Irish people in those days were as eager to get rid of their rubbish by dumping as we are today, and an excavation in the ditch might have produced a lot of valuable material; in archaeology yesterday's dump is today's treasure-house.

Michael and his colleagues most carefully removed the earth the Webbs had thrown back into the hole, and traced out the former outline of the objects. They were rewarded by revealing, still attached to the soil, two tiny panels of gold filigree, each about the size of a postage-stamp, that had become detached from the paten. It was one of the most romantic moments in my life when I looked into the hole and saw these tiny objects, still gleaming, which had lain there undisturbed for almost one thousand years.

It was clear that if the find was to join the national collection, the finders had to be given a substantial award, an amount in keeping both with the value of the hoard itself and the financial status of the finders, and the Museum proposed just such an award. Unfortunately the amount had to be decided on by cheese-paring Scrooges in the Department of Finance, and a derisory sum was offered to, and immediately rejected by, the Webbs, who initiated legal proceedings to regain the hoard; a lawyer's paradise was entered into.

Custody, possession, ownership, are words on which the legal mind loves to play. The Webbs had no claim to *ownership* of objects which they had taken from lands which they did not own, and on which they were trespassing without permission. If the objects had been concealed by persons who intended to return and claim them at a later date, then the State, continuing what had been a royal prerogative, had a claim to ownership as treasure trove, a claim which overrode the rights of the landowner. The Webbs had had the objects in their *possession*, they had handed them over voluntarily for temporary protective purposes to the Museum; could they turn up at the Museum and demand that they should be returned to their possession? In the *custody* of the Museum, the objects were fairly safe; what protective custody could the Webbs give to them? It was obvious that the tangled question of treasure trove would be a source of major legal argument, as it had been in the Broighter Case, nearly one hundred years ago. Legal developments rumbled on.

It so happened that at the time I was researching into the development of the Royal Irish Academy's collection of Irish antiquities, and became interested in the history of treasure trove in Ireland, where the operation of treasure trove is delegated to the Academy. I got to know quite a lot about it. Legal friends, when I met them in the street, asked, 'Have they come to you yet?' When I asked, 'What do you mean?', they replied, 'The Webbs, of course; they are looking for archaeologists to bolster up their claims.' And in due course, they did come. I got a letter from a firm of solicitors in Birr, saying that the Webbs' leading counsel, Mr Kinlen, would like a consultation with me. I refused, and thereby waived the quite handsome fee I would have felt entitled to ask.

But in a most ironic manner, I was later forced to disgorge my information free. When the case came to the High Court, Mr Kinlen took the bold line that there was no longer, and had not been since the signing of the Treaty in 1922, anything such as treasure trove in the twenty-six counties. In England letters in transit are deemed to be royal mail, and if you are knocked down by a post-office van, the prerogative of the Crown cannot be sued for damages. Apparently at some time, I think in the seventies, someone in this country who had been knocked down by a post-office van took an action against the post office; the post-office pleaded royal prerogative, but the court ruled that all such regal rights had lapsed on the signing of the Treaty. Mr Kinlen argued that treasure trove also had disappeared from the Republic. The court felt that the Academy ought to know about treasure trove, and asked that that information be placed at its disposal. Willy-nilly the Academy obviously had to ask me to spill the beans, and so I told the story as I knew it to the court.

The High Court was obviously impressed by Mr Kinlen's argument, and, without prejudice to the ownership of the objects, awarded possession of them to the Webbs. What were the Webbs to do? Nobody could blame them if anything happened to the objects while they were in the Museum, but if they took them out of the Museum, how were they going to safeguard them? The problem was resolved by the State appealing to the Supreme Court, which held that although royal prerogatives had disappeared in 1922, sovereign states also enjoyed such prerogatives. The State had a right to 'ownerless things', when the objects were significant artefacts of national archaeological importance. The Court granted to the Webbs the appropriate award that was their due in the first place, and which, if then awarded, would have avoided the wasting of a great deal of time, trouble and unnecessary expense.

CHAPTER 24

# The Boyne

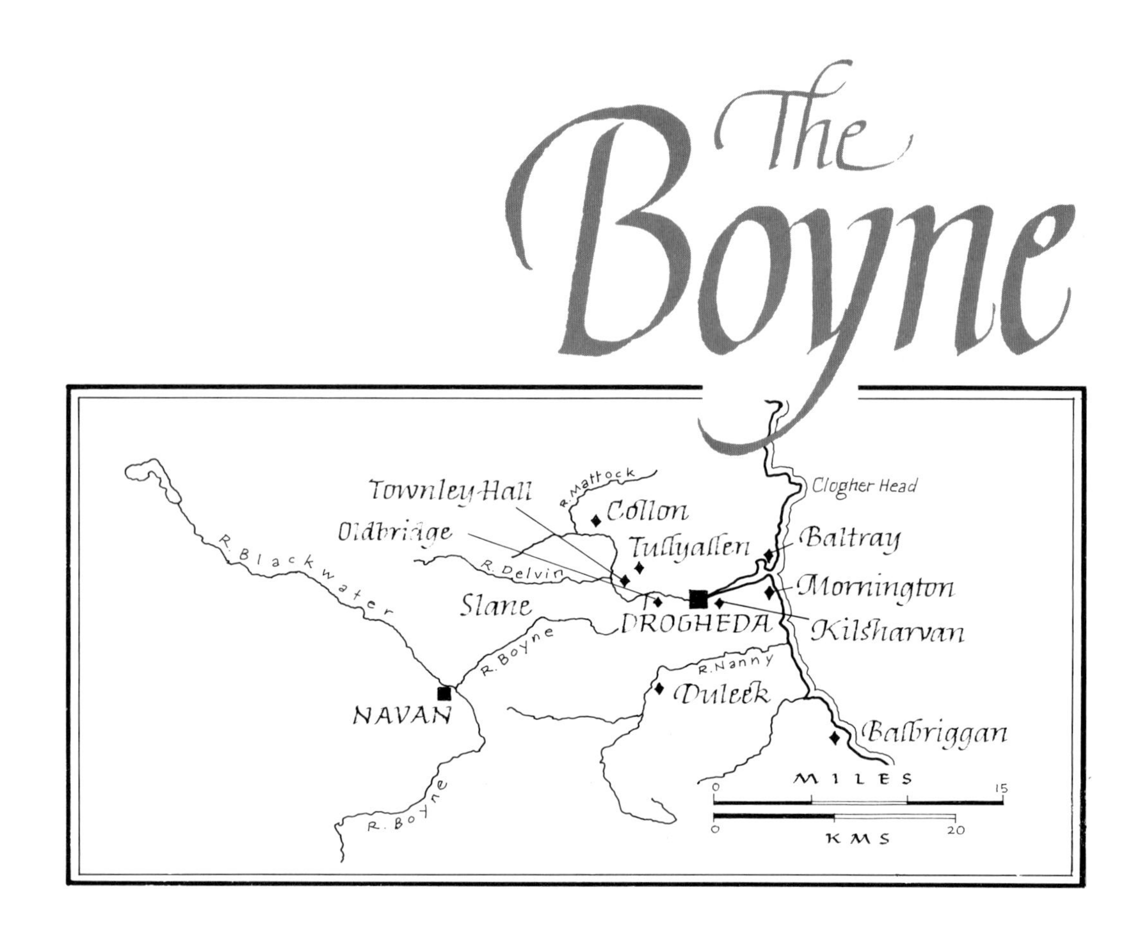


UPPER COURSE · LOWER COURSE

BRÚ NA BÓINNE · NEWGRANGE · KNOWTH

TOWNLEY HALL · DROGHEDA · THE ESTUARY

## Upper Course

We return to Croghan, but this time we set our faces to the north-east, to look out over the headwaters of the Boyne.

North of Edenderry the Boyne gradually collects itself together, and flows in an erratic course that is typical of so many of the major rivers of Ireland, first north-easterly across well-developed glacial deposits, some of which rise into spectacular eskers. *En route* it passes through Trim, a historic town, which like Kilkenny might have risen to the status of capital of Ireland had not the coastal position of Dublin given it the primacy. The castle, with its central keep and surrounding curtain wall, is one of the finest in Ireland, and there are also the remains of a cathedral and several monastic houses. In medieval times the town was one of the principal strongholds of the Pale.

## Lower Course

About 5km to the south of Navan the Boyne makes a right-angle bend to the north-west, and in the town has a head-on collision with the Meath Blackwater, which was flowing south-east from Kells and beyond. The combined streams turn at right angles to the north-east, and plunge into higher karstic limestone country. At Navan the general countryside is below 60m in level, but the rock landscape rises to over 75m on both sides of the river. We have already seen the Shannon cut into limestone country, both at Meelick and at Castleconnell. The course of the Boyne in this 10km stretch alternates between wandering across open dolines partly filled with glacial deposits through which isolated knobs of rock rise here and there, and flowing in a narrow rock gorge, well seen on the stretch between Beauparc House and Slane Castle. Praeger has an illustration of this picturesque gorge.

Above Slane the river turns east, and swings southwards into an open semi-circle which ultimately carries it northwards to meet the Mattock at Oldbridge, 5km west of Drogheda. The Mattock itself is a tributary of the Delvin River (though it imposes its name on the combined rivers), and broadly speaking the valley of the Delvin parallels that of the Boyne; thus there is a ridge of high ground between the two valleys. Here, and for a small area around, the limestone is capped by a layer of black shales, and it is on this black shale ridge-top that the magnificent concentration of imposing prehistoric monuments, known as *Brú na Bóinne*, the House on the Boyne, is situated.

## Brú na Bóinne

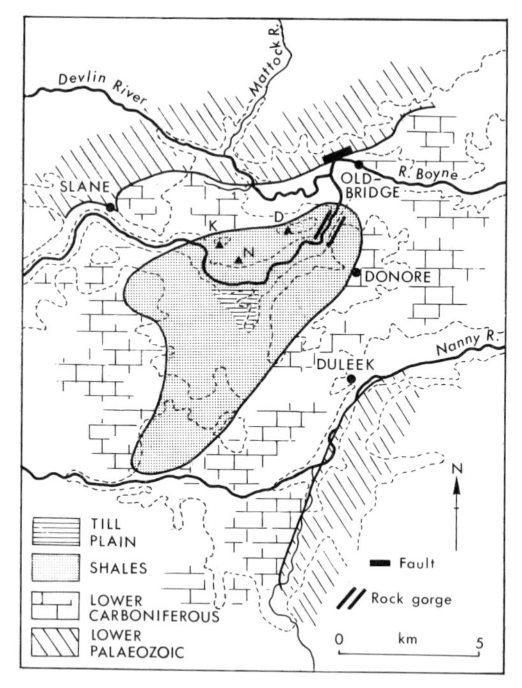


*The local geology, the course of the river and the local soils probably all played a part in the development of the intense prehistoric activity that took place in this stretch of the Boyne valley. (D = Dowth, K = Knowth, N = Newgrange)*

Newgrange, Knowth and Dowth are of course the kings of the ridge, but there are a considerable number of other monuments in the immediate vicinity, both on the ridge itself and on the broad gravel terraces of the Boyne that lie below the ridge on its southern side. The terrace soils are very fertile, as are those on the till-plain across the river, and it may have been this richness of the local soils that first attracted farmers to the area.

### Newgrange

My first visit to Newgrange was in the mid-thirties with Arthur Stelfox, Tony Farrington and R.A.S. Macalister. Though he has already bobbed up several times in my narrative, this was my first meeting with Macalister; I was no more than a student at the time. He was then Professor of Archaeology in University College, Dublin; a small alert man with twinkling eyes, he was always dressed in a blue serge suit and starched collar, and carried an umbrella;

he had a fertile imagination. Some of the slabs in the roof of the great central chamber inside the Newgrange mound carry a black encrustation of manganese oxides, deposited from evaporating water. Macalister believed that the deposit was soot from Bronze Age funeral pyres, and I had been brought along as a 'scientist', in the hope that I could convince him that large fires in such a confined area would not have left much oxygen for those in charge of the fires to breathe.

I do not know if he listened to me, but after a short interval he jumped to another ploy. He produced from his pocket a small pendulum bob attached to a length of string, and proceeded with the aid of the tip of his umbrella to try to push the bob in under the great stone basin in the right-hand recess of the tomb (in his defence I must say that the interior of the tomb was then much less tidy than it is today). He thought that the basin might be serving as the cap of an open vertical shaft, such as are found in Mycenaean tombs. If he could get the bob in, he would lower it on the string, and so ascertain the depth of the shaft. I was amazed and embarrassed by his attempts, and retired down the entrance-passage out of sight. However, he gave up after a short time, and emerged from the tomb quite undisappointed by his failure.

At Newgrange in those days candles and torches were the rule, and the overlying dilapidated mound was partly covered by trees and scrub. Today's Newgrange makes us remember Brian O'Kelly, who worked there for thirteen years in conjunction with Percy le Clerc, who directed the reconstruction of the facade of the mound carried out by the Office of Public Works (OPW). Brian excavated the chamber, straightened up the leaning stones in the entrance passage that made access difficult, and outside the tomb he also excavated around the vicinity of the entrance. Among the numerous important discoveries that he made, the most dramatic was the realisation that the sun, when rising at its winter solstice, was low enough in the sky to shine up the entrance passage and illuminate the chamber itself.

In the course of the outer excavations, large quantities of white quartz were found in the vicinity of the entrance, accompanied by numerous rugby-football-sized cobbles of granite from the Mourne Mountains; such cobbles could not be obtained in quantity less than 30km from the site. Studying the arrangement of the quartz as he found it spreadeagled on the ground, Brian came to the conclusion that white quartz interspersed with granite cobbles formed a wall-face in the front of the mound in the vicinity of the entrance. Accordingly he and Percy erected the high quartz-faced wall that is the principal feature of the monument as we approach it today. While we can never know what the original appearance of the mound was, I have to feel that the wall, as erected, overstates the case.

But nothing ever stops in archaeology, and even since Brian's campaigns ended, there have been further developments. David Sweetman of the Parks and Monuments branch of the OPW has shown that on the slope between the access road and the great tomb itself, and approaching within 10m of the mound, there is a large ring of post-holes and pits with charred wood and cremated bones, a *henge* monument on the style of Stonehenge. Finds and radiocarbon dates show that this monument is some hundreds of years later than the big tomb. The builders of the big tomb seem to have had no metal; the builders of the henge were Early Bronze Age, and clearly had metal. It would be interesting to know the range of social and economic differences that separated the two groups of monument-builders.

But success brings its own problems, and the readier access to the great tomb which O'Kelly and le Clerc provided has brought a corresponding increase in visitor numbers. On a favourable day 1200 people will make their way in and out of the chamber. Now it is proposed to set up an archaeological park in the Boyne valley, with its focus on the great tombs. Experience elsewhere shows that even such laudable developments bring their own problems, and much sensitivity and good taste will be required if the proposed park is to be made a successful reality.

**Knowth**

There is a famous American national park at Yosemite in California, where there is a giant granite dome which has been deeply cut into by glacial action, so that the park abounds in cliffs, waterfalls, trees, birds and animals. One book about it gives it, in its title, the attribute *Incomparable*. I feel that though the scale and the context are very different, the site at Knowth merits the same adjective.

At Knowth (Pl. 7) the great mound has for more than twenty years yielded secret after secret, as George Eogan continues his mammoth programme of excavation. I first met George when he assisted David Liversage in the excavation on Dalkey Island, and I rapidly got to appreciate his powers of application and persistence. George had put himself through University College, Dublin, but as he had to work in the daytime he could only attend night classes at the university. Unfortunately a college regulation did not allow those who had taken evening degrees to proceed immediately to graduate work. The rules in Trinity were less formal, and I took him on as a research student. He produced a very good thesis on Irish Bronze Age swords, and also deputised for me in some teaching. By the time he had got his Ph.D., I had adopted him as my son in archaeology, just as I had adopted Bill Watts as my son in science. George dug in Jericho with Kathleen Kenyon, and then went on to Oxford to work with Christopher Hawkes. After a spell in Queen's University, Belfast, he returned to University College, Dublin, where he is now professor.

When, as we shall see in the next section, Trinity College acquired the Townley Hall estate, also in the Boyne valley, in 1957, I was anxious that any antiquities on the property should be examined. David Liversage dug a small Neolithic house-site at the east end of the estate, and there was another small mound toward the west which George dug. Though what was left was not visually exciting, the mound contained a very simple passage-tomb which rested on a complex stone setting. But underneath the mound was the remains of a round house with decorated pottery in the style that Praeger and Macalister had found at Carrowkeel in Sligo, known as Carrowkeel ware. There were also cereal grains and charcoal, which gave a radiocarbon date of 4700 years ago.

George then located another site nearby which had a decorated stone associated with it, and he secured permission to dig there. Unfortunately after all his preparations were made, the permission was unexpectedly withdrawn. What were we to do? George and I looked at one another and said, 'What about Knowth?' So we went round to the Robinsons, on whose land the mound lay. We set out our position to old Mr Robinson, whom I can still see clearly in his chair in front of the fire in the sittingroom, and after some talk he gave his consent. The original idea was to explore the satellite smaller tombs in the vicinity of the big mound, but the work just grew and grew. I am very fortunate in that, living only a few kilometres away, I have been able to follow the yearly progress of the work, just as I was able to follow Brian O'Kelly's work at Newgrange.

What is the story of Knowth, twenty years on? The first Neolithic farmers to reach Ireland probably arrived a little more than 5000 years ago. They lived in rectangular houses, used pottery with little decoration, and did not build elaborate tombs. At Knowth these people had a small settlement on the natural rise in the rock on which the great mound was later erected.

Then the passage-tomb builders arrived about 4750 years ago, living in round houses and using pottery whose surface was roughened by stab-marks, the so-called Carrowkeel ware. Their tombs increased in size, culminating in the high mound, holding within itself two large passage-tombs; many of the large stones used were lavishly decorated with stylised ornament.

As at Newgrange, they also embellished the entrances to the large tombs with boulders of quartz and cobbles of granite.

*George Eogan (centre) demonstrates a decorated kerb stone at Knowth. Behind (left to right) Etienne Rynne (Galway), Frank Mitchell, Bohulav Chropovský (Czechoslovakia), Jacques Nenquin (Belgium)*

We have seen that at Newgrange the first users of metal then arrived and erected a large monument in their own style. These Early Bronze Age people used a thin-walled style of pottery, often geometrically decorated, known as Beaker. These people also came to Knowth, probably shortly after 4000 years ago, but beyond their pottery and their flint implements no structural features were found.

There was then an extraordinary lull, as almost no material of the later stages of the Bronze Age or the pagan Iron Age was found. Activity was renewed, perhaps about AD 400, when the strategic possibilities of the great mound were realised for the first time. Two very large ditches were dug around it, one at its base and the other around the top edge; an entrance causeway was left at the south-east. Again there appears to have been an abandonment, and the ditches began to silt up.

Around AD 800 there was renewed extensive occupation. There are houses and souterrains, and evidence for farming and industrial activities. Knowth now begins to emerge in history, and it was probably the palace of the local king.

In the late twelfth century the mound was seized on by the Anglo-Norman invaders, who saw in it a ready-made motte, or defensive mound. They erected a substantial stone building, with well-cut stone surrounds to its windows on the top of the mound. After that date there is a trickle of later pottery, and remains of late medieval houses around the big mound. And the story continues to the present day on the Robinson farm. The family cannot have realised what they were letting themselves in for when Mr Robinson granted his permission, but they have been very gallant about all the comings and goings of the past twenty years.

I have tried to give only a step by step account of the revealing of the historical continuity of the site, which it has been my privilege to follow, and which I have found so impressive. I have said nothing about the crown jewels as they have been discovered; the two great passage-graves, one a replica of Newgrange, the other in Breton style; the stylised carvings on the great stones, and the recent realisation that some of the carvings are palimpsests, the original design having been replaced by the superposition of a later style; the magnificent stone-cutting, on a large scale, in the great decorated stone bowl in one of the tomb-chambers, on a small scale, in the lavishly worked flint macehead from the same chamber; the *graffiti* in Irish which the ninth-century settlers left on the stones of the passage-grave when they re-used it, and the coins minted in Winchester which they dropped in one of their souterrain passages. The list could go on and on. I feel that Knowth truly merits the word 'incomparable'.

## TOWNLEY HALL

I do not regard myself as in any way superstitious, but I am not so sure about portents. There were three portents of Townley Hall, long before I was aware there was any possibility that I would one day be closely associated with the place.

Mrs Madeline Balfour, who lived on for many years at Townley Hall as a life tenant after her husband's death, was the daughter of John Kells Ingram, a don in Trinity College and a very distinguished sociologist. In a rash moment he wrote 'Who fears to speak of '98?', and regretted it ever after. She had been great friends with Lucy Gwynn of Parteen, also the daughter of a don, and when Lucy Gwynn returned to Dublin she asked me to drive her down to Townley Hall to see Madeline, and this I did.

John Betjeman was British Press Attaché in Dublin during the war; he had a great admiration for the buildings of Francis Johnston, especially Townley Hall, and wrote about them. Betjeman was succeeded by Reggie Ross Williamson, also a lover of the arts, and he wanted to see the house that had impressed Betjeman so much. One of Reggie's duties was to provide 'carriage exercise' for the ambassador, Sir Gilbert Laithwaite, and he asked me to arrange a visit to Townley Hall. So I came a second time, with Reggie and Gilbert.

One winter afternoon in the fifties there was a knock on the door in Merrion Square, where my family and I were living, and a man asked to see my wife. His name was Tisdall, and he was Mrs Balfour's steward. He explained that Mrs Balfour was ill, and wished to dispose of a few items of personal jewellery; her closest friend had been Lucy Gwynn, and she wished the pieces to go to my wife, who was Lucy Gwynn's niece. She died shortly afterwards. Among the items was a pearl-mounted ruby, suspended on a gold chain. When, some years later, we did arrive in Townley Hall, we found a double portrait of Mr and Mrs Balfour, in which she is shown wearing the chain. My wife used to wear it sometimes, after she had become *chatelaine* of the house.

On Mrs Balfour's death the property passed to a distant kinsman, who had his home and career in England. Not wishing to change his way of life, he decided to sell the estate. Lynn Carr Lett was the family law agent, and also farmed himself. He felt that Trinity College ought to do more about agriculture, a subject which had only a marginal place in the activities of the college. He came to me with the suggestion that the estate, which was only 50km from the college, would form a magnificent centre for agricultural work; he knew it could be purchased on reasonable terms.

At the time the Trinity medical school had received another of those ukases that come from time to time saying that Ireland produces far too many doctors, and that the size of the medical school must be reduced. In a docile way the college listened, and decided that if medicine had to shrink, engineering and agriculture should expand.

So in 1957 the college bought the Townley Hall estate of almost 400ha, part farmland, part woodland, together with the Francis Johnston mansion, and set about expanding its faculty of agriculture and forestry. The Agricultural Institute offered co-operation in research and teaching, and the Kellogg Foundation provided funds to assist in organising the house as a student residence; the future seemed rosy. I took to 'weekending' with my family in some rooms in the farmyard, and threw myself fully into the project. I carried milk-churns, I washed cows' udders, I moved electric fences, I assisted sows to farrow. I greatly enjoyed living in the country, as opposed to making occasional visits to it from the city, and also taking an active part in farming, instead of leaning on a farm gate from time to time.

But the project was fundamentally underfunded, the college as a whole regarded the matter with apathy, and the enterprise became an uphill struggle. The climax came in 1967, when the Minister for Education declared that university structures in the Republic must be reorganised, there must be amalgamations, and that the distribution of faculties must be rationalised. It was clear that whatever happened, there was going to be no major government support for agricultural education in Trinity College, and the college decided to pull out. I regretted that the enterprise had failed, but I did not regret my contact with Irish farming and its many problems.

There was no problem in disposing of the lands, where the Land Commission was a ready purchaser. But what about the house, generally recognised as one of the masterpieces of the distinguished Irish architect, Francis Johnston? If it passed to the Commission, it would probably fall into decay, and end up a miserable half-demolished ruin, as Kenure Park in Rush is today.

My wife and I had come to like the place and its setting in the Boyne valley, and we were loath to see it abandoned. The house was fitted out for use as a hostel; why not turn it to that purpose? So in 1969 we took a deep breath and bought the house and 20ha around it, just sufficient to preserve its parkland setting. Soon the house was in almost continuous use as a study centre for archaeology, natural history, politics, counselling groups and retreats, and we had many satisfied customers. It meant of course very hard work for my wife, but she thrived on it. In its prime the house would have had twenty indoor servants; we had one full-time and two part-time helpers. We used to say that it was as if the Cunard Line had decided to dispense with a crew for the Queen Mary, and sent her to sea with only my wife as captain and myself as chief engineer.

But by the time fifteen years had passed, it was clear that the pace could not be kept up indefinitely, and we began to think of withdrawal, not from the area, but into a small gardener's cottage nearby. My wife did not survive to make the move, but died in the same bedroom in the big house that Mrs Balfour had died in thirty years before.

I moved on to the cottage, and there my enjoyment of the surrounding countryside has increased. The house, where we lived on the first floor, was so big that it became almost an expedition to get out of it. In the cottage one step takes me into the country, full of all sorts of wildlife. I have taken to night-time walks, and at the right seasons I can hear the red deer stags challenging one another, or the vixen advising the local foxes that she is waiting to be called on. I cannot envisage returning to the city.

Familiarity with an area does not breed contempt; it rather deepens one's awareness of the interknit nature of the countryside. When I came to Townley Hall first, woods had been recently cleared, and the rough ground was full of grasshopper warblers. As the young trees grew, the warblers disappeared and occasional breeding woodcock took their place. For years a roding woodcock flew backwards and forwards over the cottage, and I thought how wonderful it would be to lie in bed and listen to the croaking sound go by. But by the time I got to the cottage the trees had grown too closely, and the woodcock no longer paraded. I see them occasionally on the avenues in the winter, but they do not nest any more. Years ago dippers nested under a bridge where one of the avenues crossed a stream; farm pollution cleared the stream of the dippers' food, and they vanished; recently I saw one again; will increased pollution-control allow them to return?

I reckon I have seen about sixty varieties of bird either on the ground or on the wing in the immediate vicinity of the cottage, and of these about forty nest nearby. We also have red deer, badgers, foxes, red squirrels, hares, rabbits, hedgehogs, field mice, shrews, pipistrelle and long-eared bats, and, unfortunately in the last ten years, too many grey squirrels and rats. The grounds of Townley Hall, and the Boyne valley, form what is virtually a nature reserve. The river offers otters and kingfishers as well.

Other forms of animal, and plant life, are not as interesting, as they are dominated by the fact that the land of the estate has been cultivated since Neolithic times, as the excavated sites show. In the twelfth century Cistercian farming extended from Mellifont to the Boyne, and some of the field names, such as the Sheep Walk, perhaps stretch back to those days.

The builder of the big house, Blayney Townley Balfour, spent a great deal of time and money laying out his estate, and so all the land is either field, plantation or pleasure-ground. There is no natural vegetation.

Immediately after it has collected the merged waters of the Mattock and the Delvin, the Boyne meets a wall of rock at Oldbridge, and turns at right angles to the east. This wall is the face of a fault, which has lifted up on its north side older Lower Palaeozoic shales and sandstones into juxtaposition with the local Carboniferous limestone. The uplift must be many tens of metres, and the fault-face slopes south at about 40°; at one point a stream cascades down a rock-face which slopes at 55°. The steepness of the face indicates that it cannot be 'old', and it also indicates relatively 'young' tectonic movement. A little lower, a girder bridge spans the river. Beside the bridge there is yet another knoll of limestone (on which an obelisk commemorative of the Battle of the Boyne used to stand); if we walk 100m to the north, we cross the fault onto shale and sandstone. From here to the sea the course of the Boyne, in contrast to the twistings we have already seen, is essentially a straight line, which possibly whispers at a continuation of the fault.

## DROGHEDA

The limestone between Oldbridge and the sea has been greatly affected by karstic processes. North of Drogheda town the rock rises to 45m, and was formerly extensively quarried to provide limestone for the local cement factory. In places the rock was deeply rotted by water which had descended in 'pipes', dissolved the calcite, and replaced it by insoluble debris which had been lowered from a higher level. When this chemical weathering was taking place the rock surface must have been much higher than it is today. I looked in the debris for pollen and spores which might have given some clue as to climatic conditions at the time of the weathering, but failed to find anything. The quarries are now abandoned, but have left a splendid legacy to the town, which has a space in which to dump its refuse for many years to come.

In the town itself the surface of the rock is very irregular. Solid rock can be seen at street level at the south end of the main road bridge, but along the quayside, only some hundreds of metres away, exploratory borings went to 20m without reaching rock.

This irregularity in the rock surface is largely masked by a sheet of glacial deposits, whose flat surface lies at about 35m; through this the Boyne has cut a deep trench down to sea-level. This trench raised great problems for the Dublin to Belfast railway; one line ran from Dublin to the south bank, and a second from the north bank to Belfast, and the gap was not bridged until 1855 when the magnificent viaduct was built. Its raised horizontal line gives a splendid indication of the size of the river trench.

The south side of the trench is much steeper than the north, and this had a great effect on the layout of the town, which is a Norman foundation of the late twelfth century. On the south side of the river two streams have incised their valleys down to the level of the main river, leaving a tongue of flat land between them. Here the Normans built their great motte, which still stands as the Millmount, and below it their bridge, in the protection of the motte. Given this defence, a substantial town quickly developed on both sides of the river. On the south the slope from the height above to the river below is too steep to make road-building easy, and several flights of steps, lined with houses, lead down to the river. A small flat at river level was big enough for a bull ring.

The north side had a more gentle, even slope, and here a pattern of streets, one above the other and each parallel with the river, linked by cross-streets, emerged. Coming up slope the first street is Dyer Street, where dyeing was carried on near the river. Then West Street, leading to the now-vanished West Gate; going east, at the point where it met the street from the bridge, it changed its name to Laurence Street, and continued to Laurence Gate. Though the gate itself is gone, the protective barbican built in the thirteenth century, which stood in front of it, is still there, the finest of its kind to have survived in Ireland. Fair Street, where the fair ground now provides a car-park, is the third of the parallel streets.

Just as in other early towns in Ireland, there is no doubt that a considerable sheet of medieval refuse is still in position below the foundations of later buildings. So far this has only been excavated on a very restricted scale, but in each case with interesting results. I looked at a few samples, and in some I found a considerable number of seeds of hemp (*Cannabis sativa*), the plant which provides both fibre for ropes, and seeds from which the drug *Cannabis* can be extracted. Hemp has never been grown successfully in Ireland, and I am sure that the seeds I found were shaken out of fibres imported for rope-making, and could not be regarded as an indication of early drug-taking.

A quite unspectacular find, an oyster-shell with some pigment in it, later became for me the high point of the excavations. If you are handling pigment in small quantities, the concave valve of an oyster-shell forms an excellent palette, as it sits snugly in the palm of the hand. One ore of mercury is cinnabar, a heavy metallic-looking substance; when finely ground it gives a red powder, vermilion, much used in decoration. An artist in Drogheda was embellishing some object with vermilion paint, and when the job was finished, threw away the shell.

*Kilsharvan, Meath. This 15th-century stone statue today presides over a wayside spring. It may represent one of the Magi carrying a gift; it was probably originally one of a group which stood, brightly painted, in wall-niches inside a church.*

Some years ago there was a magnificent exhibition of English medieval art in the Royal Academy in London, and I went to see it. The exhibition rooms had been arranged to resemble the interior of a church, and splendid objects had been gathered together. There was the Black Prince's personal armour, and a stained-glass window from Canterbury Cathedral. One corner of one room was used to demonstrate the craft-working of the period, and what should I see there but an oyster-shell containing gold, red and blue pigments. It had not been found thrown away in rubbish, but beside a tomb in a church in Wiltshire. The artist had been decorating the elaborate tomb of Lady Margaret Neville who died in 1338, and had neglected to carry it away when he had finished his task. There must have been similar tombs in the medieval churches in Drogheda.

At Kilsharvan, 5km south of Drogheda, at the side of the road between Julianstown and Duleek, a splendid statue of about 1450 stands above a spring. It shows a crowned figure presenting a gift, probably one of the Magi; it will have been one of a group, which stood, elaborately painted, inside a church.

## THE ESTUARY

Below the town the level of the rock surface falls, and glacial deposits are dominant. The Boyne becomes a tidal estuary, which is 6km long and gradually widens to a width of 1km before it is narrowed by a magnificent series of sand-dunes. The dunes extend southwards from Clogher Head for 15km to Benhead, north of Balbriggan.

At low tide great expanses of tidal mud, rich in food debris carried down from Drogheda, are exposed, and in winter these are frequented by large numbers of migrant waders and ducks. The area is nominally a wildlife sanctuary, but some spasmodic shooting does go on. At first I used to look for rarities, but now I am content to watch the larger patterns. Flocks of green plover close to the water go wavering across the estuary, so slowly that one doubts if they will make it to the far shore. By contrast enormous numbers of golden plover wheel and soar high in the air, sometimes in twisted ribbons, sometimes in a fluctuating sheet. Small flotillas of brent geese cruise up and down the shore-line. Over the years I have noted some rarities; an avocet feeding at the edge of a mud-bank; a grey phalarope pirouetting in shallow water; a little egret standing among some gulls, conspicuously larger in size, but as I have said my main interest is now the larger pattern.

Boats of course had to traverse the estuary if they were to reach Drogheda, and in the early nineteenth century a pair of parallel walls, extending from the town to the dunes, were constructed to define a channel. The walls were built up to spring high-tide level, and gaps were left so that falling tidal water from the flanks of the estuary had to enter the channel, and so strengthen the current to keep the channel scoured. Though the walls are rather in decay in some places, they still serve their original purpose, and enable Drogheda to maintain its position as a busy port.

Unfortunately towns at the head of estuaries tend to creep seawards as the intake of flat land beside the river provides cheap space for the expansion of industry. Dublin is a prime example of this, and now Drogheda is following suit. A cement factory, an oil and gas depot, a coal storage site, a sewage farm, all are intruding on the open space of the estuary. The same has happened at the river's exit through the dunes. The channel turns at right angles, and cuts north-west/south-east through them. On the south side, where the channel runs into the cut, there used to be a most attractive point of land. Some thirty years ago a fish-meal plant was erected there, and I am sure that An Taisce (the National Trust for Ireland) protested against the development. But the all-powerful formula 'job creation' carried the day, and the plant went ahead. It now stands abandoned and wrecked, a hazard as well as an eye-sore. A fortress-like commercial structure, accompanied by a big settling-pond, has recently appeared on the north bank of the cut; let us hope that it will not fall into dereliction too. From time to time quite impracticable schemes to construct a deep-water port at the mouth of the estuary arise. I trust they will never be attempted.

The channel through the dunes is floored with mussels, which provide an unending supply for the local fishermen. The men work in a time-honoured style, using small flat-bottomed rowing-boats of a local pattern. An implement with long tines close together, like a cross between a rake and a fork, and at right angles to a shaft about 5m long, is used to tear the mussels from the bottom and lift them into the boat; it is very heavy work. The laden boat is then beached, and the mussels dumped in a heap on the foreshore. This is the moment for the oyster catchers and the turnstones who scramble over the heap getting the most delicious pickings. The mussels are then shovelled on to horizontal riddles, and pushed round with rakes so that the smaller shells fall through. The larger mussels are then bagged, and sent to Wexford for purification. The salmon net-men also have their base here; their boats are essentially similar, except that they have a planked platform at the stern, on which the coiled net is laid to make it easy to feed it out as the boat makes a circle in the river. The ends of the net are brought together, and it is drawn ashore.

The entrance to the channel from the sea is marked in various ways, most interestingly by two stone structures, probably sixteenth-century in age. A slender square stone tower, the Maiden Tower, stands on the seaward side, and some metres behind it there is a narrow stone pillar, the Maiden's Finger, of remarkably phallic appearance. A mariner approaching the channel would align himself so that the pillar was concealed by the tower; if the pillar appeared in sight, he knew he was off course.

The village of Baltray lies on the north side of the channel at its inner end. Here there was formerly a picturesque unorganised scatter of thatched fishermen's cottages, but today it is a dormitory suburb of Drogheda, and most of the thatch has been replaced by tiles. Something remarkably like a prehistoric mariner's guide lies just north of the village. Here there is a high gravel bluff facing the sea, and it is probable that in early post-glacial time waves reached the base of the bluff. The coast then retreated, and the dunes were thrown up, leaving between them and the bluff tidal lagoons which have since been drained. Two splendid standing-stones, one 3m and the other 2m high (Pl. 8), stand side by side on the edge of the bluff, where they would have been clearly seen from the sea below. I am sure they were erected either as a sign of welcome, or as a sign of warning, to potential immigrants.

And here we end our peregrination, beside the standing-stones at the mouth of the Boyne, looking out across the Irish Sea, with Clogher Head and the Mourne Mountains to the north, and the Skerries and Lambay to the south. I shall wander on with all my senses alert, questing as ever. As I go I brood on the many facets of my surroundings, both natural and artificial, and, with gratitude, continue to marvel at the beauty of the environment which delights and embraces me.

# BIBLIOGRAPHY


de PAOR, M. & L. 1958 *Early Christian Ireland* London, Thames & Hudson

EOGAN, G. 1986 *Knowth and the passage-tombs of Ireland* London, Thames & Hudson

EVANS, E.E. 1957 *Irish Folk Ways* London, Routledge & Kegan Paul

GILLMOR, D. (Ed.) 1989 *The Irish Countryside* Dublin, Wolfhound

GODWIN, H. 1975 *History of the British Flora* (2nd edn.) Cambridge, Cambridge University Press

HARBISON, P. (Ed.) 1989 *The Shell Guide to Ireland* (revised) Dublin, Gill and Macmillan

HERITY, M. & EOGAN, G. *Ireland in Prehistory* London, Routledge & Kegan Paul

HOLLAND, C.H. (Ed.) 1981 *A Geology of Ireland* Edinburgh, Scottish Academic Press

HUGHES, K. & HAMLIN, A. 1977 *The Modern Traveller to the Irish Church* London, SPCK

HUTCHINSON, C.D. 1989 *Birds in Ireland* Calton, Poyser

JESSEN, K. 1949 *Studies in Late Quaternary Deposits and Flora-history of Ireland* Dublin, Royal Irish Academy

JESSEN, K. & FARRINGTON, A. 1938 *The Bogs at Ballybetagh, near Dublin, with remarks on Late-glacial Conditions in Ireland* Dublin, Royal Irish Academy

LAVELLE, D. 1976 *Skellig; Island Outpost of Europe* Dublin, O'Brien Press

MITCHELL, F. 1986 *Shell Guide to Reading the Irish Landscape* Dublin, Country House

1987 *Archaeology & Environment in Early Dublin* Dublin, Royal Irish Academy

1989 *Man & Environment in Valencia Island* Dublin, Royal Irish Academy

(Ed.) 1987 *The Book of the Irish Countryside* Belfast, Blackstaff Press; Dublin, Town House

PRAEGER, R. LL. 1934 *The Botanist in Ireland* Dublin, Hodges, Figgis

1937 *The Way that I Went* Dublin, Hodges, Figgis / London, Methuen

1950 *Natural History of Ireland* London, Collins

(Ed.) 1911-15 *Clare Island Report* (3 vols.) Dublin, Royal Irish Academy

WEBB, D.A. 1943 *An Irish Flora* Dundalk, Dundalgan Press

WHITTOW, J.B. 1975 *Geology and Scenery in Ireland* London, Penguin Books

# INDEX OF TOPICS


## A

agriculture, 128, 131, 238
  early, 62-3, 68, 78-81, 103-6, 110-12, 138-9, 157, 195, 238
  modern, 43, 59, 118
  ridge-and-furrow method, 99
amino acids, 112
amphi-Atlantic plants, 58, 63
archaeology, 12, 44-51, 49-50, 61, 67, 78-81, 83, 98, 118, 192-3
  industrial archaeology, 208
  protection of monuments, 106-7
axe-factories, 46, 82-3

## B

basalt, 56-7, 77, 82, 87, 175
bawns, 147
beaches. *see* raised beaches; storm beaches
beetle remains, 72, 121, 231-2
birds, 4-5, 5, 87, 115-16, 170, 173, 180, 216-7, 226, 252, 256
  corncrake, 19-20, 92, 132, 204, 211, 217
  firecrest, 180
  red-necked phalarope, 115-16
Black Pig's Dyke, 205
blanket-bogs, 113, 126, 155, 179
  artefacts found in, 12, 14, 147, 158-9, 237
  destruction of, 119-20, 234-6
  growth of, 77, 81, 123, 159-60
bogs. *see* blanket-bogs; peat; raised-bogs
booleying, 77-8, 80, 81
Bord na Móna, 215, 234-6, 237, 239
boulder clay. *see* till
breccia, 37
British Association, 69-70
Broighter Hoard, 74-5
Bronze Age, 81, 104, 110, 128, 214
  agricultural activity, 112, 113
  artefacts, 48, 83, 114, 195, 205, 211
  carvings, 88, 90
  monuments, 122-3, 126, 150, 157, 182

## C

calcite (calcium carbonate), 23, 24-5, 35, 102, 149-50
Caledonides, 22, 39, 90, 98, 107, 145
callows, 216
canals, 203-4, 208, 211, 215, 216-17, 219, 220
Carboniferous period, 23, 244
castles, 86, 88, 136, 142, 147, 148, 189-90, 210
  Athlone, 211
  Trim, 243
caves, 5-6, 25, 33-7, 102, 195, 224-5
  animal remains, 33, 34-5, 35-6, 37, 195-6
  human remains, 35-6
chalk, 23, 76-7, 97, 105
chemical weathering, 25-7, 66, 97, 188, 209
chert, 105, 205
churches, 48, 59, 90, 98, 118, 142-3, 209-10, 217, 219, 239
clachans, 88, 90
Clare Island Survey, 127
clay, 22
cliffs, 28, 94, 98, 112-13, 141, 167
climatic optimum, 74
coal deposits, 23, 102, 200-01, 237
cooking places, 46-7
copper mining, 180-81
core-stones, 94-5, 97
corries, 162-4, 184-5, 191
crannogs, 69, 194, 205
cultivation-ridges (lazy-beds), 99, 118
curraghs, 89

## D

dating. *see* dendrochronology; palynology; radiometric dating
deer-traps, 158-9
dendrochronology, 50, 68-9
Derrynaflan chalice, 239-41
desertification, 131
dolines, 25, 102, 103, 243
Dowris Hoard, 202
droving-roads, 139-40
drumlins, 67, 89, 203, 225, 226-7
Dublin Naturalists' Field Club, 3-4, 11, 126

## E

Early Christian period, 94, 118, 125, 130, 157, 226
  agriculture, 81
  artefacts, 98, 189
  monuments, 87-8, 99, 122-3
earthquakes, 27-8
Electricity Supply Board, 119, 146, 162-4, 203, 219
erosion, 22, 24-7, 97, 113, 145, 165, 172, 186, 200, 218, 224
erratics, 155, 173-7, 224, 233
eskers, 210, 211, 215, 243
etch-plains, 27, 165, 172, 183, 188
European Community, 162, 236

## F

fen-peat, 113, 128
fens, 213
field-walking, 45-7, 84
fish, 72-3, 100, 257
  pollan, 72
  salmon, 257
fishing, 86
forests, 71, 135-6
  fossil, 123-4, 235-6, 237
  submerged, 143
forts, 88, 131, 142-3, 147, 154, 157, 211, 216, 219
  Iron Age, 94, 98, 149-50
fossils, 2, 10, 30, 149
freshwater shrimp (*Mysis relicta*), 72
*fulachta fiadh*. *see* cooking-places

## G

gabbro, 59
Geological Survey, 41, 135, 155
Geological Survey of Northern Ireland, 71
giant deer, 14, 18-19, 34, 35-6, 53, 67, 72, 195, 232
dating of, 19, 56
glacial deposits, 11, 71, 99, 176-7, 201-2, 216, 254, 256
correlation, 238
glacio-marine processes, 44
granite, 42, 59, 88, 94-5, 97, 117, 143, 245
  core-stones, 66
  movement of, 155, 174
grikes, 25, 102
gypsum, 53, 56-7

## H

heathers, 124, 134
henge monuments, 246
Hercynides, 23, 145, 150, 167, 207, 218
Heritage Zones, 212
high crosses, 87-8, 98

hums, 102, 206
hydro-electric plants, 29, 162-4, 203, 226

## I

ice. *see also* corries; moraines
  erosion, 103, 104, 122, 138, 157-8, 168-9, 218-20
  flow, 27, 142-3, 202-3, 207-8
  masses, 87, 94-5, 120
Ice Age, 17-18, 29, 238
  Long stages
    Cold
      Midlandian/Fenitian, 29-30, 41, 152
      Ballybunnionian, 152
    Warm
      Gortian, 39-40, 123-4
      Glenavian, 72
      Littletonian/Post-glacial, 238
  Short phases
    Cold
      Ballybetagh, 17-18
    Warm
      Woodgrange, 67
industrial development, 146-7, 257
interglacial periods, 30, 41-2, 57-8, 72, 112, 149. *see also* Ice Age, long warm stages
interstadial periods, 72. *see also* Ice Age, short warm phases
Irish Wildbird Conservancy, 92, 116, 173, 176
Iron Age, 46, 94, 98, 162, 202, 205
iron pan, 100

## J

joints, 24, 167

## K

karsts, 25, 57, 102-3, 135, 146, 149, 194, 223
cockpit karst, 103
Kerry County Council, 163-4
kettle-holes, 41, 42
kitchen-middens, 44-5, 61-2, 91, 125, 149

## L

lakes, 130, 183-5, 194-5
  former, 14, 17-18, 62, 104, 200, 213, 215
lava. *see* basalt
lazy-beds. *see* cultivation ridges
lignite, 71, 73, 227
limestone, 23, 24, 176-7, 206, 210, 233. *see also* karsts
  Burren, 135-6, 139
  caves, 25, 33-7, 102
  erosion of, 24-5, 99, 145, 187
  pot-holing, 223-4
  quarries, 2, 10, 253
Lower Palaeozoic period, 22, 206

## M

machair, 89, 90, 117
macrofossils, 18
magnetometer, use of, 195
mammals, 33, 252. *see also* giant deer; woolly mammoth
  bear, 33, 195-6
  fox, arctic, 34, 195
  hyaena, 34-5
  lemming, 34, 36
  lemming, arctic, 195
  reindeer, 34, 36, 229, 232
marshes, 147
Mass-rocks, 143
medieval remains, 47, 49-50, 59
megalithic tombs, 67, 94, 99, 103-7, 110, 135, 138
  boulder dolmen, 182
  court-grave, 111-2
  passage-tomb, 103-4, 106, 244-9
  portal-dolmen, 138
  wedge-tomb, 157, 182
Mesolithic period, 76, 81, 84
  artefacts
    Larnian phase, 45, 46-7, 48, 49, 62, 75-6
    Sandelian phase, 84, 215
Mesozoic period, 23, 53, 77, 78
micaschists, 98
microliths, 83-4
molluscs, 53
monasteries, 130, 135, 136, 142, 147, 155-6, 216, 252
  Clonmacnoise, 211-12
  islands, 170, 171-2, 174, 226
moraines, 37, 60, 104, 105, 122, 162, 207, 219
end-moraines, 41, 142
mosses, 121, 138, 231, 232, 235
mottes, 249, 254
mussels, 257

## N

Napoleonic forts, 48, 86, 142, 209, 214
National Monuments Act, 51
National Museum of Ireland, 35, 75, 105, 125, 126, 147, 195, 237
  Derrynaflan chalice, 239-40
  Wood Quay, 49-51
natterjack toad (*Bufo calamita*), 156, 159
Neolithic period, 48, 49
  agriculture, 62, 77, 78-81, 138-9, 194-5, 238
  artefacts, 48-9, 78-81, 82, 99, 111-12, 138, 194, 247-9
  axe factories, 46, 82-3
  designs, 249
  tombs, 67, 99, 103, 105, 111-12, 247-8
neotectonics, 93
Normans, 47, 59, 81, 86, 189-90, 211, 249, 254

## O

Ogham inscriptions, 172
Old Red Sandstone, 22, 23, 145, 185, 204-6

## P

Palaeoecology Centre, QUB, 67-9
Palaeozoic period, 22, 244, 253
Pale, the, 58
palynology, 11-12, 14-16, 39-40, 42, 53, 55-6, 62-3, 68, 104, 122-3, 138
  bog-dating, 113-14, 237-8
  soil-dating, 127-8
peat, 15, 39-40, 55-6, 77, 78-81, 110-12, 127, 157
  dating, 100, 104
  for fuel, 119-20, 127, 130, 131, 138-9
pediments, 188
peneplains, 28, 188
permafrost, 43
pingos, 43
pinnacles, 102, 155
planation-surfaces, 188
plants, 11, 14-15, 55-6, 68, 131, 134, 217
  American, 63, 134
  arctic/alpine, 14, 87, 120-1, 231-2
  *Chara*, 213
  *Dulichium spathularis*, 58

dwarf willow (*Salix herbacea*), 14, 17, 20, 88, 121
grass wrack (*Zostera marina*), 150
hemp (*Cannabis sativa*), 254
inula (*Inula salicina*), 217
Mediterranean heath (*Erica erigena*), 113
mountain avens (*Dryas*), 87
mountain sorrel (*Oxyria digyna*), 121
poppy, arctic (*Papaver radicatum*), 232
rhododendron, 124, 151
rushes (*Juncus* spp), 141
St Patrick's cabbage (*Saxifraga spathularis*), 158
temperate, 17-18, 23, 43
tropical, 71
poljes, 25, 102, 135
pollen analysis. *see* palynology
pollution, 73, 106
porcellanite, 82
pot-holing, 223-4
potassium/argon method, 175
power-stations, 71, 119-20, 145-6, 162-4, 203, 204, 208, 214-15, 219, 220, 235-6
promontory forts, 48, 131, 154

## Q

quartz, 245
quartzite, 22, 88, 94, 95, 98, 136
Quaternary period, 22, 29-31, 64, 238
Queen's University, Belfast, 67-9, 78

## R

radiocarbon dating
potassium/argon method, 175
radiocarbon method, 19, 35, 36, 37, 53-8, 62, 68-9, 83, 110, 120, 181
bog-dating, 100, 104, 113-14, 158
mammals, 37, 230-33
uranium/thorium method, 57-8, 152
raised beaches, 30-31, 49, 60-61, 73-6, 148-9
raised-bogs, 55-6, 114, 208, 213, 214-15, 233-6, 237, 239
raths, 122-3, 194
reptiles, 23
rhyolite, 46
rock-folding, 22, 23, 167-8
Roman remains, 48, 150

## S

salt-marshes, 182
sand-dunes, 90-91, 118-19, 154, 258
cultivation ridges, 99-100
protection of, 156-7
sandstone, 22, 176-7, 186, 187, 191, 206, 207, 208, 213-14, 219
sea-level, changes in, 30-31, 60, 62, 72, 87, 89, 169, 182, 209
shale, 22, 23, 140-1, 145, 148, 150-51, 200, 206, 207, 208, 237, 243-4
Shannon Commissioners, 205, 211, 216
sheep-grazing, 128
shell deposits, 22-3, 100, 102, 112, 125, 213
shell-middens, 49
skerries, 117
slate, 22, 167
Sligo County Council, 106-7
snow-beds, 121
soaks, 234
sphagnum-moss, 235
spotted slug (*Geomalachus maculosus*), 159
stalactites, 24, 25
stalagmites, 24, 25, 35-6, 37
standing-stones, 59, 258
storm beaches, 117, 215
storms, 117-18

## T

tectonic movement, 24, 27-9, 93-4, 98, 112-13, 167, 184-5, 253
Tertiary period, 22-9, 53, 59, 70, 77, 94, 188
chemical weathering, 25-7
tillite, 99
tills, 44, 46, 99, 112, 149, 151-2, 244
tors, 66, 94
tourism, 165-6, 167, 170-71, 204, 246
treasure trove, 74-5, 240-41
trees, 123, 138, 235-8
alder, 42
birch, 123
clearances of, 62-3, 68, 138-9, 160
fir (*Abies*), 24
fossils, 40-42, 71, 113-14, 123-4
hazel, 40, 72, 123
juniper, 57, 238
oak, 112, 159-60
palm, 71
pine, 40, 72, 104, 112, 113-14, 123, 128, 143, 158, 159-60, 235-6
redwood (*Sequoia*), 136
sequences, 30, 72, 123, 135-6
spruce (*Picea*), 40, 72, 124
yew, 72, 158-9, 235
Trinity College, Dublin, 8-10, 36-7, 49, 54, 60, 183
radiocarbon laboratory, 70, 205
Townley Hall, 250-51
turloughs, 103, 135, 155, 206

## U

Upper Palaeozoic period, 22-3

## V

Vikings, 50, 142, 172, 175
volcanic activity, 9, 29, 39
volcanic rock, 233

## W

walls, 110-11, 139, 157
water-table, 24-5
weeds, 62-3
woolly mammoth, 33, 34, 229-30, 232, 233
dating of, 35, 37

## Y

Yosemite National Park, 247

# INDEX OF PERSONAL NAMES


**A**

Ahlmgren, L., 195
Allberry, E.C., 179
Armstrong, E.C.R., 103
Ashby, E., 69-70

**B**

Baillie, M., 68-9
Balfour, B.T., 253
Balfour, M., 249-50, 252
Barnosky, T., 19
Beckett, S., 8-9
Bersu, G., 149-50
Blackett, P., 69, 70
Boyle. R., 190
Brenan, E., 33
Breuil, Abbé, 214
Bridle, J.W., 8
Brodigan, M., 45
Browne, C.R., 131
Brunker, J.P., 4 (p), 5, 82, 92
Burrell, Sir J., 193
Burton, P., 189, 190
Butler, J. Bayley, 35

**C**

Cabot, D., 117
Cahill, M., 239
Carter, W., 100
Case, H., 78, 80-81
Casement, Sir. R., 151
Caulfield, S., 110-12
Charlesworth, J.K., 37, 41, 43, 67, 69, 209
Clarke, G., 84, 205
Coffey, G., 74-5, 76
Colley, G., 51
Collins, Sir W., 116
Coope, R., 121, 231, 233
Coudé, A., 120
Coxon, P., 68, 123, 127-8, 135, 152
Craig, A., 43
Culleton, E., 42

**D**

Davies, G.H., 119, 186
Davies, M., 221
Davies, O., 67
de Paor, M., 122
, de Valera, E., 11, 16-17, 150
de Valera, R., 111
de Vries, H., 57
Deigan, S., 238
Delaney, C.F.G., 54
Dick, R., 115-6
Dickson, J., 121, 231, 232
Dillon, E.P., 139
Dixon, H.H, 9
Dodson, J., 157, 158
Donner, K., 125
Dorman-O'Gowan, E., 192-3
Dunlop, M., 133
Dunne, P., 92, 116

**E**

Eogan, G., 40, 48, 51, 126, 193, 246-7, 248 (p)
Erdtman, G., 14-15
Evans, D., 82
Evans, E.E.E., 66, 67, 77-8, 80, 88

**F**

Farrington, A., 4, 11, 13, 39, 41, 69, 152, 176, 188, 230, 234, 244
Fisher, J., 115, 116
Fitzgerald, J.M., 9
Fleck, Lord, 70
Flegg, A., 135
Flynn, J., 179-80
Flynn, M., 180
Flynn, T., 180
Fox, J., 20
Freeman, W., 60

**G**

Gatenby, J.B., 9-10
Gibbons, M., 103
Godwin, Sir H., 53-6, 55 (p), 67, 133, 191, 238
Gogarty, O. St. J., 8
Goodwillie, R., 117
Grogan, E., 193
Guthrie, Mrs, 230
Gwynn, A.M., 5, 36
Gwynn, E., 196
Gwynn, L., 196, 250

**H**

Hackett, F., 234
Hamilton, Mr Justice, 51
Hannon, G., 123-4
Harbison, P., 194
Hardy, E., 12
Harrison, J.H., 78
Hart, L., 193
Hawkes, C.F.C., 247
Hencken, H., 12, 16, 69, 75
Henry, F., 75, 87-8, 118
Herity, M., 110
Hill, A.V., 69-70
Hill, D., 93
Hodgers, D., 84
Holland, C.H., 145, 185
Horn, W., 169
Hosking, E., 115
Hudson, R.G.S., 151
Hunt, J., 193-4
Hunt, P., 193-4, 197
Hyde, H.A., 56

**I**

Iversen, J., 62 (p), 63

**J**

Jackson, J.S., 125, 151, 181, 182 (p), 183, 196
Jennings, J., 177
Jessen, K., 11-12, 13-16, 17 (p), 18-19, 54, 56, 62 (p), 63 (p), 64, 104, 114, 133, 134, 190, 229, 231, 237
Johnston, Francis, 250, 251
Joly. J, 9, 10
Jonassen, H., 13, 17 (p), 18, 133
Joseph, J.K. St J., 105

**K**

Kelly, N., 240
Kennedy, P.J., 92, 116
Kinahan, G.H., 40
Kinlen, D., 241
Knowles, M., 197
Knowles, W.J., 197

**L**

Lavelle, Des, 166, 167, 171
le Clerc. P., 245, 246
Leask, H., 219
Lett, L.C., 250
Lewis, F.J., 127
Libby, W.F., 53-4, 56, 57
Lisney, A., 5
Liversage, G.D., 45, 48, 49, 196, 246, 247
Lynch, A., 138

**M**

Macalister, R.A.S., 103, 214, 233, 244-5, 247
McAulay, I.R., 54
McCutcheon, J., 231, 232
McMillan, N., 6
Mahr, A., 11-12, 14, 75

Martin, F.X., 50-51
Mason, A., 19-20, 92, 115-16
Mason, T.H., 1, 2, 19-20, 93
Max, M., 155
May, A., 126
Millard, J., 91
Miller, A., 188
Moffat, C.B., 92
Mohr, P., 175
Molyneux, Sir T., 229
Moore, J., 205
Morrison, M., 78
Movius, H.L., Jr., 36, 75, 76

## N

Nevill, T., 229
Newbould, P., 73, 84, 99-100

## O

O'Brien, D., 196-7
O'Brien, W., 181
O'Connell, M., 68, 110, 114, 130
O'Hare, P.J., 113
O'Kelly, M.J. (Brian), 51, 172, 219, 245-6, 247
Ó Nualláin, S., 111-12
Ó Ríordáin, B., 49, 51
Ó Ríordáin, S.P., 121, 122-3, 180, 181, 192, 193
Osvald, H., 55, 133, 134

## P

Parkes, H.M., 53, 205, 237-8
Paxton, J., 189
Pearson, G., 68
Philipps, A., 125
Pitt-Rivers, Gen., 45, 69
Pochin Mould, D., 171
Poole, J.H.J., 54
Porter, K., 12
Praeger, R. Ll., XI, 11, 25, 35, 37, 55, 63, 74-5, 76, 82, 86, 87, 103, 115, 126-7, 132, 197, 214, 225, 233, 243, 247
Proudfoot, B., 78

## Q

Quane, M., 75

## R

Raftery, J., 12, 51, 205
Rennison, H. W., 61
Rennison, H.H., 44
Renouf, L.P.W., 183
Richardson, L.J.D., 56
Riley, F.T. (Bill), 6, 16-17, 75
Robinson, T., 247, 249
Roche, B., 179
Roche, May, 179
Ryan, M., 239-40

## S

Scannell, M.J.P., 57
Scott, M., 180
Shee, E., 239
Sheehan, Jer., 108
Sheehan, John, 191
Sidebottom, J., 78, 80
Smith, A., 67-8
Smith, C., 236
Smyth, L.B., 4, 10
Stacpoole, G., 45, 47, 84, 90, 149
Stelfox, A.W., 2, 3 (p), 4, 5, 6, 12, 14, 40, 53, 158, 244
Stephens, N., 119
Stephenson, R., 87-8
Stillman, C., 175
Sutcliffe, A. J., 34
Swain, I., 1
Sweetman, D., 246
Synge, F.M., 41, 120, 123, 141, 149, 174

## T

Tansley, Sir A., 55, 133
Ters, M., 149
Tizard, H., 69
Tohall, P., 126
Tratman, T.K., 33, 35, 36
Trench, W.F., 8

## U

Ussher, R.J., 33-5

## V

von Post, L., 14-15, 55

## W

Wallace, P., 49
Walsh, P., 57
Warren, R., 33
Warren, W., 149, 152
Watts, W.A., 39 (p), 40, 43, 57, 58, 113, 114, 123-4, 135, 138, 205, 237, 246
Webb, D.A., 183
Webb, M., 239
Wells, J., 176
Westport, Marquis of, 124-5
Wheeler, T., 69
Whitlock, C., 159
Whittow, J.B., 184
Williams, T., 5
Woodman, P., 47, 83-4
Wyatt, J., 124

## Z

Zeuner, F., 238

# INDEX OF IRISH LOCALITIES

The spelling of the names follows that of the *National Atlas*. Entries give a grid reference, in bold, consisting of a three-figure Easting coordinate and a three-figure Northing coordinate, shown in that order, followed by the page numbers.

B. Bay, Cas. Castle, co. County, Harb. Harbour, Hd. Head, Hse. House, I(s). Island(s), L. Lake, Lough, Mt(s). mt. Mountain (s), Mount, Pen. Peninsula, Pk. Park, Pt. Point, R. River, reg. Region, Sd. Sound, V. Valley.

## A


Aasleagh Falls **089 264** 29
Achill I. **068 303** 28, 120-21, 126
Achill Sd. **073 299** 119
Adoon, L. **053 107** 157-8
Allen, L. **196 321** 198, 200, 203, 205
Altawinny B. **182 433** 95
Anaffrin, L. **158 390** 99
Annaghmakerrig **258 321** 230
Antrim **314 386** 73
Aran Is. **086 209** 94, 154, 155
Ardara **173 390** 96, 97, 98
Ardboe **397 376** 73
Ardcavan **306 124** 38, 41-2
Ardee **296 290** 58
Ardnacrusha **158 161** 196, 202, 219, 221
Arigna **192 314** 201
Arrow, L. **179 312** 104
Ashleam B. **069 297** 101, 109, 120-21
Athlone **204 241** 210, 211, 216, 233
Attamoney, R. **096 306** 122
Aughinish I. **128 153** 129, 137, 144, 146, 209
Awbeg, R. **153 114** 37


## B


Balboru **170 174** 219
Balbriggan **320 264** 45, 242, 256
Ballina, Mayo **124 318** 101, 109, 110
Ballinamore **213 311** 203
Ballinasloe **185 231** 214
Ballinderry, Westmeath **221 239** 12, 69
Ballinloghig **042 107** *Pl. 4*, 153, 159-60, 161, 178
Ballinskelligs **042 065** 174-5
Ballintra **192 369** 102
Ballybetagh **320 221** 14, 16-20, 38, 53, 104, 120-21, 134, 159, 229, 230, 237
Ballybunnion **086 141** 45, 129, 137, 141, 144, 145, 147-50, 152
Ballycastle, Antrim **311 440** 81-2
Ballycastle, Mayo **110 337** 52, 65, 110
Ballyconnell **227 318** 203, 226, 227
Ballycorus **323 221** 2
Ballydehob **098 035** 183
Ballyferriter **033 106** 46
Ballyglass **122 277** 122
Ballyhiernan B. **218 445** 85, 89-90
Ballyhillin **241 459** 85, 87
Ballylongford **099 145** (estuary) *Pl. 3*, 129, 137, 141, 144, 146, 148
Ballylumford **343 402** 71
Ballymackstocker B. **225 439** 89
Ballymakegogue **077 115** 229
Ballymoney **294 425** 52, 65, 71
Ballymote **166 315** 36
Ballyshannon **187 361** 29, 225, 226
Ballysodare **166 329** 107
Ballyvaughan **122 207** 140
Baltray **314 277** *Pl. 8*, 242, 258
Banagher **200 215** 210 (p), 215
Bann, R., Ballymena **296 410** 72
Banna Strand **075 122** 151
Bantry **099 048** 153, 161, 178
Bantry B. **086 046** 180
Barrow I. **072 117** 150-51
Barrow, R. **273 146** 233-4
Beaghmore, Tyrone **268 384** 126
Beara Pen. **065 047** 179
Beauparc Hse. **294 272** 243
Beginish **041 078** 165, 172
Behy V., Kerry **065 089** 162-4
Behy, Mayo **107 340** 101, 109, 110-12
Belcoo **208 338** 201, 223
Belderg **099 339** 101, 109, 112, 114
Belfast **334 374** 74, 254
Bellacorick **096 320** 119
Belleek, Donegal **194 359** 225
Bellonaboy Bridge **085 332** 113-14
Belmullet **070 332** 110, 114-16, 119-20, 143
Belturbet **236 317** 225
Benhead **317 269** 256
Benwee Hd. **081 344** 28, 101, 109, 112
Binevenagh, mt **269 430** 85, 87
Birr **206 205** 210, 216
Black Pig's Dyke **192 302** 205
Black R. **202 331** 201, 203
Blackbrink B. **198 257** 209
Blacksod B. **068 317** 117

| | | |
|---|---|---|
| Blackwater Bog | **203 229** | 212 (p), 213 |
| Blackwater R., Meath | **276 273** | 228, 242, 243 |
| Blackwater R., Waterford | **200 098** | 32, 39, 187, 189 |
| Blaskets | **027 097** | 159, 167 |
| Blennerville | **081 112** | 154 |
| Bloody Foreland | **182 434** | 85, 95 |
| Boa I. | **211 364** | 226 |
| Boderg, L. | **201 291** | 206, 207 |
| Bofin, L., Galway | **102 245** | 207-8 |
| Boora | **216 218** | 210, 215 |
| Boora, L. | **216 218** | 215 |
| Boyle | **180 302** | 104, 204 |
| Boyne, R. | **300 272** | 220, 228, 233-4, 242, 243-58 |
| Brandon B. | **056 114** | 158 |
| Brandon Hd. | **046 116** | 28, 155, 157, 159 |
| Brandon Peak | **047 109** | 159 |
| Bray Hd., Kerry | **032 072** | 167 |
| Brittas B. | **331 183** | 47 |
| Brockley | **312 452** | 82 |
| Broighter | **264 424** | 74-5, 240 |
| Brosna, Little R. | **205 219** | 210, 216 |
| Brosna, R., Offaly | **207 222** | 210, 215 |
| Brú na Bóinne | **301 274** | 244 |
| Buncrana | **234 432** | 85, 86, 88 |
| Bunnyconnellan | **133 318** | 110 |
| Burnfoot | **238 423** | 85, 89 |
| Burren, Clare | **128 211** | 25, 101, 102-3, 109, 129, 136, 137, **138-40**, 144 |
| Burren, Mayo | **114 297** | 123-4 |

## C

| | | |
|---|---|---|
| Caha Mts | **085 058** | 179 |
| Caher | **205 125** | 187, 191 |
| Caher, R. | **116 208** | 140 |
| Caherconree, mt | **073 107** | 153, 154, 164, 178 |
| Cahersiveen | **046 079** | 153, 161, 164, 165, 172, 178, 188 |
| Camaross | **288 124** | 38 |
| Camlin, R. | **208 277** | 208 |
| Camp | **070 109** | 154 |
| Cappagh | **217 097** | 33 |
| Caragh, L. | **072 090** | 162 |
| Carlingford L. | **320 313** | 59 |
| Carlingford Mt | **316 312** | 58, 59, 60 |
| Carndonagh | **247 445** | 85, 87-8 |
| Carnsore Pt. | **312 103** | 38, 42, 45 |
| Carran | **127 199** | 135 |
| Carranadoe | **200 290** | 206, 207 |
| Carrauntoohil, mt | **080 084** | 162 |
| Carrick-on-Shannon | **194 299** | 203, 204, 205 |
| Carrickart | **212 436** | 90 |
| Carrickmacross | **284 303** | 53 |
| Carrig I. | **098 148** | 147 |
| Carrigacappeen | **102 074** | 136, 139, 153, 161, 176-7, 178 |
| Carrigafoyle Cas. | **099 148** | 147 |
| Carrowkeel, Sligo | **176 311** | 101, 103-4, 109, 204, 247 |
| Carrowmore | **118 334** | 101, 105-7, 109 |
| Carrowmore L. | **083 329** | 114 |
| Carrownaglogh | **133 318** | 101, 109, 110 |
| Cashel | **207 141** | 228 |
| Cashen, R. | **090 133** | 148, 149 |
| Castle Archdale Forest Pk. | **218 359** | 225 |
| Castle Roche | **299 312** | 52, 58, 65 |
| Castlebar | **114 290** | 123 |
| Castleconnell | **166 163** | 219-22, 226, 243 |
| Castlegregory | **062 113** | 153, 154, 156, 161, 174, 178 |
| Castleisland | **099 109** | 141 |
| Castlemaine Harb. | **074 100** | 162 |
| Castlepook Cave | **158 109** | 32, 33-5 |
| Castletownroche | **168 102** | 32, 36-7 |
| Cathleen Falls | **188 361** | 29 |
| Cats' Hole | **210 334** | 224, 228 |
| Cavan | **242 305** | 226 |
| Ceanannas Mór = Kells | | |
| Charleville = Rath Luirc | **153 122** | 37 |
| Church I. | **043 078** | 165 |
| Cladagh R. | **313 336** | 225 |
| Clare I. | **068 286** | 28, 126-8, 130, 136 |
| Claregalway | **137 233** | 136 |
| Cleggan | **060 258** | 132 |
| Clew B. | **086 288** | 121, 126 |
| Clifden | **065 250** | 29 |
| Clogheen | **200 113** | 191 |
| Clogher Hd. | **317 284** | 242, 256, 258 |
| Cloghfarmore | **302 304** | 52, 59, 65 |
| Clones | **250 326** | 225, 226, 228, 229 |
| Clonfinlough Stone | **205 230** | 212, 213-14 |
| Clonmacnoise | **200 230** | 204, 210 (p), 211-14 |
| Clonmany | **237 446** | 88 |
| Clonsast Bog | **255 220** | 228, 234-6 |
| Coleraine | **284 432** | 83-4 |
| Colgagh | **174 337** | 101, 103, 109 |
| Collon | **299 281** | 242 |
| Cong | **115 255** | 135 |
| Connor Pass | **049 105** | 157 |
| Cooley Pen. | **323 308** | 59-60 |
| Cork | **167 072** | 32, 153, 161, 178, 186, 224 |
| Cork Airport | **166 066** | 185-6, 188 |
| Corr Cas. | **326 239** | 49 |
| Corrib, L. | **116 246** | 135 |
| Corrib, R. | **128 229** | 28-9 |

Coumanare **051 105** 153, 158-9, 161, 178
Craggaunowen **146 176** 194
Cranagh, R. **235 434** 88
Croagh Patrick, mt **090 280** 136
Croaghmoyle **110 298** 123
Crocknapeast **169 384** 98
Croghan **248 233** 228, 233-4
Crossfintan Pt. **313 105** 38, 46-7
Cuilcagh, mt **212 328** 224
Curlew Mts **178 306** 204
Curraghcloe **309 128** 38, 41-2
Cush, Limerick **169 126** 122
Cushendall **323 427** 82
Cushendun **256 216** 46, 52, 65, 76
Cushrush I. **213 337** 203

**D**

Daingean **247 227** 233
Dalkey I. **327 226** 38, 47-8, 62, 196, 246
Dawros Hd. **163 397** 96, 97, 100
Delvin, R. **297 278** 242, 243, 244, 253
Derg, L., Clare **170 185** 200, 209-10, 217-20
Derrycarhoon **099 040** 181-2
Derrycarne Narrows **202 291** 206 (p), 207, 218, 220
Derrynaflan Bog **218 148** 228, 239-41
Devenish I. **222 347** 226
Dingle **044 101** 153, 159, 161, 162, 178
Dingle Pen. **060 106** 150, 155, 167, 173
Doagh **243 450** 90
Dodder, R. **315 230** 4
Dog's Bay **069 239** 132
Donard, Wicklow **293 197** 95
Doneraile **160 107** 33
Dooey Pt. **176 403** 96, 98
Doon L. **155 174** 98
Doonass, Leap of **166 163** 220
Dorsey, The **295 319** 205
Dowris **204 205** 202
Dowth **302 274** 244
Drogheda **309 275** 242, 253-7
Drowse, R. **180 359** 86
Drumdaff **191 270** 206, 207
Drumgoosat **282 303** 52, 53, 56-8, 65
Drumharlow L. **190 302** 204
Drumsna **199 297** 205-7
Drumurcher **252 318** 228-33
Duleek **304 268** 242, 244, 256
Dun Aengus Fort **081 211** 94, 154
Dunaff Hd. **230 448** 85, 88
Dundalk **304 307** 45, 59, 60
Dundalk B. **310 300** 44, 58, 59, 60, 61
Dunfanaghy **201 437** 85, 90-91
Dungannon **279 362** 73
Dungarvan, Waterford **226 093** 5, 32, 35
Dunmanus B. **082 034** 182
Dunree Hd. **228 439** 85, 88
Dunshaughlin **296 252** 12
Dyrick **207 106** 32, 187-8, 189

**E**

Eagle, Mt **033 099** 159
Edenderry **263 232** 243
Ennis **133 177** 218
Enniscorthy **297 139** 40
Enniskerry **322 217** 14
Enniskillen **223 344** 223, 225
Erne, Lower L. **216 356** 225, 226
Erne, R. **238 312** 29, 201, 203, 225-6
Erne, Upper L. **229 333** 225, 226-7
Errisbeg **070 240** 132

**F**

Fahamore **061 119** 154, 155
Fahan **233 426** 88
Falcarragh **193 432** 85, 92
Fanad Hd. **223 447** 89
Fanad, reg. **218 441** 85, 99
Fawnmore **052 266** 131
Feale, R. **105 130** 149
Feenagh **140 126** 140
Feeagh, L. **096 300** 122
Fenit **072 115** 25, 26 (p), 145, 150, 153, 154, 161, 178
Feohanagh V. **044 108** 159
Ferbane **211 224** 210, 215
Fin Lough **203 229** 210, 212 (p), 213, 215
Five Alley **183 177** 219
Fogher **038 077** 167
Forbes, L. **208 281** 206, 208
Formoyle **117 207** 140 (p)
Foyle, L. **254 429** 86-7
Foynes **125 151** 141
Freestone Hill **233 166** 149-50
Furnace, L. **097 297** 121, 122

**G**

Gabriel, Mt **093 034** 180-81, 183
Galey, R. **103 139** 147-8
Galty Mts **190 123** 191
Galway **129 225** 129, 137, 144
Gap of Mamore **232 443** 88
Gara, L. **170 300** 204-5, 207
Giant's Causeway **294 445** 175
Gill, L., Kerry **060 114** 103, 105, 156-7

Glen, R. **160 382** 98
Glenamoy **089 333** 28, 101, 109, 113-14
Glenavy **315 373** 52, 65, 71-2
Glenbeigh **067 091** 153, 161, 162, 178
Glencar, L. **173 343** 103
Glencolumbkille **153 384** 96, 99
Glencullen **318 220** 20
Glengad Hd. **252 454** 87
Glengarriff **092 056** 153, 161, 178, 179-80
Glenlough **158 391** 96, 99
Glenties **181 394** 96
Glenveagh National Pk. **199 418** 12
Glin **113 147** 141
Glinsk **078 238** 28
Goat I. **180 194** 218
Goodland **320 441** 52, 65, 76-81
Gort **145 202** 39-40, 124
Gortahork **191 430** 92
Gortatole **211 337** 223, 225
Gorteen B. **070 238** 132
Gowna, L. **230 290** 225-6
Graiguenamanagh **270 143** 234
Great Blasket I. **027 097** 159, 167
Great Skellig **024 060** 153, 156, 161, 167-71, 173-4, 178
Greencastle, Donegal **265 440** 61, 85, 86-7
Greenore **327 310** 52, 60, 65
Greystones **329 212** 45
Grianán of Aileach **337 420** 98
Gur, L. **164 140** *Pl. 6*, 121, 192-6, 204, 211

**H**

Headford **126 247** 135, 139
Horn Hd. **201 442** 90, 91
Howth **328 238** 49
Hyne, L. **109 028** 153, 161, 178, 183-5

**I**

Ilen, R. **113 035** 183
Illaunloghan **036 073** 155, 171
Illauntannig **062 121** 155-6
Inch, Kerry **065 101** 162
Inchbofin **205 254** 209
Inchcleraun **199 259** 209-10
Inishbofin I., Galway **053 265** 129, 130-32, 137, 144
Inishcealtra **170 185** 217
Inishkea North, I. **056 323** 101, 109, 117-19
Inishkea South, I. **055 321** 101, 109, 117-19
Inishmore, I. **085 209** 154
Inishowen Hd. **268 443** 87
Inishowen, reg. **265 443** 86-9
Inishkeel **171 400** 98
Iveragh Pen. **070 080** 155, 162, 165

**J**

Jamestown **198 297** 205
Jenkinstown **311 309** 61
Julianstown **313 270** 256

**K**

Keeragh I. **286 106** 38, 42
Kells, Meath = Ceanannas Mór **274 275** 58, 243
Kenmare **090 070** 161, 176, 178, 179
Kenmare B. **066 058** 175
Kenmare R. **066 058** 173
Kenure Pk. **326 256** 251
Kerry Hd. **067 130** 129, 137, 144, 145-6
Kesh, Fermanagh **218 363** 225
Kesh, Sligo **170 311** 36
Key, L. **183 305** 204
Kilbaha **073 148** 129, 137, 143, 144
Kilbeg **246 102** 38, 39-40, 124
Kilcoole **329 208** 4
Kilcredaun Pt. **085 149** 143
Kilcunmin **056 112** 157
Kilglass L. **198 286** 206, 207
Kilkee **088 159** 148
Kilkenny **250 156** 243
Kilkenny, co. **250 146** 237
Killabuonia **070 040** 156, 174
Killadangan **096 283** 124-6, 182
Killadoon **074 274** 118
Killadysert **125 158** 141
Killala **120 330** 110
Killaloe **170 172** 203, 217 (p), 218, 219, 220, 234
Killarney **096 090** 141, 145, 153, 161, 165, 178
Killimer **180 212** 146
Killiney, Dublin **326 224** 45
Killorglin **077 096** 162, 163
Killybegs **171 376** 96, 97, 98
Kilmacthomas **239 106** 39
Kilmastulla R. **175 171** 218-19
Kilgraeny **217 096** 5, 21, 32, 35-6
Kilrush **099 155** 141, 142, 145
Kilshannig **181 089** 154, 155
Kilsharvan **309 270** 242, 255 (p), 256
Kilternan **320 221** 14
Kindrum **219 442** 89
King John's Weir **158 160** 196
Kingscourt **278 295** 53

Kinnagoe B. **264 446** 85, 87
Kinvarra **137 210** 129, 135-8, 144
Knightstown **042 077** 165-6, 172
Knockadoon **165 141** *Pl. 6*, 194
Knockalla Mt **224 435** 88, 89
Knockbridge **299 303** 59
Knockcroghery **193 258** 209
Knockmaa **136 248** 135
Knockmealdown Mts **205 108** 187, 189, 191
Knocknacran **281 302** 53, 56
Knocknadobar, mt **050 084** 165
Knocknarea **162 335** 101, 104-5, 109, 135
Knockonna **108 035** 183
Knockvicar **187 306** 204
Knowth **299 274** *Pl. 7*, 246-9

## L

Lagore **298 253** 12
Lamb's Hd. **052 056** 155
Lambay I. **332 251** 38, 48, 126, 127, 258
Lanesborough **200 269** 204, 207, 208
Larne **340 402** 46, 52, 65, 73-6, 83
Lecarrow **197 255** 209
Lee, R. **125 065** 186
Leenaun V. **087 262** 29
Leitrim **195 304** 203
Lenankeel **231 444** 88
Letterkeen **097 305** 101, 109, 121-3
Liffey, R. **297 230** 49-50
Limavady **268 424** 74
Limerick **158 157** 141, 196, 217, 218, 219, 220, 221
Lisbellaw **230 341** 226
Lisdoonvarna **113 198** 129, 137, 140-1, 144
Lismore **204 098** 32, 187
Lismore Cas. **204 098** 189-91
Listowel **099 133** 145, 148, 149
Little Brosna, R. **198 210** 216
Littleton **217 154** 228
Littleton Bog **223 155** 237-9
Lixnaw **090 129** 149
Log na Síonna **205 332** 201 (p), 202
Long I. **035 072** 171
Longford **213 275** 206, 207, 228
Loop Hd. **068 147** 129, 137, 142-5
Lougheraherk **158 389** 96, 99
Loughros B. reg. **165 392** 99-100
Louisburgh **080 280** 118
Lurgan **308 358** 73

## M

Maam Cross **097 246** 135
Macnean Lower, L. **210 337** 201, 203, 223, 225
Macnean Upper, L. **203 339** 201, 203
Maghera **166 391** 96, 99-100
Magilligan Pt. **265 438** 85, 87
Maharee Is. **163 121** 153, 154-7, 161, 178
Malahide **323 246** 10
Malin **246 450** 85, 87, 99
Malin Hd. **238 459** 85, 87
Mallow **155 098** 32, 224
Manorhamilton **188 339** 107
Marlbank Loop **210 335** 224
Marble Arch **212 335** 224-5
Mattock, R. **301 276** 242, 243, 244, 253
Meelick **194 213** 210 (p), 211, 216, 220, 243
Mellifont Abbey **301 278** 252
Melvin, L. **189 354** 86, 225
Mevagh **212 439** 90
Mill R. **236 431** 86
Millford **219 426** 90
Milltown, R. **043 104** 159
Milverton **323 259** 2
Mitchelstown **181 112** 32
Mitchelstown Caves **196 113** 25, 191
Mizen Hd., Wicklow **330 180** 38, 47
Money Point **105 151** 145, 146
Mongan Bog **203 229** 210, 212 (p), 213
Monvoy **257 103** 38, 46
Mornington **313 276** 242
Mount Melleray Abbey **206 104** 187
Mourne Mts **330 326** 29, 52, 59, 60, 65, 66, 245, 258
Moy, R. **125 300** 134
Muckros B. **162 374** 96
Muinhin Bridge **084 325** 114
Mullet Pen. **065 330** 117, 119
Mullingar **244 253** 228
Mulroy B. **220 434** 89-90
Muntermellan **203 439** 91
Murlough B. **320 442** 78
Murrough, The **332 200** 5

## N

Nanny, R. **310 270** 242, 244
Navan = an Uaimh **286 267** 228, 234, 242, 243
Neagh, L. **304 374** 52, 65, 70-73, 83, 227
Nenagh **186 179** 217, 219
Nephin Beg, mt **093 310** 122
New Ross **272 127** 42
Newcastle West **128 133** 141, 148, 237

Newcastle, Wicklow **329 204** 4
Newgrange Tumulus **300 273** 103, 171, 244-6, 247
Newport, Mayo **098 293** 123
Newrathbridge **329 197** 4
Newry **308 326** 60

## O

O'Briensbridge **166 166** 217, 218, 219, 220
Oileán na gCanóg **034 068** 173-4
Oldbridge **305 276** 243, 244, 253
Oranmore **138 224** 136
Owenmore **204 329** 201
Ox Mts. **140 320** 107, 110, 123

## P

Parteen **158 160** 196-7, 198, 220, 221
Plassy **162 158** 219, 220
Pollnahallia **133 247** 129, 134-6, 137, 144, 149, 177
Pomeroy **269 372** 126
Port **155 389** 96, 99
Port Laoise **247 198** 134, 228
Portacloy **083 344** 101, 109, 113
Portadown **301 354** 73
Portarlington **254 212** 234, 236
Portnablagh **205 437** 91
Portmagee **037 073** 28, 155, 156, 165, 167, 172, 188
Portmagee Channel **042 075** 165, 171
Portmarnock **323 242** 45
Portnoo **170 399** 96, 97-8, 132
Portumna **185 204** 210, 217
Poulaphouca Falls **294 208** 2
Poulnabrone **123 201** 138
Puffin I. **034 067** 153, 161, 173-4, 178

## Q

Quin **141 174** 194

## R

Rahan **225 225** 221 (p)
Rathcroghan **180 284** 205
Rathfarnham **314 229** 19
Rathlin I. **313 451** 46, 52, 65, 82-3
Rath Luirc. *see* Charleville
Rathmelton **222 421** 89
Ratoath **302 252** 229
Red Cellar Cave **165 141** 195
Ree, L. **202 252** 206, 207, 208, 209-10, 217, 218
Reenard Pt. **043 078** 165
Richmond Harb. **206 276** 208
Rinevella B. **082 149** 129, 137, 143, 144
Rinmore Pt. **201 254** 89
Roaringwater B. **100 031** 183
Rockmarshall **312 308** 52, 61-4
Roddanstown **364 364** 67
Roonagh Quay **074 281** 126
Roosky, Leitrim **205 287** 203, 206
Rosguill **210 441** 85, 89, 90
Ross Abbey **127 247** 135
Rossan Pen. **148 384** 96, 97, 98-100
Roundstone **072 240** 55, 129, 132-4, 137, 144

## S

Saleen **101 146** 147
Saltee Is. **295 097** 38, 40, 42
Sandel, Mount **285 432** 52, 65, 83, 215
Scalp, The **321 220** 14
Scarriff **164 184** 218
Scattery I. **097 152** 129, 137, 141-2, 144, 155, 202
Shandon Cave **226 094** 32, 33
Shannon Harb. **203 218** 210, 215
Shannon Pot **205 332** 201 (p), 202
Shannon, R. **200 222** 196, 198-222, 233-4, 243
Shannonbridge **197 225** 210 (p), 214-15
Shearwater I. **034 068** 173-4
Sheen, R. **093 068** 179
Sheep Haven **206 439** 90-92
Shehy Mts **112 062** 186
Silver, R. **213 217** 215
Skellig, Gt **026 062** 153, 161, 167-71, 173-4, 178
Skelligs **026 062** 156, 167-71
Skerries **325 260** 2, 258
Skibbereen **112 033** 183
Skreen, Sligo **152 332** 101, 107-8, 109, 136
Skull **092 031** 153, 161, 178, 180-83
Slane **296 274** 242
Slane Cas. **296 274** 243
Slaney, R. **298 147** 28, 41
Slea Hd. **031 096** 159
Slieve Bignian **332 323** 66
Slieve Elva **115 204** 140
Slieve Gullion **302 320** 58
Slieve League **154 378** 98
Slieve Mish Mts **075 107** 150, 154
Slievetooey **160 390** 98, 99
Sligo B. **156 337** 203
Slyne Hd. **051 241** 129, 137, 144
Sneem **069 066** 166

Spa **077 115** 150-52, 153, 161, 178, 229
Sruh Croppa R. **211 333** 224, 225
St Doulagh's **321 242** 10
St Finan's B. **036 066** 156, 173, 174
Staigue Fort **061 063** 98
Stormanstown **291 294** 52, 59, 65
Strangford L. **358 349** 67
Strokestown **193 280** 206, 207
Sugarloaf mt **087 052** 180
Suir, R. **226 122** 28
Sutton **326 239** 38, 45, 49, 62
Swilly, L. **230 435** 86, 88

**T**

Tarbert **106 147** 129, 137, 144, 146
Termonbarry **205 277** 206, 208
Tievebulliagh, mt **319 427** 52, 65, 82-3
Toome B. **298 390** 52, 65, 83
Tory I. **186 446** *Pl.* 2, 28, 85, 92-5, 112, 131, 155
Townley Hall **303 277** 242, 247, 249-53
Tralee **083 114** 150, 153, 154, 161, 163, 178
Tramore **258 101** 46
Tranarossan B. **211 443** 90
Trawbreaga B. **245 449** 88
Trim **280 256** 243
Truskmore **176 347** 85, 89, 90
Tuam **143 252** 135
Tullyallen **304 277** 242
Twelve Pins, The, mts **078 252** 134

**U**

Uisneach **228 252** 233
Urris Hills **230 441** 88

**V**

Valencia Harb. **041 078** 164, 165
Valencia I. **037 075** *Pl.* 5, 28, 111, 153, 155, 161, 165-7, 171-2, 173, 178, 191

**W**

Warren Point **314 318** 210
Waterford **260 112** 5, 32
Waterville **050 066** 175
Westport **100 284** 107, 124-5, 182
Wexford **304 121** 38, 40, 41, 46-7
White I. **217 362** 226
Whitehead **347 391** 71
Wicklow **331 193** 4, 11, 38, 46-7
Wicklow Mts **303 192** 95, 97
Wood Quay **315 234** 49-51, 175, 38
Woodgrange **347 348** 52, 65, 67
Worm Ditch **192 302** 205

**Y**

Youghal B. **212 073** 218-19